HIGH
Pressure
BOILERS

Second Edition

AMERICAN TECHNICAL PUBLISHERS, INC.
HOMEWOOD, ILLINOIS 60430

Frederick M. Steingress
Harold J. Frost

2 3 4 5 6 7 8 9 – 94 – 9 8 7 6 5 4

Printed in the United States of America

ISBN 0-8269-4415-9

Contents

Acknowledgements

The authors and publisher are grateful for the technical information and assistance provided by the following companies, organizations, and testing agencies.

The American Society of Mechanical Engineers
Aurora Pump, Unit of General Signal
Babcock & Wilcox Company
Bacharach, Inc., Division of United Technologies
Block and Associates
Cleaver-Brooks
Combustion Engineering
Crosby Valve & Gage Co.
Eugene Ernst Products Co.
Factory Mutual System
Fireye, Inc.
Hays Republic Corporation
Honeywell, Inc.
Jenkins Bros.
The Kraissl Co., Inc.
Lawler Automatic Control, Inc.
McDonnell-Miller
The Permutit Co., Inc.
Riley Stoker Corporation
Rosemount Analytical
Sarco Company, Inc.
Superior Boiler Works
Teledyne Farris Engineering
Uehling Instrument Co.
Walter Kidde
Worthington Pump
Alaska Department of Labor
    Mechanical Inspection Division
Arkansas Department of Labor
    Boiler Inspection Division

The Commonwealth of Massachusetts
    Department of Public Safety
    Engineering Section, Division of Inspection
State of New Jersey
    Department of Labor
    Division of Workplace Standards
    Office of Boiler and Pressure
        Vessel Compliance
State of Ohio
    Department of Industrial Relations
City of Dearborn
    Department of Public Works
    Building and Safety Division
City of Elgin
City of Milwaukee
    Building Inspection and Safety Engineering
City of Philadelphia
    Department of Licenses and Inspections
Salt Lake City Corporation
    Department of Building and Housing Services
City of Sioux City
    Board of Examiners of Mechanical
        Stationary Engineers
    Inspection Services Division
City of Terre Haute
    Office of the Board of Examining Engineers
Province of Alberta
    Labour
    General Safety Services Division
    Boilers Branch

INTRODUCTION

High Pressure Boilers, 2nd Edition provides information on the safe and efficient operation of high pressure boilers and related equipment. The content and format of the book are specifically designed for use in preparation for obtaining a boiler operator's license.

Boiler operation and boiler components are broken into separate topics in the book. Chapters 1 through 10 cover steam boiler theory, equipment, and accessories. Chapter 11, Steam Boiler Operation, covers operator duties and responsibilities. Chapter 12, Testing, contains six tests that can be used as a comprehensive review.

Key words defined in the chapter are listed at the end of each chapter for review. The illustrated glossary and the index are provided for easy reference. Answers to all questions in *High Pressure Boilers* are listed in the *Instructor's Guide.* The following information is provided to assist the user of *High Pressure Boilers.*

Arrowhead Symbols

Arrowhead symbols are used to identify the flow of material in a boiler system or various parts of a boiler system. As a material changes, the arrowhead symbol also changes. For example, water when heated changes to steam. When two materials are flowing in the same path, alternating arrowheads of the two materials are shown.

KEY TO ARROWHEAD SYMBOLS			
◭ - Air	▲ - Water	▲ - Fuel Oil	⌂ - Air to Atmosphere
◭ - Gas	△ - Steam	⚠ - Condensate	⌂ - Gases of Combustion

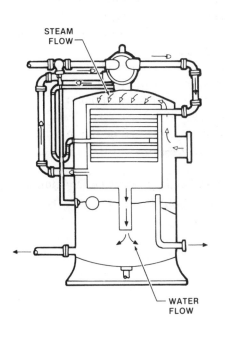

STEAM FLOW

WATER FLOW

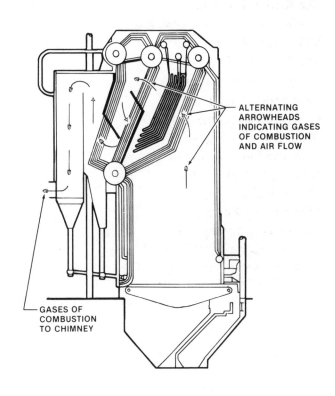

ALTERNATING ARROWHEADS INDICATING GASES OF COMBUSTION AND AIR FLOW

GASES OF COMBUSTION TO CHIMNEY

Tech Checks

Tech Checks follow the text in a chapter and are used to test understanding of the information presented in the chapter. Questions in Tech Checks are answered in the following manner. Place the letter of the correct answer in the blank next to the question.

___C___   1. Rank refers to the _____ of the coal.
  A. ash content
  B. Btu content
  C. degree of hardness
  D. clinker formation

___D___   2. Vertical fire tube boilers require _____.
  A. high ceilings
  B. less floor space
  C. the use of staybolts
  D. all of the above

___C___   3. Casing
___A___   4. Impeller
___D___   5. Packing gland
___B___   6. Shaft bearing

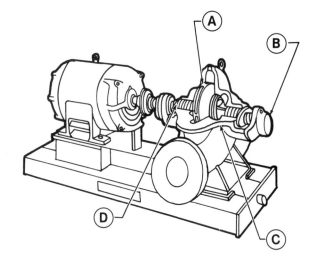

Chapter 12—Testing

Chapter 12—Testing is comprised of six tests, each including questions similar to those that may be found on a licensing examination. Sample questions from actual licensing examinations from various states and Canada have been included. Multiple Choice questions are answered in the same manner as Tech Checks. True-False questions are answered by circling the letter T if the statement is true and F if the statement is false.

T   (F)   1. Scale protects the boiler heating surfaces.

(T)   F   2. To prevent water hammer, water should be drained out of all high pressure steam lines.

(T)   F   3. Waterwalls permit a greater heat release per cubic foot of furnace volume than refractory walls.

Chapter 1

STEAM BOILERS

Modern society depends on steam for many uses. Steam generated by boilers is used to supply electricity, water, and gas. Steam is also used to heat water and buildings, including residential buildings, and in various industrial processes and commercial applications.

A steam boiler is a closed vessel containing water. The water in the steam boiler is pressurized and turned into steam when heat is added. When a fuel is burned, the chemical energy (ability of the chemical to do work) in the fuel is transformed into heat. This heat, which is a form of energy, is released in the steam. The total heat in the steam is called enthalpy.

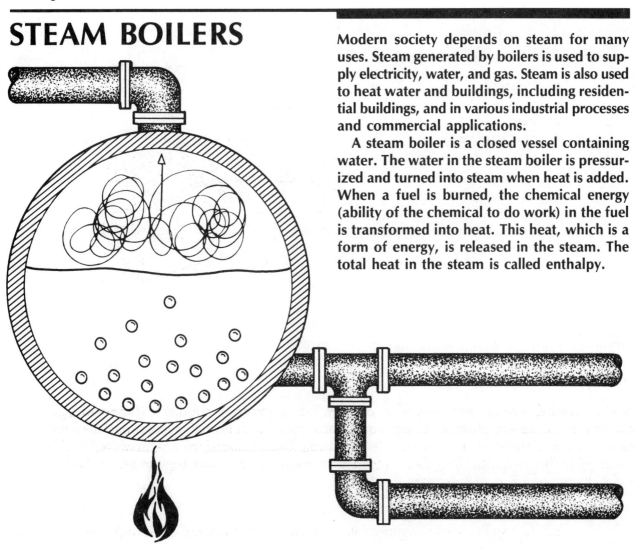

KEY TO ARROWHEAD SYMBOLS			
△ - Air	▲ - Water	▲ - Fuel Oil	⌂ - Air to Atmosphere
⚠ - Gas	△ - Steam	⚠ - Condensate	⚠ - Gases of Combustion

1

STEAM BOILER TYPES

Steam boilers (often referred to simply as boilers) are generally classified as either *low pressure steam boilers* or *high pressure steam boilers*. Steam boilers, however, can be further classified as *fire tube steam boilers* or *water tube steam boilers*. The type of steam boiler used in a particular application depends on the pressure, temperature, and amount of steam required.

Low Pressure Steam Boilers

Low pressure steam boilers are used primarily for heating buildings such as schools, apartments, warehouses, and factories, and for heating domestic water. These boilers can be of fire tube, water tube, or cast iron sectional type. Boiler size will vary based on the quantity of steam required.

A low pressure steam boiler has a maximum allowable working pressure (MAWP) of 15 pounds per square inch (psi). This may vary in some states. Check your local pressure vessel code to determine the maximum psi allowed for low pressure steam boilers.

High Pressure Steam Boilers

High pressure steam boilers are used in generating electricity and in processing operations in industry. Paper mills use steam for dryers. Breweries use steam in equipment such as brew kettles and mash tubs. Pasteurizing and sterilizing facilities use steam generated by high pressure boilers in their processes.

A high pressure steam boiler operates at pressure above 15 psi and over 6 *boiler horsepower*. A boiler horsepower is defined as the evaporation of 34.5 pounds of water per hour from and at a feedwater temperature of 212°F. Check your local pressure vessel code for variations.

Fire Tube Steam Boilers

In a fire tube steam boiler, heat and gases of combustion pass through tubes surrounded by water. See Figure 1-1. Fire tube steam boilers may be either high or low pressure boilers. Three types of fire tube steam boilers are the *horizontal return tubular boiler, scotch marine boiler,* and *vertical fire tube boiler.*

All fire tube boilers have the same basic operating principles. The heat produced by gases of combustion pass through the tubes while the water surrounds the tubes. However, fire tube boilers have different designs, based on application and installation considerations. Fire tube boiler tubes are always measured by their outside diameter (O.D.). Fire tube boilers are designed for pressure up to a maximum of 250 psi and approximately 750 boiler horsepower.

The following are advantages of a fire tube boiler:

1. can be factory assembled, thus giving better quality control
2. initial cost is less than a water tube boiler
3. requires little or no setting (brickwork)
4. contains larger volume of water for a given size compared to a water tube boiler
5. requires less headroom and floor space

Some of these advantages can turn out to be disadvantages. Because of the larger volume of water these boilers contain, disastrous explosions may occur. See Figure 1-2. Explosions may occur because of a sudden drop in pressure without a corresponding drop in temperature. Knowledge of the following basic principles of boiler operation can prevent serious accidents.

1. Water will boil and turn to steam when it reaches 212°F at atmospheric pressure.
2. The higher the steam pressure, the higher the boiling point of water in the boiler.
3. As steam pressure in a boiler increases, there is a corresponding increase in temperature. See Figure 1-3.

When a steam boiler is operating at 100 pounds per square inch gauge pressure (psig), the temperature of the water and steam will be about 337°F. If there is a sudden drop in pressure from 100 psig to 0 psig without a corresponding drop in water temperature, the

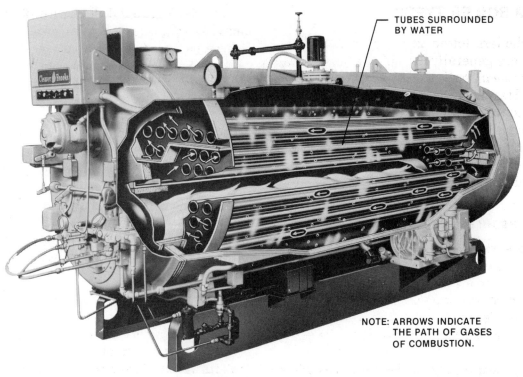

TUBES SURROUNDED
BY WATER

NOTE: ARROWS INDICATE
THE PATH OF GASES
OF COMBUSTION.

Figure 1-1. Combustion gases and heat pass through tubes surrounded by water in fire tube boilers. *(Cleaver-Brooks)*

Figure 1-2. A sudden drop in pressure without a corresponding drop in temperature caused this scotch marine boiler to explode. *(Factory Mutual System)*

GAUGE PRESSURE (PSI)	TEMPERATURE (°F)
20	258
30	274
40	287
50	298
60	307
70	316
80	324
90	331
100	337
150	366
200	388
250	406
300	421

NOTE:
gauge press. + atmospheric press. (14.7) = absolute press.
100 psig + 14.7 = 114.7 psia

Figure 1-3. The boiling point of water increases as steam pressure increases.

water at 337°F immediately flashes into steam. When water flashes into steam, its volume increases tremendously. This can result in a disastrous explosion. Approximately 13% of the water flashes into steam. The remaining water cools to 212°F at the corresponding atmospheric pressure.

Principles of Fire Tube Boiler Operation

When water is heated, it increases in volume and becomes lighter. See Figure 1-4. This warmer water, now lighter, rises and the cooler water drops to take its place. The steam bubbles that eventually form break through the surface of the water and enter the steam space.

The addition of tubes inside the drum containing water increases the heating surface. See Figure 1-5. The heating surface is that part of a boiler with water on one side, and heat and gases of combustion on the other. By increasing the heating surface, more heat is taken from the gases of combustion. This results in more rapid water circulation and faster formation of steam bubbles.

When larger quantities of steam are released, the *thermal efficiency* of the boiler increases. Thermal efficiency is the ratio of heat supplied from the fuel to the heat absorbed by the water. Modern fire tube boilers with improved design and heat transfer rates have achieved thermal efficiency rates as high as 80% to 85%.

Placing an internal furnace within the boiler

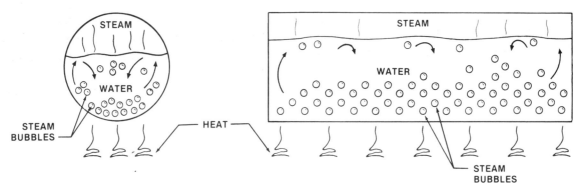

Figure 1-4. Water becomes lighter when heated. This warmer water, now lighter, rises releasing steam bubbles, as colder, heavier water drops.

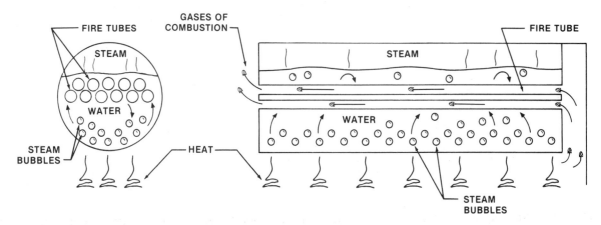

Figure 1-5. As the number of tubes in a boiler is increased, the boiler efficiency is increased.

shell greatly increases the heating surface. This allows maximum absorption of heat. Also, the boiler creates steam in less time. See Figure 1-6.

Horizontal Return Tubular Boilers. For many years the horizontal return tubular (HRT) boiler was the workhorse in industry. The HRT boiler is a type of fire tube boiler. It is fired with fuel oil, gas, or coal. It consists of a drum suspended over a firebox. The two methods used to support the drum are:

1. columns and a suspension sling,
2. supporting brackets resting on metal plates in a brick setting.

The tube sheets of an HRT boiler are supported with through stays and diagonal stays (braces). See Figure 1-7.

The feedwater pipe extends approximately three-fifths of the length of the drum. It enters the front tube sheet. The location of the feedwater pipe helps increase water circulation in the boiler.

The HRT boiler is also equipped with a dry pipe to ensure a higher quality of steam. All connections to HRT boilers, such as steam nozzles and safety valve connections, must be approved by The American Society of Mechanical Engineers (ASME).

The drum is riveted and since its bottom is in the firebox, leaks often develop around the rivets. The bottom blowdown line also has to pass through the firebox. This is protected by a sleeve and a refractory pier or by wrapping with a protective insulation. Today modern boiler drums are welded.

Scotch Marine Boilers. Scotch marine boilers were used on ships for many years. These boilers have a corrugated furnace, combustion chamber, and tubes passing through the boiler to the front tube sheet. The boilers used in industry today are not true scotch marine boilers, but rather, boilers that have been modified to meet the demands of stationary plants. See Figure 1-8. The furnace is completely surrounded by water. This increases the boiler heating surface, therefore increasing boiler efficiency.

The arrows in Figure 1-8 indicate the path of the gases of combustion. By inserting baf-

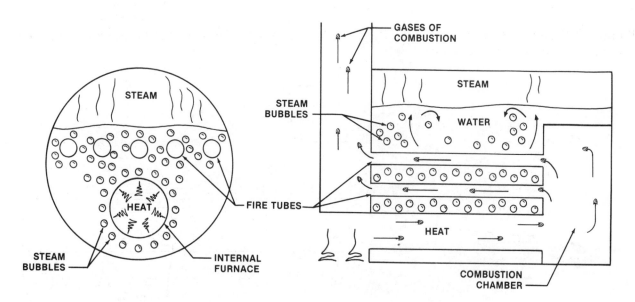

Figure 1-6. Adding an internal furnace to a boiler increases the heating surface, maximizing boiler efficiency.

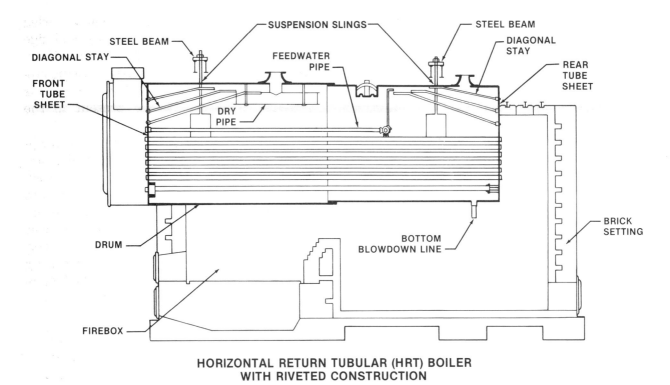

**HORIZONTAL RETURN TUBULAR (HRT) BOILER
WITH RIVETED CONSTRUCTION**

Figure 1-7. On an HRT boiler, the drum is suspended over the firebox. Stays are used to support the flat surfaces.

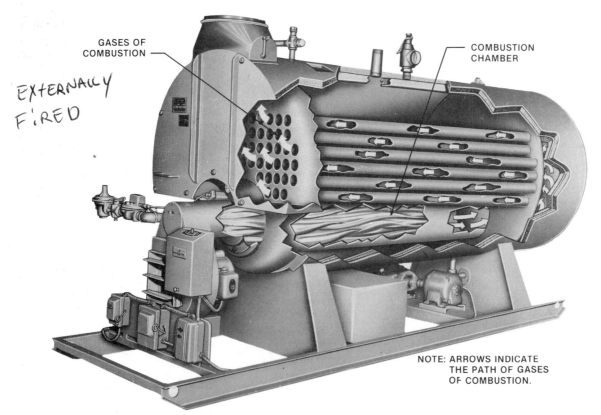

Figure 1-8. The furnace is inside the drum of a scotch marine boiler. (*Superior Boiler Works, Inc.*)

fles on the fireside, the boilers can be made into a two-, three-, or four-pass boiler. Figure 1-8 shows a two-pass boiler. In a scotch marine boiler, the gases of combustion will make many passes before leaving the boiler. By increasing the number of passes, more heat can be absorbed by the water, therefore increasing thermal efficiency.

Vertical Fire Tube Boilers. Vertical fire tube boilers are one-pass boilers. The gases of combustion cannot be retained in the boiler by the use of baffles. See Figure 1-9.

The combustion chamber (firebox) of a vertical fire tube boiler is supported by staybolts. A waterleg is formed by the construction of the inner and outer wrapper sheets. The waterleg is subject to overheating if deposits of sludge and sediment are allowed to accumulate. *NOTE:* Sludge is the accumulated residue produced from impurities in water. Sediment is particles of foreign matter present in the water.

Vertical fire tube boilers are designed as dry-top or wet-top boilers. The dry-top boiler produces steam that is slightly superheated, which causes tubes in the upper tube sheet to be prone to leaks. The wet-top boiler does not produce superheated steam because the upper tube sheet is surrounded by water. The vertical fire tube boiler requires a high ceiling because of its height. Vertical fire tube boilers are commonly used on steam pile drivers.

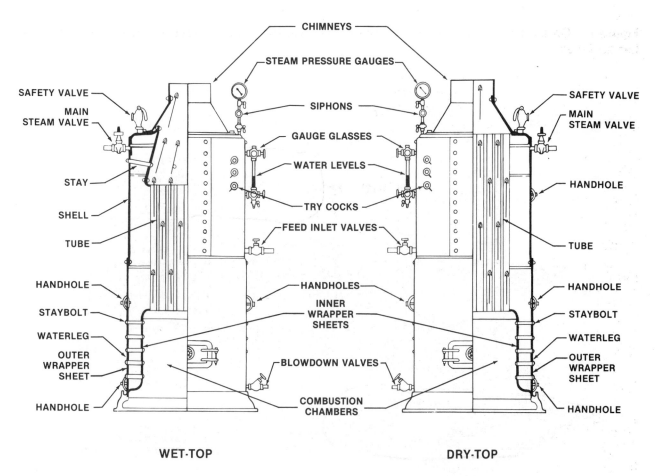

Figure 1-9. Vertical fire tube boilers require less floor space than HRT boilers.

Water Tube Steam Boilers

A water tube steam boiler has water inside the tubes. The heat and gases of combustion pass around these tubes. See Figure 1-10. As with fire tube boilers, the boiler tubes are measured by their outside diameter.

Water tube boilers were developed as the rapid growth of industry prompted a need for steam at higher pressures. Water tube boilers have been designed to operate at pressures as high as 3206 psi, also known as the *critical pressure of steam*. Critical pressure of steam is the point at which the density of the water and steam is the same. Fire tube boilers needed such large drum diameters and plate thicknesses to meet the demand for higher capacities and pressures that they were no longer practical or safe.

The development of the water tube boiler

does not mean that there is no place for fire tube boilers in industry. The fire tube boiler continues to be used where moderate pressures are needed and large quantities of steam are not required.

Unlike the fire tube boiler, the water tube boiler has the heat and gases of combustion surrounding the tubes. The heated water inside the tubes becomes lighter, causing it to rise. The cooler water drops to the mud drum. The mud drum is the lowest part of the water side of a water tube boiler. The steam bubbles that form at the heated surfaces rise and finally break through the water surface in the steam and water drum.

It is always desirable to absorb as much heat as possible from the gases of combustion before they enter the chimney (stack). This is accomplished by baffles located in the path of the gases of combustion. See Figure 1-11. These baffles are designed to direct the gases so that they come into close contact with the boiler heating surface. Baffles are constructed of refractory (firebrick) material and must be maintained for optimum efficiency. If broken baffles are not replaced, the gases of combustion will take a direct path to the chimney. This will result in a sudden increase in the temperature of flue gas going up the chimney. Some of the early water tube boilers had box headers that required the use of staybolts to prevent bulging. The introduction of sinuous headers eliminated the need for staybolts and made for a safer, more efficient boiler. See Figure 1-12.

The steam and water drum is dished (concave) and therefore requires no braces or stays. The water tube boiler carries a smaller volume of water per unit of output than the fire tube boiler. It is also capable of handling large steam loads and responds quickly to fluctuating steam loads. Because of their construction, these boilers can carry extremely high steam pressures and temperatures. They are also less likely to produce explosions, but require a more highly skilled operator.

Some water tube boilers are equipped with waterwalls for the purpose of increasing the life of the furnace refractory. See Figure 1-13.

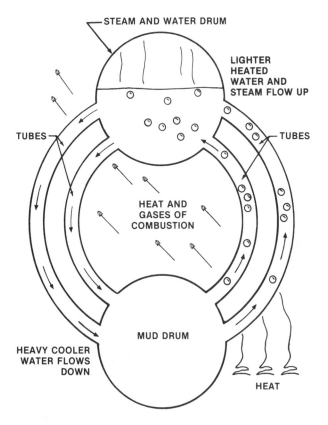

Figure 1-10. Water tube boilers provide rapid water circulation.

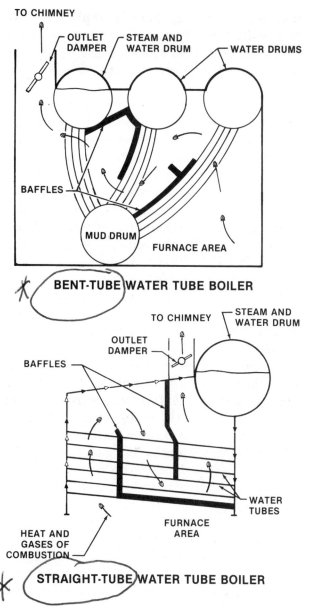

Figure 1-11. Baffles direct the flow of gases of combustion across generating tubes.

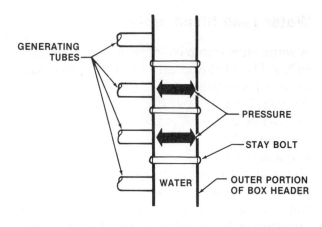

SIDE VIEW OF BOX HEADER WITH STAY BOLTS

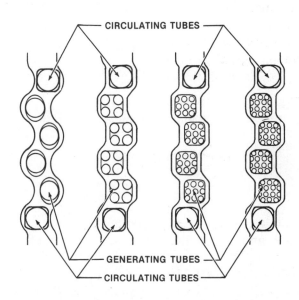

FRONT VIEW OF SINUOUS HEADERS

Figure 1-12. Sinuous headers eliminate the need for staybolts.

The waterwalls not only lengthen the life of the refractory, but also increase the steaming capacity of the boiler. Additional benefits of the waterwalls are

1. smaller furnace volume per unit of output,
2. higher heat release in the furnace area,
3. increased firing rate per unit of furnace volume.

Without the use of waterwalls, stokers and pulverized coal burners could never have been developed. The steam generated by the use of waterwalls is expressed in pounds of steam per hour per square foot of waterwall heating surface. On a hand-fired coal boiler, 8 pounds of steam are generated per hour for every square foot of waterwall heating surface. When using

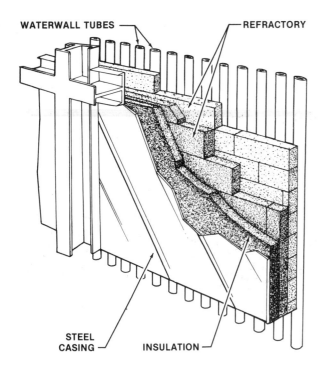

Figure 1-13. Waterwalls extend refractory life and increase the steaming capacity of boilers.

a stoker-fired boiler, 12 pounds of steam are generated per square foot of waterwall heating surface. When burning fuel oil, gas, or pulverized coal, 16 pounds of steam are generated per hour per square foot of water-wall heating surface.

WARNING: Waterwalls should never be blown down during furnace operation. (See Chapter 2 for blowdown procedures.)

Water tube boilers can also be fitted with superheaters to increase the heat content of the steam. Superheaters are convection type, radiant type, or a combination of both. See Chapter 2 for a detailed discussion of superheaters. Two types of water tube steam boilers are the *straight-tube boiler* and *bent-tube boiler.*

Straight-tube Boilers. In a straight-tube water tube boiler, the water enters the steam and water drum through an internal feedwater

line. It passes through *downcomer nipples* into the front header. Downcomer nipples are short pieces of steel tubes rolled and expanded in the bottom of the steam and water drum. They are connected to the sinuous front headers.

When heated, the water expands in volume, becomes lighter, and moves toward the rear header where the steam bubbles begin to form. The steam bubbles rise up the rear header to the steam and water drum. Here they break through the surface of the water, entering the steam space. See Figure 1-14. Generally, the tubes in straight-tube water tube boilers are

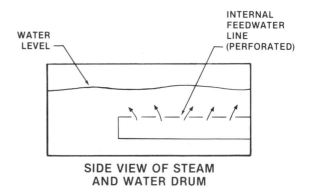

SIDE VIEW OF STEAM AND WATER DRUM

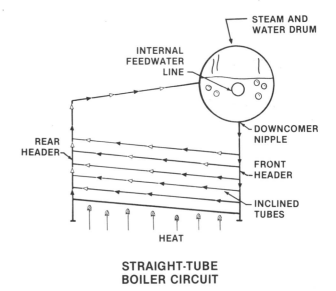

STRAIGHT-TUBE BOILER CIRCUIT

Figure 1-14. Straight-tube boilers have inclined tubes to increase circulation. Water is introduced to the boiler through an internal feedwater line.

expanded into the drums and headers and are slightly flared to prevent leakage.

Bent-tube Boilers. Circulation becomes more complex in a bent-tube boiler. The rear tube bank acts as a downcomer to the mud drum. Most of the steaming occurs in the front tube banks. The steam and water mixture enters the steam and water drum both above and below the water surface. Bent-tube boilers operate at higher pressures and higher steam capacities than straight-tube boilers. The design eliminates the need for headers. See Figure 1-15.

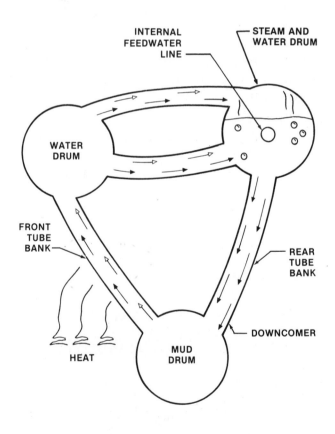

Figure 1-15. Bent-tube boilers operate at higher pressures and steam capacities than straight-tube boilers, and their design provides for improved water circulation.

ASME CODE STANDARDS

Most states have adopted the code of The American Society of Mechanical Engineers (ASME). The ASME code was instituted to govern and control the types of material, the methods of construction, and the procedures used in installation of steam boilers. ASME symbol stamps show that parts within the boiler system conform to ASME standards. See Figure 1-16.

The materials used in boiler construction must withstand various boiler temperatures and pressures. Boiler drums and shells, braces, stays, and tubes are subjected to continuous stress when the boiler is in operation.

The ASME code ensures that boilers and fittings are strong enough and made of suitable materials to withstand this stress. The types of stress commonly found in boilers include *compressive, shear,* and *tensile stress.* See Figure 1-17.

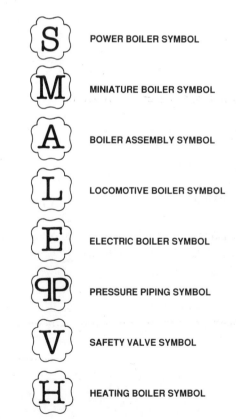

Figure 1-16. ASME symbol stamps denote conformance of boiler components to ASME standards.

Compressive stress occurs when two forces of equal intensity act from opposite directions, pushing toward the center of an object. Shear stress occurs when two forces of equal intensity act parallel to each other but in opposite directions. Tensile stress occurs when two forces of equal intensity act on an object, pulling in opposite directions.

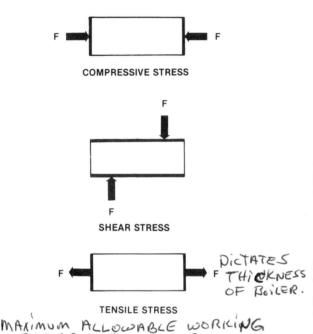

DICTATES THICKNESS OF BOILER.

MAXIMUM ALLOWABLE WORKING PRESSURE. MAWP.

Figure 1-17. Boiler materials and fittings are subjected to compressive, shear, and tensile stress.

Boiler plates and staybolts are subjected to tensile stress. Rivets are subjected primarily to shear stress. Fire tubes in a fire tube boiler are subjected to compressive stress. Compressive stress also occurs when a vacuum is allowed to develop within the boiler.

The construction of a fire tube boiler limits the pounds of steam per hour it is capable of producing and its operating pressure. The flat tube sheets must be adequately supported and require careful use of stays. See Figure 1-18.

Through stays are used to prevent bulging in the HRT boiler. Staybolts hold the inner and outer wrapper sheets of vertical fire tube boilers together. Diagonal stays are needed in the upper steam space of modified HRT boilers to hold flat and curved surfaces together.

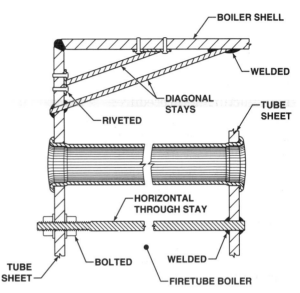

Figure 1-18. Stays are essential in fire tube boiler construction. They are used to support flat surfaces and prevent bulging.

In fire tube boilers, the tubes are expanded in both the front and rear tube sheets. The protruding ends of the tubes are then rolled to ensure a tight fit and prevent water leakage. The tubes are then beaded over to prevent the tube ends from burning. See Figure 1-19.

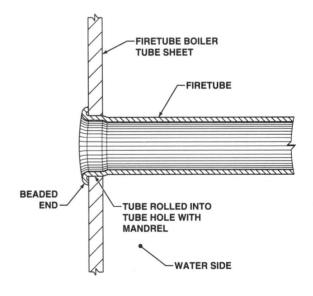

Figure 1-19. Fire tubes are expanded and beaded over to help support the tube sheets.

PACKAGE BOILERS

Package boilers are preassembled before installation. The boilers are shipped on beams and arrive ready for operation. As modern manufacturing procedures and technology were developed, the package boiler became more popular. Package boilers enabled steam boiler manufacturers to assemble boilers in their plants, where the quality of construction could be closely monitored.

The package boiler is a self-contained unit complete with feedwater pump, fuel pump, burner assembly, and combustion controls. It requires connecting only the feedwater lines, steam lines, fuel lines, electrical connections, and a tie into the breaching and chimney. This takes a relatively short period of time, and then the boiler is ready for firing.

Package boilers can be either a fire tube or water tube type. See Figures 1-20 and 1-21. Package boilers are shipped by rail, truck, or overseas on ships. The only limitations of package boilers are the pounds of steam per hour capability and the size of the unit.

FIELD-ERECTED BOILERS

Field-erected boilers are used to generate electricity or large amounts of steam and must be built on site. Some of these boilers are five or six stories high. Field-erected boilers require very careful quality control during construction. It is much easier, however, to build a package boiler in a plant using jigs and automated construction techniques than to have a boiler field-erected. Field-erected boilers are checked by field inspectors to ensure their compliance with ASME code standards.

ELECTRIC BOILERS

Electric boilers operate similarly to boilers fired by fuel oil, gas, or coal. The primary difference is that electric boilers have heat produced by electric resistance coils, or electrodes. In resistance coil electric boilers, electricity flows through a coiled conductor. Resistance created by the coiled conductor generates heat. Resistance coil electric boilers are used in low ca-

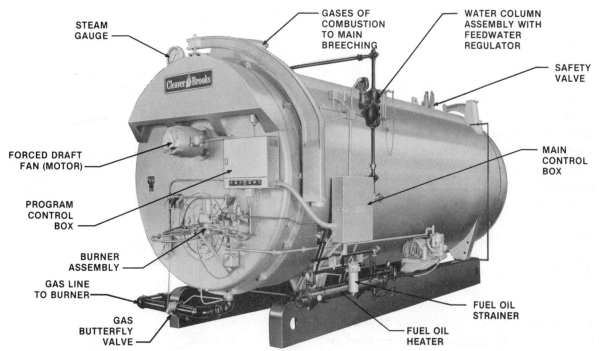

Figure 1-20. Package fire tube boilers are preassembled at the factory and allow quick installation. (*Cleaver-Brooks*)

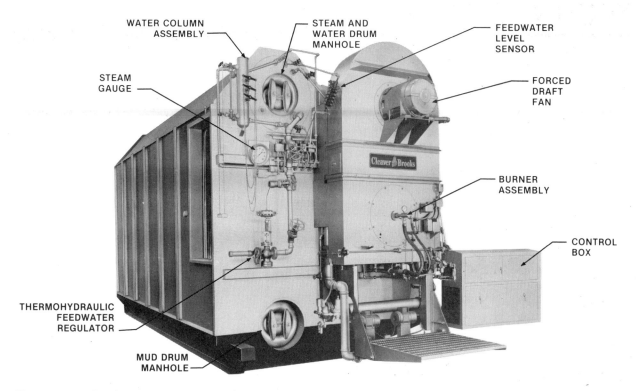

WATER COLUMN ASSEMBLY

STEAM AND WATER DRUM MANHOLE

FEEDWATER LEVEL SENSOR

STEAM GAUGE

FORCED DRAFT FAN

BURNER ASSEMBLY

CONTROL BOX

THERMOHYDRAULIC FEEDWATER REGULATOR

MUD DRUM MANHOLE

Figure 1-21. Package water tube boilers are used where steam pressure demand does not require a field-erected boiler. (*Cleaver-Brooks*)

pacity boilers and are not as common as electrode electric boilers.

In electrode electric boilers, heat is generated by electric current flowing from one electrode to another electrode through the boiler water. Conductivity of the boiler water will affect the flow of electricity and the amount of heat generated.

Conditions which affect boiler water conduc-

tivity must be carefully monitored to assure safe and efficient operation. For optimum efficiency, consult the manufacturers recommendations for boiler water conditioning. **WARNING: Electric boilers operate at voltages up to 16,000 volts. Before maintenance work is performed on an electric boiler, the main electrical disconnect must be turned off and locked out.**

Key Words

ASME code
bent-tube boiler
boiler horsepower
compressive stress
critical pressure of steam
dry-top boiler
electric boiler
enthalpy
field-erected boiler
fire tube steam boiler
high pressure steam boiler

horizontal return tubular boiler
low pressure steam boiler
package boiler
scotch marine boiler
shear stress
straight-tube boiler
tensile stress
thermal efficiency
vertical fire tube boiler
water tube steam boiler
waterwall
wet-top boiler

TECH CHECK ✓ 1

_A_

1. A low pressure steam boiler has a maximum allowable working pressure (MAWP) of up to _____.
   A. 15 psi
   B. 35 psi
   C. 100 psi
   D. no MAWP

_B_

2. The evaporation of 34.5 pounds of water per hour from and at a feedwater temperature of 212°F is defined as _____.
   A. a factor of evaporation
   B. one boiler horsepower
   C. latent heat of fusion
   D. an evaporation test

   ONE BOILER HORSEPOWER

_A_

3. In a fire tube boiler, the heat and gases of combustion pass _____.
   A. through the tubes
   B. around the tubes
   C. only through the combustion chamber
   D. both A and B

_C_

4. A fire tube boiler may be used _____.
   A. only in low pressure plants
   B. only in high pressure plants
   C. in high or low pressure plants
   D. only for process steam

_B_

5. Because of the large volume of water, the boiler most likely to cause a boiler explosion is _____.
   A. a water tube boiler
   B. a fire tube boiler
   C. either a water tube or fire tube boiler
   D. boilers cannot explode

   (CHAPER 1)

_A_

6. As steam pressure in a boiler increases, there is a corresponding increase in the _____.
   A. temperature
   B. superheat
   C. volume of steam
   D. boiler horsepower

_B_

7. A sudden drop in boiler steam pressure without a corresponding drop in boiler water temperature could result in _____.
   A. a loss of efficiency
   B. a boiler explosion
   C. an increase in surface tension
   D. no effect on the boiler

____D____ 8. The part of a boiler that has the heat and gases of combustion on one side and water on the other side is known as the _____.
  A. water surface
  B. steam surface
  C. fire side
  D. heating surface

____C____ 9. The comparison, or ratio, of heat supplied in fuel to heat absorbed by water is defined as _____ efficiency.
  A. combustion
  B. water tube
  C. thermal
  D. overall plant

____A____ 10. A horizontal return tubular (HRT) boiler is _____ boiler.
  A. a fire tube
  B. a water tube
  C. either a fire tube or a water tube
  D. none of the above

____D____ 11. Vertical fire tube boilers require _____
  A. high ceilings
  B. less floor space
  C. the use of staybolts
  D. all of the above

____B____ 12. In a water tube boiler, the heat and gases of combustion pass _____.
  A. through the tubes
  B. around the tubes
  C. through and around the tubes
  D. only through the combustion chamber

____A____ 13. The _____ boiler has a large volume of water in relation to horsepower size.
  A. fire tube
  B. water tube
  C. process steam
  D. vertical water tube

____C____ 14. Stays and braces are needed to prevent bulging in _____.
  A. any water tube boiler
  B. a high pressure water tube boiler
  C. a fire tube boiler (high or low pressure)
  D. none of the above

____C____ 15. The _____ boiler was developed to provide steam at higher pressures.
  A. HRT
  B. fire tube   300 PSI
  C. water tube   3260 PSI
  D. combination

_____B_____ 16. The mud drum is the lowest part of the water side of a(n) _____ boiler.
      A. HRT
      B. water tube
      C. low pressure fire tube
      D. high pressure fire tube

_____D_____ 17. Baffles are designed to direct the gases of combustion so that they come into close contact with the _____.
      A. feedwater
      B. combustion chamber
      C. superheater
      D. boiler heating surface

_____C_____ 18. The steam and water drum of water tube boilers is dished (concave) to eliminate the need for _____.
      A. brickwork
      B. waterwalls
      C. stays
      D. baffles

_____D_____ 19. To increase the life of a furnace refractory, some water tube boilers are equipped with _____.
      A. waterwall blowdown lines
      B. sinuous headers
      C. box headers
      D. waterwalls

_____A_____ 20. Boiler plates and staybolts are subjected to _____ stress.
      A. tensile
      B. compressive
      C. shear
      D. no stress when boiler is under pressure

_____C_____ 21. Safety valve connections must be approved by the _____.
      A. fire department
      B. shift foreman
      C. American Society of Mechanical Engineers (ASME)
      D. American Boiler Manufacturers Association (ABMA)

Identify the parts of the fire tube boiler.

_____C_____ 22. Heat
_____A_____ 23. Steam
_____B_____ 24. Water
_____D_____ 25. Gases of combustion

Identify the parts of the water tube boiler.

B _____ **26.** Tubes
C _____ **27.** Heat
D _____ **28.** Mud drum
A _____ **29.** Steam and water drum

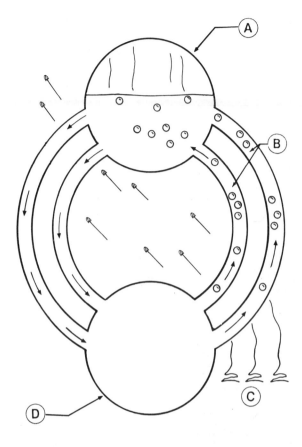

Identify the parts of the straight-tube water tube boiler.

D _____ **30.** Baffles
B _____ **31.** Water tubes
C _____ **32.** Heat and gases of combustion
A _____ **33.** Steam and water drum

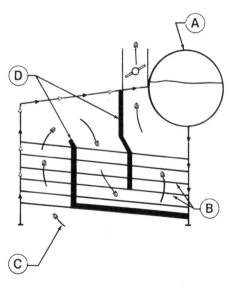

Chapter 2

STEAM BOILER FITTINGS AND ACCESSORIES

The boiler is the largest piece of equipment in the boiler room. To operate a boiler safely and efficiently, certain fittings and accessories are required. Whether a boiler is a fire tube or water tube type, the fittings are located in the same area of the boiler and serve the same purpose.

Fittings and accessories must be constructed in accordance with the ASME code. The ASME code requires that all fittings used in boilers be constructed of materials that will withstand the temperatures and pressures the boilers will be subjected to.

The code also specifies how these fittings will be attached to the boiler. This will vary according to temperatures and pressures. In addition, the ASME code has a suggested procedure for testing and operation of all fittings found on boilers. These procedures will vary, depending on the temperatures and pressures at which the boilers operate.

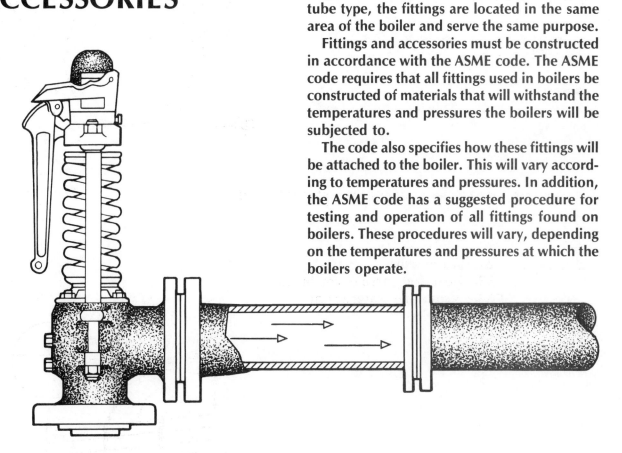

KEY TO ARROWHEAD SYMBOLS			
△ - Air	▲ - Water	▲ - Fuel Oil	⌂ - Air to Atmosphere
△ - Gas	△ - Steam	△ - Condensate	⌂ - Gases of Combustion

FITTINGS

Fittings (trim) on the boiler include valves, gauges, and other components required for safe and efficient operation. The location of the fittings necessary for operation is the same for fire tube and water tube boilers. See Figure 2-1.

There is no ornamental chrome on a steam boiler. Every fitting has a definite purpose. It is there for safety, efficiency, or a combination of safety and efficiency. Materials used for fittings are dependent upon temperatures and pressures involved.

For example, cast iron is used for the construction of water columns up to 250 psi. Malleable iron is used for water columns operating up to and including 350 psi. Steel is used for water columns operating over 350 psi.

Brass or bronze is used to construct fusible plugs, which have a core filled with pure tin. The melting point of the tin is 450°F and provides the last warning to the boiler operator before the highest heating surface overheats.

In a horizontal return tubular (HRT) boiler, the fusible plug is located in the tube sheet

(front or rear) about 2" to 3" above the top row of tubes. In the scotch marine boiler with a wet-top combustion chamber, fusible plugs are located in the top of the combustion chamber (crown sheet). At one time fusible plugs were commonly used on both fire tube and water tube boilers. However, fusible plugs are seldom found on newly installed boilers. With age, fusible plugs crystallize which alters the melting temperature of the core. This can result in the failure of a fusible plug to quickly melt when the heating surface overheats. All fusible plugs must be removed and replaced during a boiler inspection.

All fittings found on a boiler are necessary. However, most boiler operators and boiler inspectors feel that safety valves are the most important fittings.

Safety Valves

Steam boilers are designed for a *maximum allowable working pressure* (MAWP). If this

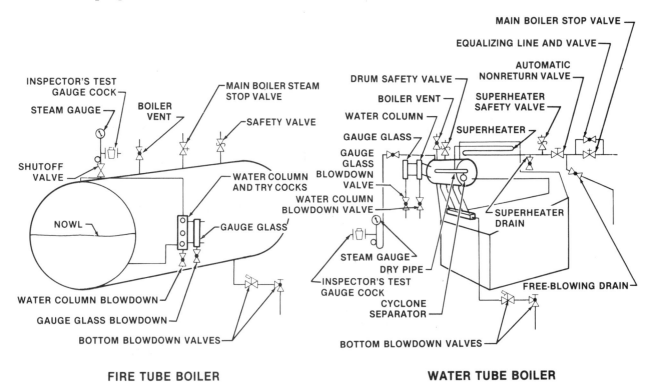

Figure 2-1. Fittings on boilers are located for visibility and accessibility.

pressure is exceeded, a failure can occur on the pressure side. A boiler failure occurs when there is a sudden drop in pressure without a corresponding drop in temperature. A portion of water in the boiler drum will flash into steam, causing a violent release of uncontrolled energy.

To prevent a failure from occurring, all steam boilers are equipped with at least one safety valve. The purpose of the safety valve is to protect the steam boiler from exceeding its MAWP according to the ASME code. Boilers having more than 500 square feet of heating surface require two or more safety valves. The capacity of the safety valves must be large enough to discharge all the steam that the boiler can generate. This must be done without allowing the pressure to rise more than 6% above the MAWP.

Electric boilers require one safety valve. Electric boilers exceeding 500 kW input require two

safety valves. The minimum safety valve relieving capacity for electric boilers is $3\frac{1}{2}$ lb/hr/kW.

Safety valves are located at the highest part of the steam and water drum and on the superheater header outlet. They must be connected to the boiler shell according to the ASME code, without any valves between the safety valve and the boiler, or superheater header outlet.

The safety valve connection will be either a screw or flange type, depending upon the size, operating pressure, and temperature of the boiler. Low pressure boilers usually have screw connections. High pressure boilers have flange connections.

When discharge piping is used in connection with a safety valve, it must be adequately braced and must not place a strain on the valve. Drains are placed at the lower sections of the discharge piping to remove any conden-

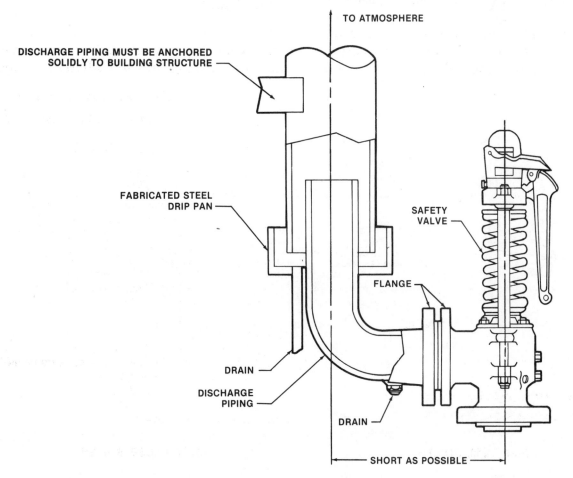

Figure 2-2. The piping layout for the safety valve must allow for the proper drainage of condensate.

sation that may form. See Figure 2-2. Discharge piping must be solidly connected to the building structure. A flexible joint is used to prevent strain on the safety valve.

The two basic types of safety valves found on steam boilers are the *spring-loaded pop-type* and the *super-jet type*. These valves are of simple construction and are very reliable. Lever-type and deadweight-type safety valves cannot be used on steam boilers.

Pop-type safety valves are used for pressures up to 600 psi. See Figure 2-3. Super-jet type safety valves are used for pressures up to 3,000 psi and are designed to withstand extremely high pressures and temperatures.

Safety valves are designed to open fully at a predetermined pressure and will remain open until there is a definite drop in pressure. This drop in pressure is known as *blowdown* (blowback) of a safety valve. The blowdown is usually 2 to 8 psi below the popping pressure,

but never more than 4% of the set pressure. For pressures between 200 and 300 psi, the blowdown shall not be less than 1% of the set pressure. (See Section I, ASME code.)

A safety valve must close tight without chattering. Once it has reseated, it must remain closed until its popping pressure is reached again.

Normally, whenever a valve under pressure is opened, it is opened slowly. This is not true with a safety valve. It pops open. This does not happen by accident, but by design. See Figure 2-4. A spring exerting a downward force keeps the valve closed. The steam pressure, acting on the safety valve disc, is exerting an upward force, trying to force the valve to open. The total force trying to overcome the spring force is equal to the area of the safety valve disc times the steam pressure.

To find the total force, first determine the area of the valve disc of the safety valve. This

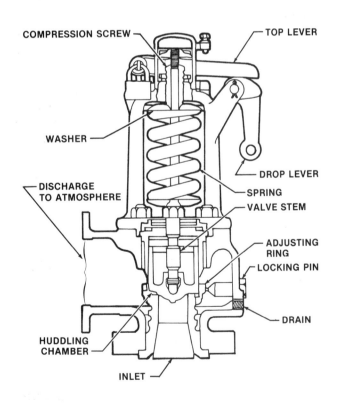

Figure 2-3. The pop-type safety valve is used as the steam drum safety valve on steam boilers with pressures of up to 600 psi.

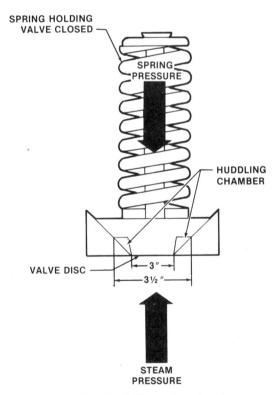

Figure 2-4. The huddling chamber increases the total force of the steam, causing the safety valve to pop open.

is found by using the formula:

$$area = 0.7854 \times d^2$$

Next, multiply the area times pressure. For example, a steam pressure of 100 psi and a valve disc diameter of 3″ has a total force of 706.86 pounds. In the following equations, *TF* is *total force*, *A* is *area*, *P* is *pressure*, and *d* is *diameter*.

$$TF = A \times P$$
$$TF = 0.7854 \times d^2 \times P$$
$$TF = 0.7854 \times 3″ \times 3″ \times 100 \text{ psi}$$
$$TF = 706.86 \text{ pounds}$$

The spring must exert a downward force equal to the upward force to keep the valve closed. As soon as the steam pressure starts to overcome the force of the spring, the valve will slowly start to open (feather). This allows the steam to enter a huddling chamber, which exposes a larger area for the steam pressure to act on.

This increases the total upward force, causing the safety valve to open quickly, or pop open. Using the dimensions from Figure 2-4, the diameter of the valve disc and the huddling chamber exposed to steam pressure is now 3½″. The total force will then be:

$$TF = A \times P$$
$$TF = 0.7854 \times d^2 \times P$$
$$TF = 0.7854 \times 3.5″ \times 3.5″ \times 100 \text{ psi}$$
$$TF = 962.11 \text{ pounds}$$

The total force jumps from 706.86 pounds to 962.11 pounds, an increase of 255.25 pounds. This greater total force overcomes the spring force, causing the valve to pop open.

Safety Valve Testing. Safety valves should be tested at regular intervals, either manually or by pressure. Testing assures that the valves are functioning properly. The interval between tests will vary from plant to plant because of operating steam pressures, local codes, and plant routine. A suggested testing procedure follows:

1. Boilers 16 psi up to, and including, 900 psi—

a. Manually test once a month.
b. Pressure test once a year.
2. Boilers above 900 psi—
a. Manually test once every six months (preferably when the boiler is going to be removed from service).
b. Pressure test once a year or have completely overhauled by factory, including factory setting and testing.

When testing a safety valve manually, always be sure that the boiler has at least 75% of the popping pressure. This will prevent possible damage to the valve. Safety valves should only be tested to assure that they function correctly. If tested too frequently, there would be a needless waste of steam and fuel and a lowering of boiler efficiency.

The capacity of a safety valve is measured in pounds of steam per hour that it is capable of discharging under a given pressure. The safety valve on steam boilers must be capable of discharging all of the steam the boiler can generate without the pressure increasing more than 6% above the set pressure. In no case can the pressure be greater than 6% above the MAWP for that boiler.

An accumulation test is used to determine if the safety valve capacity is large enough to protect the boiler. This test should not be conducted without a boiler inspector present. Boilers equipped with superheaters should not be subjected to an accumulation test because the superheater tubes could be damaged, due to overheating from the lack of steam flow through them.

The accumulation test is made by shutting off all steam outlets from the boiler and increasing the firing rate to a maximum. The safety valves should relieve all the steam without the pressure increasing more than 6% above the set pressure. During this test, the boiler operator must maintain a *normal operating water level* (NOWL).

NOTE: It takes one pound of water to make one pound of steam. The steam lost during this test must be replaced with additional feedwater makeup. An adequate water supply must be available during this test.

Safety Valve Adjustments and Repairs.
The setting or adjusting of the popping pressure and the blowdown of a safety valve should only be done by a qualified person who is familiar with the construction, operation, and maintenance of safety valves. Repairs should only be done by the manufacturer or a manufacturer's authorized representative. Always check local code requirements for the setting, adjustment, and testing procedures of safety valves.

Each boiler safety valve has a data plate attached. See Figure 2-5. The information shown on the data plates may vary slightly from manufacturer to manufacturer. However, all data plates must provide the following information:

1. manufacturer's name or trademark
2. manufacturer's design or type number
3. size of valve in inches, seat diameter
4. popping pressure setting in psig
5. blowdown in pounds per square inch
6. capacity in pounds per hour
7. lift of the valve in inches
8. year built or code mark
9. ASME symbol
10. serial number

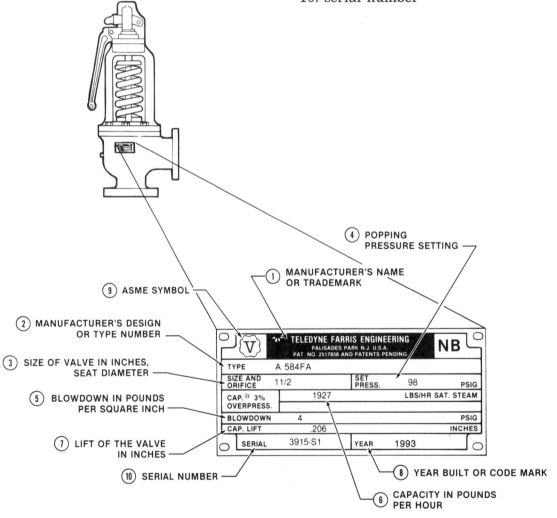

Figure 2-5. The ASME code requires certain data on all safety valve data plates. (*Teledyne Farris Engineering*)

Water Column

The main purpose of the water column on a steam boiler is to reduce the turbulence in the gauge glass to give the operator a more accurate reading. The water column also serves as a fitting to which the following may be attached: *gauge glass, try cocks, high and low water alarm whistles,* and *gauge glass blowdown lines.*

The gauge glass is a primary water level indicator. The try cocks are a secondary water level indicator. The high and low water alarm whistles only warn the operator of a dangerous water condition. Blowdown lines for the water column and gauge glass are used to remove any buildup of sludge or sediment.

The location of the water column differs slightly in fire tube and water tube boilers. See Figure 2-6. On fire tube boilers it is located at

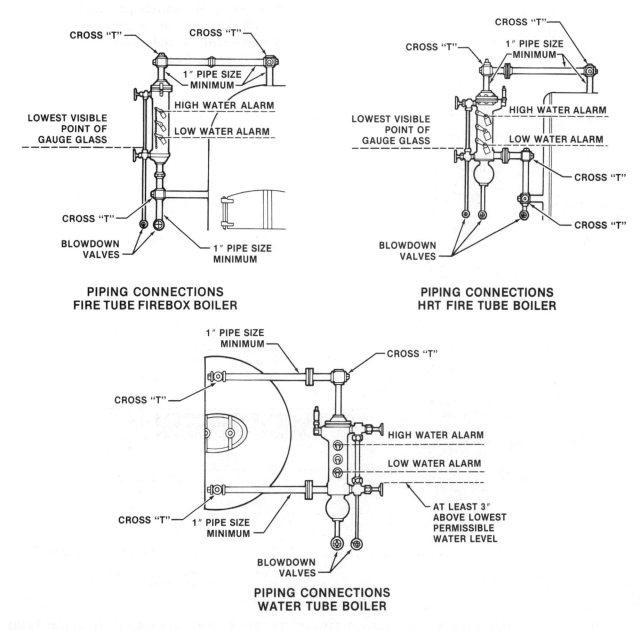

PIPING CONNECTIONS
FIRE TUBE FIREBOX BOILER

PIPING CONNECTIONS
HRT FIRE TUBE BOILER

PIPING CONNECTIONS
WATER TUBE BOILER

Figure 2-6. The location of the water column varies on different types of boilers.

the NOWL so that the lowest visible part of the gauge glass is 2″ to 3″ above the highest heating surface. On water tube boilers the water column is located at the NOWL so that the lowest visible part of the gauge glass is 3″ above the lowest permissible water level, as specified by the manufacturer.

The water column is connected to the highest part of the steam space and to the water side of the boiler. The connecting pipe size must be a minimum of 1″ and must meet the requirements of the ASME code for both pressure and temperature. Provisions must be made for cleaning and inspection by installing cross "T's" in pipe connections.

Valves are permitted between the water column and boiler if they are as specified in the ASME code, either outside stem and yoke (os&y) or stopcocks with levers permanently fastened. Both are to be sealed or locked in an open position. Lines cannot connect to the water column that would cause a flow of steam or water because this would result in a false water level reading.

The position of the steam and water connection for a water column is specified in the ASME code. See Figure 2-7. Water columns are made of cast iron, malleable iron, or steel.

Cast iron can be used with pressures up to 250 psi, malleable iron with pressures up to and including 350 psi, and steel with pressures higher than 350 psi.

Gauge Glass. The gauge glass is normally attached to the water column by a screw or flanged fitting. Most are equipped with quick-closing stop valves that can be closed in the event of a glass failure. Tubular glass is used at pressures up to and including 250 psi, and flat glass is used above 250 psi. See Figure 2-8. The gauge glass should be protected by a shield to prevent accidental breakage and to protect the operator.

Steam boilers that operate at 250 psi and up have either two gauge glasses, or one gauge glass and an electrical level indicator. A broken gauge glass can be replaced while a steam boiler is under pressure.

WARNING: Never work on a gauge glass without using eye protection.

The following procedure should be observed when replacing a broken tubular gauge glass:

1. Secure water and steam gauge glass stop valves.

2. Open blowdown valve for the gauge glass.

3. Check water level by secondary means.

4. Remove gauge glass guard.

5. Remove gauge glass nuts.

6. Remove all broken glass and old washers.

7. Cut a new glass, leaving a ¼″ clearance for installation.

8. Place nuts and new washers on the gauge glass.

9. Center the glass so that it does not touch any metal.

10. Tighten nuts by hand and then make a one-quarter turn with a wrench.

11. Crack open the steam gauge glass stop valve and allow the glass to be heated and expand.

12. When the glass has been heated, close the gauge glass blowdown valve and open the water gauge glass stop valve.

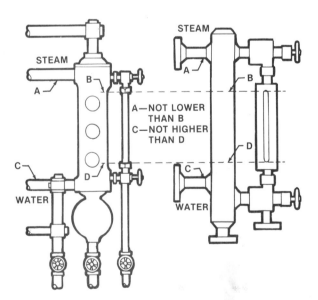

Figure 2-7. The arrangement of steam and water connections for a water column is specified in the ASME code.

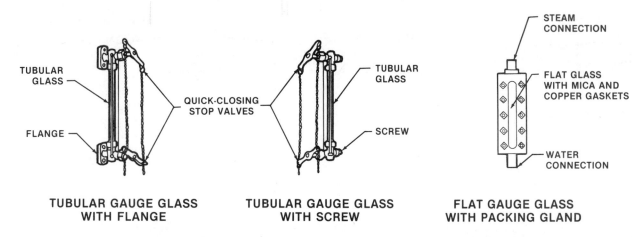

TUBULAR GAUGE GLASS
WITH FLANGE

TUBULAR GAUGE GLASS
WITH SCREW

FLAT GAUGE GLASS
WITH PACKING GLAND

Figure 2-8. Tubular gauge glasses are used for pressures up to 250 psi. Flat gauge glasses are used for pressures above 250 psi.

13. Open the steam gauge glass valve fully.

14. Check for leaks and tighten nuts if necessary.

15. Replace gauge glass guards.

A broken flat gauge glass can be replaced while a steam boiler is under pressure as follows:

1. Secure water and steam gauge glass stop valves.

2. Open blowdown valve from gauge glass.

3. Remove packing gland nuts and gland (top and bottom).

4. Remove old packing.

5. Remove gauge glass assembly.

6. Install new gauge glass assembly.

7. Repack and replace glands and nuts.

8. Close gauge glass blowdown valve.

9. Heat and expand glass by cracking open water side of glass only.

10. If leakage occurs, tighten as per manufacturer's specifications using proper tools. Tighten in sequence.

11. If no leakage occurs, open steam and water side fully.

Try Cocks. Try cocks are used while a broken gauge glass is being replaced or if there is doubt as to the true water level in the boiler.

Try cocks are mounted at two or three points on the water column and are used to determine the water level within the steam boiler. The middle cock is at the NOWL, the bottom cock indicates a low water level, and the top cock indicates a high water level.

Try cocks are very effective up to 250 psi. Above that point it is difficult to distinguish between the water and the flash steam that blows out of the try cock.

SECONDARY ONLY IN LOW PRESSURE BOILERS.

Alarm Whistles. Alarm whistles are often mounted on a water column. They alert the operator of a high or low water level condition. The two types of alarm whistles are *float type* and *weight type.* See Figure 2-9.

In the float-type alarm whistle, two floats are attached to rods and are connected independently to the valve levers. One float is set at a high level and opens the valve if the float is lifted by high water. This will cause steam to pass through the valve to the whistle.

The other float is set at a low level. If the water drops, the float opens the valve, allowing steam to pass through to the whistle, which signals low water. *NOTE:* This whistle is an alarm indicating a dangerous water level. The operator must determine high or low water by using the gauge glass or a secondary means

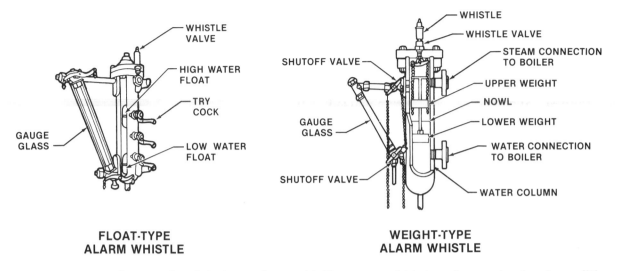

FLOAT-TYPE ALARM WHISTLE

WEIGHT-TYPE ALARM WHISTLE

Figure 2-9. Both float and weight-type alarm whistles warn of high or low water level condition.

(try cocks) of establishing the water level.

In the weight-type alarm whistle, two weights are attached to rods and connected independently to the valve levers. As water rises in the column, the upper weight is surrounded by water and gains sufficient buoyancy. This opens the whistle valve, indicating a high water level. The lower weight is normally covered with water. If the water level should drop, the weight will lose buoyancy and open the whistle valve, indicating a low water level.

Blowdown Procedure. The water column and gauge glass should be blown down once during every shift or whenever the operator is in doubt as to the true water level. This is necessary to remove sludge and sediment that may collect in the piping connections. A build-up of either would give a false water level.

On boilers equipped with flat gauge glasses, follow manufacturer's recommendations for blowing down. Some flat glasses have mica between the glass and steam or water to prevent the steam or water from coming into direct contact with the glass. The mica prevents etching and discoloration of the glass. The mica in the gauge glass can be damaged when steam is blown across it.

Steam Pressure Gauge

The principle of the modern pressure gauge was discovered in 1849 by a French scientist named Eugene Bourdon. Bourdon was coiling copper tubing to make a still and during the process, one side was flattened by accident. To save the coil, he filled it with water and connected it to a pump, thinking hydraulic pressure would cause the tubing to pop back into shape.

Because the tubing was coiled, instead of going back into its original shape it started to uncoil. The more pressure Bourdon applied, the more the tubing uncoiled. As the pressure was released, the tubing coiled back up.

He made notes of what he observed, and from these notes came the beginning of our modern pressure gauge. Bourdon's findings were recognized and the tube inside a pressure gauge is called a *Bourdon tube*. See Figure 2-10.

Boiler plants have pressure gauges to indicate all of the various pressures an operator must be aware of to ensure safe and efficient plant operation. Pressure gauges are calibrated in pounds per square inch. *Gauge pressure* is the pressure above atmospheric pressure. *Absolute pressure* is gauge pressure plus atmospheric pressure.

The boiler pressure gauge should be plainly visible to the operator. The pipeline that connects the pressure gauge comes from the highest part of the boiler steam and water drum. Connections to the boiler shall not be less than ¼″. If steel or wrought iron is used, it must not be less than ½″. The steam gauge must be protected by a siphon to prevent steam from damaging the Bourdon tube. Pipe siphons may be pigtail or U-tube. See Figure 2-11.

It is also advisable to install a gate valve to facilitate changing of the gauge in the event

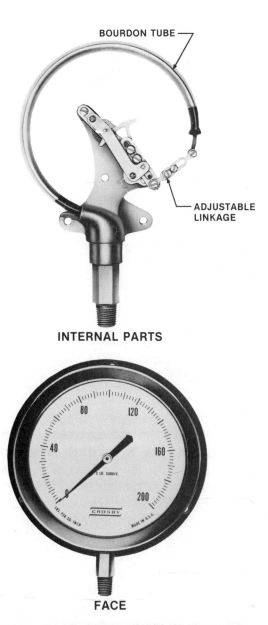

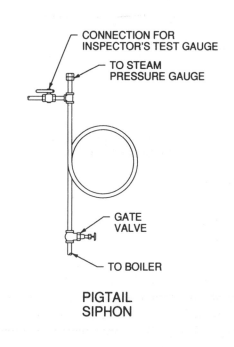

PIGTAIL SIPHON

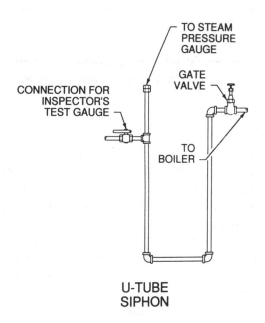

U-TUBE SIPHON

Figure 2-10. The Bourdon tube and adjustable linkage make the setting and correction of a pressure gauge possible. (*Crosby Valve & Gage Co.*)

Figure 2-11. The steam siphon protects the Bourdon tube from the high temperature of the steam. An inspector's test gauge is connected when checking the pressure gauge for accuracy.

of a failure. A connection for an inspector's test gauge is also recommended by the ASME code.

A boiler steam pressure gauge should have a range of up to two times the safety valve setting. It should never be less than one-and-one-half times the safety valve setting. If for any reason a steam pressure gauge is not accurate to within 2% of the working pressure, it must be recalibrated or replaced. A pressure gauge can be recalibrated using a test gauge or a deadweight tester. See Figure 2-12.

What is the hydrostatic pressure?
Hydrostatic Pressure = Vertical Feet × .433 psi/vertical foot
20 × .433 = 8.66
Hydrostatic Pressure = **8.66 psi**

Pressure Gauge Reading Above Steam and Water Drum	91.34 psi
+ Hydrostatic Pressure	8.66 psi
Pressure Gauge Reading Below Steam and Water Drum	100 psi

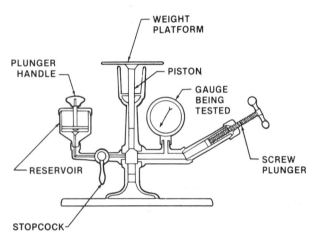

Figure 2-12. The deadweight tester is used to recalibrate pressure gauges.

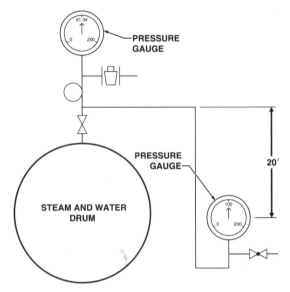

Figure 2-13. A pressure gauge reading made below the steam and water drum must be corrected for hydrostatic pressure (0.433 psi per vertical foot).

When a boiler pressure gauge is located below the steam and water drum, it must be corrected to compensate for the vertical height of condensate above the pressure gauge. This is called *hydrostatic pressure*. The correction factor for hydrostatic pressure is 0.433 psi per vertical foot. See Figure 2-13.

Boiler Vents

Boiler vents are sometimes called *drum vents* or *air cocks.* Boiler vents

1. remove air from the steam and water drum while filling and during warm-up, prior to putting the boiler into service,

2. prevent a vacuum from developing within the boiler drum when the boiler is removed from service, or when draining the boiler.

The boiler vent is connected to the highest part of the steam and water drum with suitable piping and valves that must meet temperature and pressure requirements of the ASME code. When warming up a boiler, the boiler vent is in an open position until the boiler gauge registers 25 psi, according to the ASME code.

At that point, all air has been removed from the boiler drum and the vent is manually closed. After removing the boiler from service, and allowing the steam pressure to drop to 25 psi, the vent should be opened manually. This prevents a vacuum from developing as the steam in the drum condenses.

PART OF BOILER FITTINGS.

WARNING: Before removing a handhole or manhole cover, the boiler vent should be opened to make sure there is no vacuum in the boiler. Failure to do so could result in serious injury to the operator and/or internal damage to the boiler.

Steam Separators

Steam separators are found in the steam and water drum of boilers. They work on the basic principle of changing the direction of flow of the steam, causing the heavier water droplets to separate. The purpose of the steam separator is to remove as much moisture from the steam as possible. In doing so, the steam separator

1. conserves the energy of the steam,
2. prevents water hammer or steam engine damage due to carryover of water,
3. protects valves, pistons, cylinders of reciprocating engines, and turbine blades from the erosive action of wet steam.

When a steam boiler is operated at high loads or with a high water level, there is a tendency to carry water droplets with the steam. One method used to control this carryover is to use a *dry pipe separator*. Another method uses *a cyclone separator*. See Figure 2-14.

Dry Pipe Separator. A dry pipe separator consists of a pipe that is in the upper part of the steam and water drum and is closed at both ends. The top half is drilled with many small holes and is connected at top center to the main steam outlet from the boiler. It has drains on the bottom that allow the trapped moisture to return to the boiler drum. The operation of the dry pipe separator is based on change of direction of the steam flow.

Steam enters the small holes on top. The steam has to change direction to leave through the steam outlet. This change in direction causes any trapped moisture to be separated and returned to the boiler through the drains. The dry pipe separator is very effective for small boilers or boilers with light steam loads.

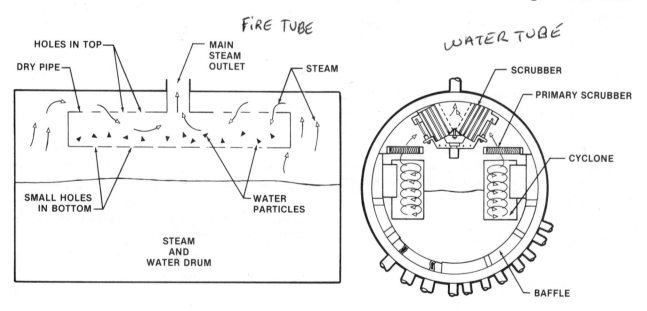

DRY PIPE SEPARATOR (SIDE VIEW)

CYCLONE SEPARATOR (END VIEW)

Figure 2-14. Dry pipe and cyclone separators remove moisture from the steam, thereby improving the quality of the steam.

As the capacity of a boiler increases, efficiency of the dry pipe separator is reduced.

Cyclone Separator. A cyclone separator consists of a number of cyclones set side by side along the length of the drum and a baffle arrangement that directs steam into the cyclones. Moisture is removed by centrifugal force as the steam is forced to rotate when it passes through the cyclones. For improved separation of steam and moisture, baffles are set up over the top of each cyclone.

Cyclone separators are essential when a boiler has a superheater and when it is necessary to keep carryover to a minimum. Scrubbers remove any moisture and solids remaining in the steam before it leaves the steam and water drum.

Superheaters

Superheaters are used to increase the amount of heat in the steam. *Saturated steam* is steam at a temperature that corresponds with its pressure. See Figure 2-15. When any heat is removed from the steam, a portion of the steam condenses back into the liquid state. The temperature of saturated steam is the same as the temperature of the water it is in contact with.

GAUGE PRESSURE (PSIG)	ABSOLUTE PRESSURE (PSIA)	SATURATION TEMPERATURE (°F)
0	14.7	212
5.3	20	228
50.3	65	298
100.3	115	337
200.3	215	388
450.3	465	460
500.3	515	470
600.3	615	489

Figure 2-15. Temperature varies with pressure in a steam boiler. To change gauge pressure to absolute pressure, add 14.7 psi to gauge pressure.

The temperature of the water is dependent upon pressure inside the drum. For example, water boils at 212°F at 0 psi, but water boils at 337°F at 100 psi. In both cases, the steam and the water are at the same temperature, 212°F in the first example and 337°F in the second example. The temperature of saturated steam increases as the pressure increases.

Steam may be either dry or wet. If all steam that leaves the water is completely evaporated, the steam is dry. If there are water droplets in the steam, it is wet. The quality (water present) of saturated steam is expressed as a percentage of the total steam evaporated. If steam leaving the boiler has a quality of 98%, it is 98% evaporated and contains 2% water. A throttling calorimeter is used to determine the moisture content in steam.

Superheated steam is steam at a temperature higher than its *corresponding pressure*, which is the pressure at which both the water and steam are at the same temperature. Superheated steam, which is completely evaporated steam, has a higher heat content than saturated steam. Therefore, superheated steam can produce more work than saturated steam can produce at the same pressure. For example, saturated steam at 100 psi has a temperature of 337°F. If this steam at 100 psi had a temperature of 500°F, it would be superheated steam.

Initially, steam power plants using reciprocating engines were designed to operate with saturated steam. Steam separators were introduced between the boiler and the engine to remove condensate from the steam. This improved the quality of the steam but did not remove all moisture. Definite drawbacks to using this wet steam were

1. erosion of engine parts,
2. erosion of pipes and fittings caused by *impingement* of the steam (impingement is the wearing away of metal caused by the water in the steam striking metal surfaces),
3. loss of heat to metal, causing condensation of steam.

These drawbacks were almost eliminated by

using superheated steam. *NOTE:* In an average steam turbine, there is a gain of 1% in efficiency for every 35° of superheat. The increase can go as high as 15% for 200° of superheat in larger turbines.

Heat is added to the steam after it has been removed from its liquid. Saturated steam can be superheated by passing it through a heater after the steam has been removed from the steam and water drum. The degree of superheat will depend on the difference in temperature of the saturated steam compared to the superheated state of the same steam.

For example, saturated steam at 100 psi is at a temperature of 337°F. If it were heated to 500°F it would have a superheat of 500°F − 337°F, or 163°F of superheat. Based on this example, the gain is 163°F of superheat (500°F − 337°F = 163°F). To find the increase in efficiency, divide the gain by 35. This equals a 4.7% increase in efficiency.

Superheaters are nests of tubes located in the *radiant zone* (furnace area) or in the direct path of the gases of combustion. See Figure 2-16. Superheaters may be classified as *radiant* or *convection.* A consistent steam temperature during fluctuations in load can be maintained by using both the radiant and convection superheater in the same unit.

Superheaters have smooth or extended surfaces. Extended surface superheaters have cast-iron fins or grills mounted on a smooth tube that increases the heating surface.

Superheaters come in many different shapes and forms. This variety is necessary because of the difference in boiler sizes and designs and the amount of space available for the superheater in the boiler. A radiant superheater receives its heat from the radiant heat zone. A convection superheater receives its heat from the flow of the gases of combustion.

The multi-loop superheater is made up of

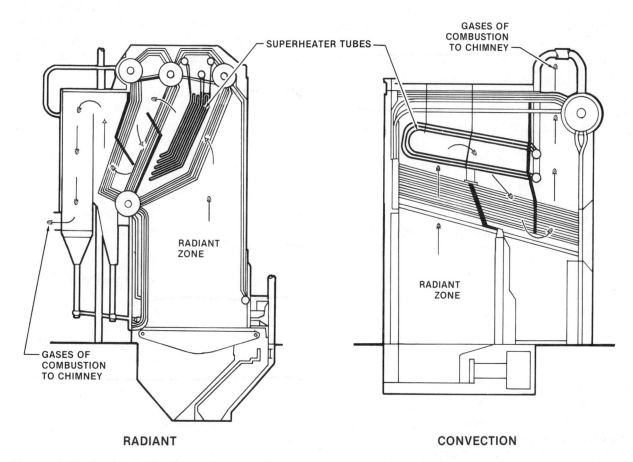

Figure 2-16. Steam boilers may have radiant or convection superheaters.

many tubes bent back a number of times between the inlet and outlet headers. By placing the superheater headers outside the high radiant heat zones, the tube connections are readily available for maintenance.

This also reduces or minimizes the possibility of leaks. Detachable metal-to-metal ball joints connect the tubes to the header and are held in place by steel studs and clamps. This arrangement makes the removal of any joint of a superheater tube for cleaning or inspection a relatively simple operation.

Superheater Operation. When operating a steam boiler equipped with a superheater, a flow of steam must be maintained through the superheater at all times. The flow of steam should never be less than 25% of boiler capacity. Failure to maintain steam flow will result in overheating, warping, or burning of superheater tubes.

A safety valve is required at the superheater outlet header. The safety valve must be of sufficient capacity to relieve 25% of the steam the boiler can produce. Superheater safety valves are set at a lower popping pressure than the safety valves on the steam and water drum to ensure this flow of steam.

Superheaters must also be fitted with a drain on the outlet side. This drain remains open when warming up a boiler and is left open until the boiler is cut in on the line. The drain must also be opened as soon as the boiler is taken off-line. This ensures a flow of steam through the superheater at all times.

This flow of steam keeps the superheater tubes from overheating during start-up and shutdown. Superheaters must be kept free of soot to maintain the transfer of heat. For optimum efficiency, follow the manufacturer's recommendations for start-up and shutdown procedures.

Soot Blowers

Soot blowers are used to remove soot deposits and to permit better heat transfer in the boiler. In order to have a transfer of heat, there must be a difference in temperature between two

substances. The greater this difference is, the greater the heat transfer will be. Boiler efficiency will increase with better heat transfer, thus reducing fuel consumption. *Soot* is carbon (unburned fuel). Soot acts as an insulator when deposited on the heating surface of the boiler. Soot deposits on heating surfaces result in increased fuel consumption. See Figure 2-17.

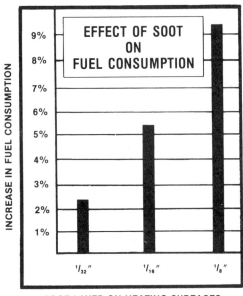

Figure 2-17. Soot is an insulator and will reduce the efficiency of a boiler.

In a fire tube boiler, gases of combustion pass through the tubes. To remove soot deposits in a fire tube boiler, it is necessary to take the boiler off-line and use brushes or scrapers. Soot blowers are not very effective in fire tube boilers but are found on some of the older HRT boilers. In water tube boilers, gases of combustion pass around the tubes. Soot deposits can be easily removed by using soot blowers. See Figure 2-18. Most modern water tube boilers are equipped with permanently installed soot blowers.

Soot blower elements are located in the direct path of the gases of combustion. These elements are made of a steel alloy to withstand

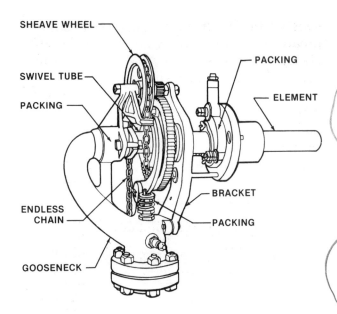

Figure 2-18. Soot blowers are used on most water tube boilers to increase their efficiency.

the high temperature of the gases of combustion. The nozzles in the element are spaced so they will allow steam or air to blow between the rows of tubes. They are held in place by bearings clamped or welded to the boiler tubes. These bearings allow the element to rotate.

Element alignment is important. If the element were to shift, steam impinging on the boiler tubes would cut through the boiler tube in a very short time.

Soot Blower Operation. The soot blower element is connected to a cam-operated valve in the head of the soot blower. It is chain operated. As it rotates the element, the steam valve is opened at the proper time, allowing steam to blow through the nozzles. As it is rotated further, the steam valve will close when the arc of soot blowing is completed. The steam line feeding the soot blowers must come from the highest part of the steam side of the boiler to ensure moisture-free steam. It is important that the soot blower lines be thoroughly warmed and completely drained. Any water discharged with the steam would cause the soot to cake up, and the sulfur in the

soot mixing with the water would cause damage to the boiler heating surface.

To blow soot, it is necessary to warm up and drain the steam lines, increase boiler draft, and follow boiler manufacturer's instructions on which elements to blow first. To blow soot, follow the path of the gases of combustion, from the first to the last pass.

Boiler Stop Valves

The ASME code states that high pressure boilers in battery (two or more boilers connected to a common header) and equipped with manhole openings must have two main steam stop valves with an ample free-blowing drain between them. Additionally, these valves should be of the os&y type that will show by spindle position whether the valve is open or closed. See Figure 2-19.

The valve should be a gate valve since it offers no resistance to the flow of steam. It should

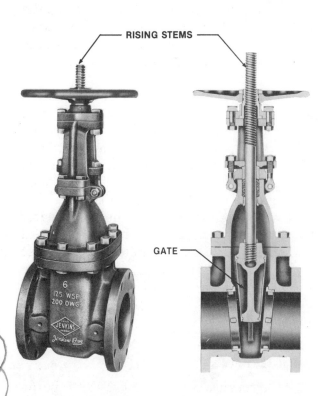

Figure 2-19. The os&y valve is used as the steam boiler stop valve. It will not restrict the flow of steam. *(Jenkins Bros.)*

always be either wide open or completely closed. An automatic nonreturn valve may be used in place of one of the stop valves. However, the automatic nonreturn valve must be located as close to the shell of the boiler as practical. See Figure 2-20.

The main stop valve is used to place a boiler in service or isolate it from the system for cleaning, inspection, or boiler repairs. The automatic nonreturn valve improves the safety and efficiency of the plant. It can cut a boiler in on the line automatically and protect the system in the event of a failure on the pressure side of any boiler on the line.

If a boiler dropped some tubes and the pressure in the boiler dropped below header pressure, the nonreturn valve would close, taking the boiler off the line and preventing steam from flowing out of the other boiler.

Both the main stop valve and the automatic nonreturn valve should be dismantled, inspected, and overhauled annually. During boiler inspection, these valves are closed, locked, and tagged while the drain between them is open.

Boiler Stop Valve Operation. In order to cut a boiler in on a line that is equipped with an automatic nonreturn valve, proceed as follows:

1. After making all necessary safety checks and warming up the boiler slowly, open the bypass around the main steam stop valve to warm up the line and equalize pressure on both sides of the valve.

2. When about 85% of the line pressure is on the incoming boiler, slowly open the main steam stop valve.

3. Open the free-blowing drain to remove any condensate trapped between the two valves.

4. Open the automatic nonreturn valve.

5. Slowly bring the pressure of the incoming boiler up to line pressure and let the automatic nonreturn valve cut the boiler in on the line.

6. Close the free-blowing drain. The automatic nonreturn valve will start to open when the pressure of the incoming boiler is slightly higher than line pressure.

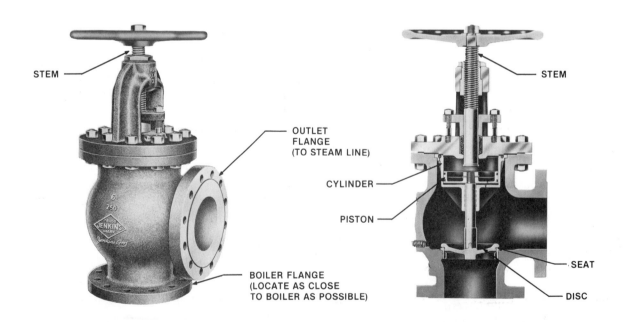

Figure 2-20. The automatic nonreturn valve is located as close to the boiler shell as is practical. It cuts the boiler in on the line and off the line automatically. *(Jenkins Bros.)*

For two valves that are hand-operated, follow steps 1, 2, and 3. Then, when the pressure of the incoming boiler is about 5 psi below header pressure, slowly crack open the main stop valve nearest the shell of the boiler. The header pressure, being a little higher than the incoming boiler pressure, will force any trapped condensate in the line back into the boiler. This helps to prevent carryover.

During normal usage the main steam line expands and contracts continuously. To allow for this expansion and contraction, expansion bends are used. This prevents excessive stress on the boiler and header. See Figure 2-21.

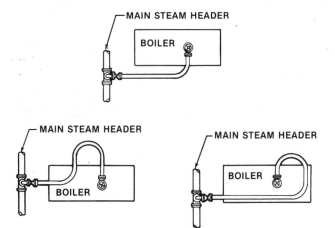

Figure 2-21. Expansion bends allow for expansion and contraction of the main steam line.

Blowdown Valves and Lines

All raw water (city water) contains a certain amount of scale-forming salts. These scale-forming salts start to settle out when the temperature of the water reaches about 150°F. The salts settle on the boiler heating surface, insulating the surface. The salts can cause the boiler tubes to overheat and burn out. To prevent this, chemicals are added to the boiler water.

The chemicals turn these scale-forming salts into a nonadhering sludge. The sludge will stay in suspension or settle to the lowest part of the water side of the boiler.

All boilers have a blowdown pipe fitted with a valve or cock. This is located at the lowest part of the water side of a fire tube boiler or the mud drum of a water tube boiler. Boilers operating at 100 psi or more are required to have two bottom blowdown valves.

The two valves may be two slow-opening valves, which require five full turns of the hand wheel to open or close fully, or one quick-opening valve and one slow-opening valve. If a quick-opening valve is used, it must be the valve closest to the shell of the boiler. See Figure 2-22.

When the MAWP exceeds 125 psi, the blowdown pipe and the fittings between the boiler and the valve must be composed of extra-heavy bronze, brass, or malleable iron suitable for the temperature and pressures involved, according to the ASME code. They must run full size with no reducers or bushings. Each bottom blowdown pipe is fitted with at least two 250 psi standard valves, both of which are extra heavy, according to the ASME code.

When the bottom blowdown pipe is exposed to direct furnace heat, it must be protected by a refractory pier or by wrapping with a protective insulation. The bottom blowdown pipe should be installed so the pipe can be inspected.

The opening in the boiler setting for the blowdown pipe should be arranged to provide for free expansion and contraction. The minimum size for pipes and fittings is 1″. The maximum size is 2½″, including surface blowdown pipes. The most accurate means of determining the frequency of blowing down is through boiler water analysis. However, a boiler should be blown down at least once every 24 hours. Four reasons for using bottom blowdown valves are to

1. remove sludge and sediment,
2. control high water,
3. control chemical concentration,
4. drain boiler for cleaning and inspection.

Pressure must be on the boiler when blowing down. The only time there is no pressure

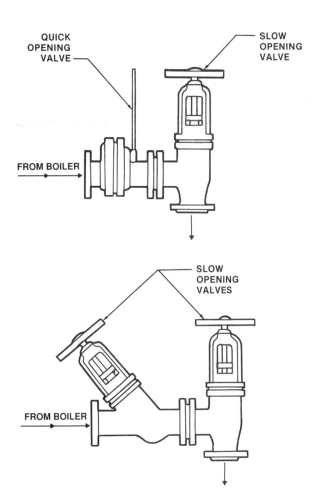

Figure 2-22. The quick-opening valve should be located closest to the boiler shell on the blow-down line.

is when the boiler is being drained. The boiler must be cool and the boiler vent open before draining.

Blowing Down a Boiler. When blowing down a boiler, the quick-opening valve should be opened first and closed last. This is a sealing valve. The slow-opening (screw-type) valve that is farthest from the shell of the boiler is the blowing valve. This valve takes the wear and tear of blowing down.

WARNING: Never walk away from an open blowdown valve. Keep your hand on the valve until it is closed.

The best time to blow down a boiler is at its lightest load. The procedure to use when blowing down a boiler is as follows:

1. Check water level.
2. Open the valve closest to the shell of the boiler first. Then open the slow-opening valve. Open valves slowly but fully.
3. Check or have someone else check the water level in the gauge glass while blowing down.
4. Close the slow-opening valve first. Close the valve closest to the shell of the boiler last.

When seatless-type valves are used on blowdown lines, follow the manufacturer's recommended operating procedure.

Some water tube boilers are equipped with waterwall blowdown valves. The valves are locked or sealed closed to avoid being opened by mistake while the boiler is firing. Waterwall blowdown valves should only be blown down after the furnace has had a chance to cool. They are usually blown down when the boiler is being taken off-line.

The blowdown valves must close tightly. If they are leaking, it will be indicated by a hot blowdown line and a drop in chemical concentrations. With a small leak, the boiler can still be operated if the water level can be easily maintained. However, the boiler should be removed from service for repairs as soon as possible.

If maintaining a NOWL is difficult, the boiler should be secured immediately. Any leaks on the blowdown line are considered dangerous. The boiler must be removed from service and cooled slowly. Before repairs are made, the boiler inspector must be notified and proper recommendations followed. The repair must be made in accordance with the ASME code.

Surface Blowdown

Surface tension on the water in a steam and water drum is increased by impurities that float on the surface of the water. These impurities enter the boiler through the feedwater system. An increase in the surface tension can cause foaming, resulting in rapid fluctuations in the water level.

The immediate danger is that large amounts of water will be carried over into the steam header and cause water hammer, which could lead to possible header rupture.

A surface blowdown line is connected to the steam and water drum at the NOWL. The valve on the surface blowdown line is opened to remove any impurities that may collect on the surface of the water. The maximum size of a surface blowdown line is 2½ ", according to the ASME code.

Continuous Blowdown

All boilers are equipped with some type of blowdown connections to remove sludge and sediment from the boiler. The bottom blowdown connection is designed for intermittent use, usually once in every 8- to 24-hour period.

Large boilers, instead of using a batch method of chemical treatment and a bottom blowdown one to three times a day, use a continuous, proportioning type of chemical treatment with a continuously controlled blowdown. The advantage of this system is that as solids are formed in the boiler water due to the chemical treatment, solids are being removed through the continuous blowdown system.

The continuous blowdown connection is made at a point just below the low water level in the steam and water drum. The discharge from the continuous blowdown line goes to the blowdown tank or to a flash tank. With this system it is possible to maintain a fairly constant total solids count in the boiler water. It is still occasionally necessary to use the bottom blowdown, but this can be done when the boiler is off or on a light load so that a greater concentration of solid matter is removed.

ACCESSORIES

Boiler accessories are required to operate a boiler. These accessories are not attached directly to the boiler but are necessary for its safe and efficient operation. Accessories commonly found in boiler systems are blowdown tanks and flash tanks used in the heat recovery system. Other boiler accessories, such as

steam, feedwater, fuel, and draft systems are discussed in Chapter 3.

Blowdown Tank

The discharge from the blowdown line cannot be connected directly to a sewer system because of the pressures and temperatures involved. If connected directly, it would be a violation of the Pressure Vessel Code.

In order to prevent hot water and steam from entering the sewer system, a blowdown or flash tank must be used between the blowdown line and the sewer. The blowdown lines are connected to this tank. The hot water and steam enter at the top of the tank. The flash steam leaves through the vent and the hot water stays in the tank.

As the level in the tank rises, cooler water from the bottom of the tank overflows into the sewer. The blowdown tank equipment should be of sufficient capacity to prevent discharging water over 150°F and/or 5 psi into the city sewer. It may be necessary to have a cold water line introduce city water into the blowdown tank outlet connection. See Figure 2-23.

After blowing down a boiler, the water remains in the blowdown tank to cool until another boiler is blown down. A siphon breaker (vent) is installed to prevent possible siphoning of the water from the tank.

Flash Tank and Heat Recovery System

Boilers have bottom blowdown valves, surface blowdown valves, and continuous blowdown valves. Usually, the bottom blowdown and surface blowdown valves discharge into a blowdown tank and then go to waste. In order to reclaim the heat from the continuous blowdown, a flash tank is used.

Water coming from the continuous blowdown is piped to the flash tank. As its pressure drops, some of the water flashes into steam. The steam is sent to the open feedwater heater.

The city water line passes through coils below the water level in the flash tank, picking up heat. When the water level in the flash tank gets too high, the internal overflow will remove the water and a trap will discharge it to waste. See Figure 2-24.

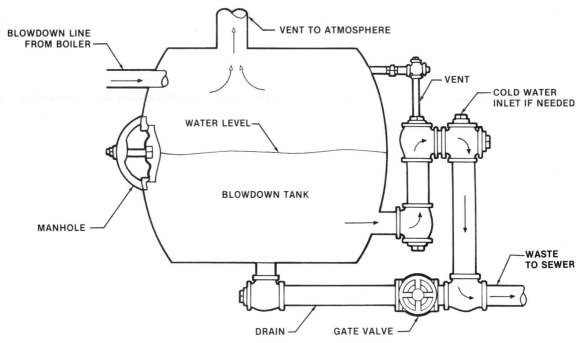

Figure 2-23. A blowdown tank prevents pressure buildup and allows boiler water to cool.

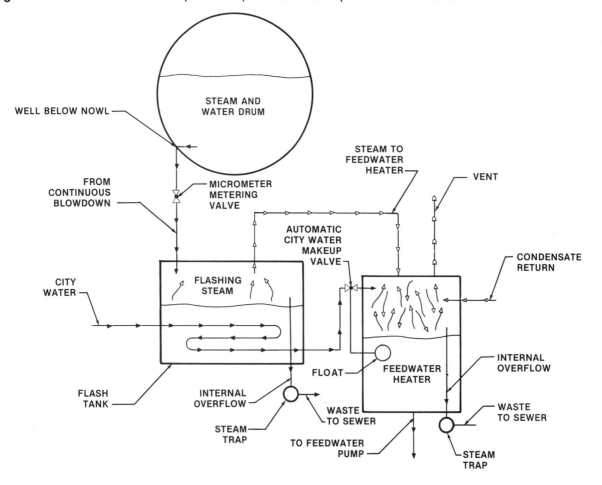

Figure 2-24. Continuous blowdown systems reclaim heat normally lost during boiler blowdown.

A heat recovery system using a flash economizer utilizes flash or exhaust steam to raise the temperature of feedwater. A 10°F rise in feedwater temperature gives approximately a 1% saving in fuel. See Figure 2-25.

In the heat recovery system, stop valves (1) are open during normal operation. The proportioning valve (2) regulates the flow of city water to the flash economizer (3). Water flows through strainers (4) and the continuous blow-down valves (5). Stop valves (6) bypass continuous blowdown to the bottom blowdown separator (7). The solenoid valve (8) controls automatic makeup (city water) and the alarm for low water in the deaerating feedwater heater (9). The overflow trap (10) removes excess water from the flash economizer. Mounting brackets (11) are used when dropping the economizer coil for cleaning.

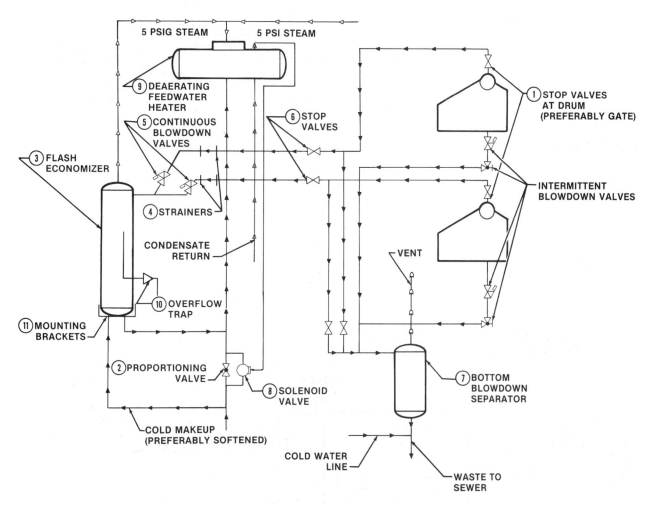

Figure 2-25. A blowdown heat recovery system increases the overall efficiency of the steam plant.

Key Words

absolute pressure
accessories
accumulation test
alarm whistle
blowdown
blowdown tank
blowdown valve and line
boiler vent
Bourdon tube
continuous blowdown
convection superheater
corresponding pressure
cyclone separator
data plate
dry pipe separator
fittings
flash tank
gauge glass
gauge glass blowdown line
gauge pressure
heat recovery system

huddling chamber
hydrostatic pressure
impingement
MAWP
NOWL
popping pressure
radiant superheater
radiant zone
safety valve
saturated steam
soot
soot blower
steam pressure gauge
steam separator
stop valve
superheated steam
superheater
surface blowdown
try cock
water column

_D_ 1. Boiler fittings are necessary for _____.
   A. safety only
   B. efficiency only
   C. cosmetic purposes
   D. both A and B

_D_ 2. The most important fitting on a boiler is the _____.
   A. low water fuel cutoff
   B. feedwater regulator
   C. superheater
   D. safety valve

_A_ 3. The fittings on a fire tube boiler and the fittings on a water tube boiler _____.
   A. serve the same purpose
   B. vary in their purpose
   C. are never found on the other boiler
   D. can never serve the same purpose

_C_ 4. A safety valve will _____.
   A. control the boiler operating range
   B. control high or low water
   C. prevent the boiler from exceeding its MAWP   BY 6%
   D. control high and low fire

_B_ 5. Safety valves are designed to _____.
   A. open slowly to prevent water hammer
   B. pop open   P.34
   C. open only by hand
   D. open and then close with no drop in pressure

_B_ 6. Superheater safety valves are set to open _____.
   A. after the main safety valves are opened
   B. before the main safety valves are opened   P.34 LOWRER POPPING
   C. only when header pressure is 6% above the MAWP   PRESSURE
   D. when the boiler is coming off-line

_A_ 7. When testing a safety valve by hand, there must be _____.
   A. at least 75% of the popping pressure
   B. no pressure on the boiler
   C. an inspector present
   D. someone watching the water level

_C_ 8. Any repairs to a safety valve should be done by the _____.
   A. chief engineer
   B. state inspector
   C. safety valve manufacturer or manufacturer's authorized representative
   D. maintenance department

_____ D

9. The setting or adjusting of a safety valve should only be done by the _____.
   A. boiler inspector
   B. state inspector
   C. person in charge of the shift
   D. qualified person who is familiar with the construction and operation of a safety valve

_____ A

10. If it is necessary to test the relieving capacity of a safety valve, a(n)_____.
    A. accumulation test is put on the boiler
    B. hydrostatic test is put on the boiler
    C. boiler must be secured and off-line
    D. bench test must be done

_____ D

11. The relieving capacity of a safety valve is measured in _____.
    A. British thermal units (Btu's)
    B. boiler horsepowers
    C. Btu's per boiler horsepowers
    D. pounds of steam per hour that it is capable of discharging under a given pressure.

_____ A

12. The main purpose of a water column is to _____.
    A. reduce turbulence in the gauge glass to get a more accurate reading of the water level in the boiler
    B. reduce surface tension
    C. provide a means of putting an accumulation test on the boiler
    D. provide a place to install the boiler gauge glass

_____ C

13. Try cocks are _____.
    A. only found on water tube boilers
    B. only found on fire tube boilers
    C. a secondary means of determining water level in a boiler
    D. used to collect boiler water samples

_____ C

14. When replacing a broken gauge glass, the water level is checked by _____.
    A. blowing down the gauge glass
    B. blowing down the water column
    C. using the try cocks
    D. never check the water level; secure the boiler during repairs

_____ B

15. The water column and gauge glass should usually be blown down _____.
    A. once a week
    B. once a shift
    C. when the boiler is coming off-line
    D. never blow down under pressure

_____ C

16. A whistle valve is used to _____.
    A. indicate it is 12:00 noon
    B. indicate a shift change
    C. warn the operator of high or low water
    D. warn the operator of a leaking blowdown line

D

17. A steam pressure gauge is calibrated in _____.
   A. pounds per cubic inch
   B. inches of water column
   C. pounds per temperature increase
   D. pounds per square inch

B

18. A siphon protects the steam pressure gauge from _____.
   A. boiler pressure
   B. high temperature of steam
   C. water entering the Bourdon tube
   D. air entering the Bourdon tube

A

19. The pressure at the base of a vertical foot of water is _____ psi.
   A. 0.433   P 30
   B. 8.3
   C. 14.7
   D. 34.5

D

20. The boiler vent is located at the _____.
   A. main steam line
   B. superheater outlet
   C. highest part of the mud drum
   D. highest part of the steam side of the boiler

B

21. The boiler vent is open when warming up a boiler until _____.
   A. the boiler is cut in on the line
   B. there is approximately 25 psi of steam pressure on the boiler
   C. the superheater drain is closed
   D. never left open during warm-up

D

22. Steam separators work on the principle of _____.
   A. potential energy
   B. kinetic energy
   C. trapping steam and letting water through
   D. changing the direction of the steam flow

A

23. The dry pipe is located in the _____.
   A. upper part of the steam and water drum
   B. superheater outlet header
   C. main steam line
   D. line before the turbine throttle

used in Firetube Boiler.
Cyclone Steam Seperator
used in watertube Boiler.

B

24. Cyclone separators are used in _____.
   A. low to medium pressure boilers
   B. boilers equipped with superheaters   WATER TUBE BOILERS.
   C. boiler chimneys
   D. boiler breeching

B

25. Saturated steam is steam at _____.
   A. a higher temperature than its corresponding pressure
   B. its corresponding temperature and pressure
   C. a dry state
   D. the superheater outlet

C

26. When steam is superheated the _____.
   A. pressure is increased along with its temperature
   B. volume increases
   C. temperature increases with no increase in pressure
   D. pressure increases

A

27. Superheater tubes are protected from warping or burning out by _____.
   A. a continuous flow of steam
   B. circulation of steam and water
   C. circulation of hot air
   D. circulation of flue gases

NOT LESS THAN 25% OF BOILER CAPACITY

A

28. Soot should be _____.
   A. removed from boiler tubes for better heat transfer
   B. left on boiler tubes to protect them from burning out
   C. only left on superheater tubes
   D. saved to cover lines running outside

B

29. Soot blowers are mainly found on _____.
   A. waterwalls
   B. water tube boilers
   C. fire tube boilers
   D. main breeching

B

30. Steam impinging on boiler tubes would _____.
   A. keep tubes exceptionally clean
   B. cut through the boiler tubes in a very short period of time
   C. have no effect on boiler tubes
   D. cause undue thermal shock

C

31. To ensure that moisture-free steam goes to the soot blower, the steam line to the soot blower must come off the _____.
   A. main steam line
   B. superheater outlet header
   C. highest part of the steam side of the drum
   D. waterwall outlet

A

32. Boilers in battery equipped with manhole openings must have _____ according to the ASME code.
   A. two main steam stop valves
   B. one main steam stop valve
   C. no valves between boiler and header
   D. boilers in battery have no manhole openings

A

33. Main boiler stop valves must be _____ valves.
   A. os&y gate
   B. os&y globe
   C. quick-closing lever-type
   D. plug-type

_B_   **34.** The ASME code will allow an automatic nonreturn valve to be used as a main steam stop valve. If one is used it must be _____.
   A. located between the main stop and main header
   B. installed as close to the shell of the boiler as practical on the main steam line
   C. used only on low pressure boilers
   D. none of the above

_D_   **35.** The main steam stop valves should be gate valves because they _____.
   A. can restrict the flow of steam
   B. can be used as throttling valves
   C. do not have to be fully open
   D. offer no restriction to the flow of steam

_B_   **36.** When a boiler is being inspected, the two main steam stop valves are _____.
   A. left wide open
   B. closed, locked, and tagged
   C. left as the operator prefers
   D. none of the above

_A_   **37.** During boiler warm-up, to remove any condensate trapped between the two boiler stop valves the _____.
   A. free-blowing drain should be open
   B. superheater drain should be open
   C. boiler vent should be open
   D. equalizing line should be closed

_C_   **38.** When the boiler is equipped with hand-operated, main steam stop valves, to cut the boiler in on the line, the steam pressure on the incoming boiler should be _____.
   A. slightly higher than line pressure
   B. equal to line pressure
   C. slightly lower than line pressure
   D. makes no difference; pressure will equalize

_B_   **39.** During normal usage, the main boiler steam line expands and contracts. To allow for this _____.
   A. rigid pipe hangers are used
   B. expansion bends are used
   C. the main steam line must be welded to external braces
   D. nothing has to be done; this will take care of itself

_A_   **40.** Bottom blowdown lines on a water tube boiler are located on the _____.
   A. mud drum
   B. bottom of the steam and water drum
   C. superheater outlet header
   D. lowest part of the combustion chamber

C

41. According to the ASME code, boilers operating at 100 psi or over must have _____.
- A. no bottom blowdown valves
- B. only one bottom blowdown valve
- C. two bottom blowdown valves *IN SERIES*
- D. up to manufacturer of boiler

A

42. When blowing down a boiler equipped with a quick-opening valve and a screw-type valve, the quick-opening valve is _____.
- A. opened first and closed last
- B. opened last and closed first
- C. opened first and closed first
- D. opened as operator prefers

A

43. If a quick-opening valve is used as a bottom blowdown valve, it must be located _____.
- A. between the boiler and the slow-opening (screw-type) valve
- B. furthest from the shell of the boiler
- C. cannot be used on high pressure boilers
- D. none of the above

B

44. The maximum size of the bottom blowdown line and the surface blowdown line is _____.
- A. 1½″
- B. 2½″
- C. 3″
- D. no maximum size required

C

45. The most accurate means of deciding the frequency of blowdown of a boiler is determined by a _____.
- A. flue gas analysis
- B. boiler operator
- C. boiler water analysis
- D. the feedwater chemical sales representative

A

46. Surface tension on the water in the steam and water drum is increased by _____.
- A. impurities that float on the surface of the water
- B. inexperienced boiler operators
- C. very soft water
- D. a high steam load

B

47. To protect sewer lines from the high temperature and high pressure coming from the boiler blowdown lines, _____.
- A. traps are used
- B. blowdown tanks are used
- C. steam separators are used
- D. nothing has to be used. They can handle all temperatures and pressures

Chapter 3

BASIC BOILER ROOM SYSTEMS

(handwritten: STEAM HEADER, NONE RETURN VALVE, SUPER HEATER, CYCLONE SEPARAT.)

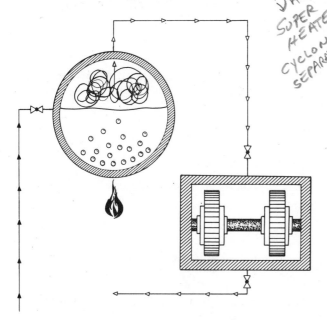

Four separate systems must function in order for a steam boiler to operate. These systems and their accessories are separate and independent of each other. However, they are all necessary for operation of the boiler. The failure of any one of these systems will result in a plant shutdown.

The steam system controls and directs the steam to the point where its energy is used for process, heating, or generation of electricity. In addition, the system includes accessories that reclaim all uncontaminated steam in the form of condensate and return it to the feedwater system for reuse.

The feedwater system supplies suitable water to the boiler at the proper temperature and pressure to sustain the steaming cycle. This system includes all the equipment necessary to supply the boiler with properly heated and treated boiler water for maximum boiler efficiency.

The fuel system supplies fuel in the proper condition for the combustion process. The combustion process changes the chemical energy of the fuel to heat energy in the steam. The fuel system includes all the necessary equipment and accessories to safely store, heat, filter, and transport the fuel to the boiler in the proper state for safe and efficient burning.

The draft system provides air for combustion and discharges the gases of combustion into the atmosphere in a nonpolluted condition. This system includes all the equipment necessary to supply and regulate air to achieve complete combustion in order to reduce, or if possible, eliminate air pollution.

KEY TO ARROWHEAD SYMBOLS			
△ - Air	▲ - Water	▲ - Fuel Oil	⌂ - Air to Atmosphere
△ - Gas	△ - Steam	△ - Condensate	⌂ - Gases of Combustion

STEAM SYSTEM

One pound of water is needed to produce one pound of steam. In the interest of economy, much of the used steam is reclaimed in the form of condensate and returned to the boiler. See Figure 3-1.

NOTE: The numbers in the following step-by-step explanations correspond to the numbers in the circles on the figures.

Water from the open deaerating feedwater heater (1) flows to the suction side of the feedwater pumps (2). One pump should be steam-driven and the other electrically driven for safety and maximum efficiency.

The feedwater then passes through a closed feedwater heater (3), through an automatic feedwater regulating valve (4), and into the steam and water drum (5). It is further heated, turns to steam, leaves the boiler drum, and enters the superheater (6).

The steam is heated to a temperature above its corresponding pressure and becomes superheated steam. When steam is superheated, more heat energy is added to the steam. Heat energy is extracted from the steam when it is put to work.

The superheated steam leaves the superheater through the main steam line (7). Some steam is sent out to the auxiliaries, and the desuperheating and pressure-reducing station. (8). The bulk of the steam goes to the steam turbine (9). The turbine is connected to the generator (10). The generator produces electricity.

This turbine has two steam extraction lines (11). *Extraction steam* is steam that is removed from the turbine at a controlled pressure after it has passed through some of the turbine stages. Extraction steam is used for process work in the plant. The second extraction line extracts steam at a lower pressure than the

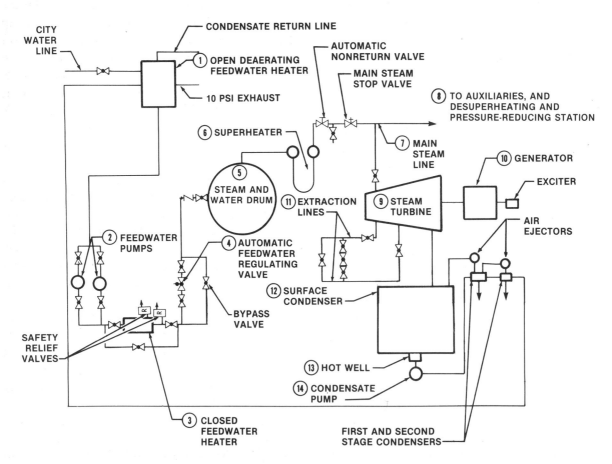

Figure 3-1. Condensate (uncontaminated, used steam) is reclaimed to achieve maximum economy.

first extraction line.

After the steam has passed through the rest of the turbine stages, it enters the surface condenser (12). A surface condenser has water passing through tubes, causing the steam to cool and condense. In this condensing process, a vacuum is formed in the condenser.

This vacuum on the exhaust side of the turbine reduces the back pressure on the turbine, thereby reducing the amount of steam needed to run the turbine. When the back pressure is reduced, the steam or water rate is reduced.

The condensate collects in the hot well (13). The condensate pump (14) takes its suction from the hot well and discharges the condensate back to the open deaerating feedwater heater. The cycle is now ready to be started again.

The air ejectors on the condenser are used to remove air and other noncondensable gases in the condenser. If all the condensate cannot be reclaimed, makeup water will automatically be added in the feedwater heater.

FEEDWATER SYSTEM

The boiler operator must know various ways of getting water to the boilers. A steaming boiler can have the water in the gauge glass go from half a glass to an empty glass in a matter of minutes. A boiler that is on-line and loses its water could burn up or even explode, causing injury or loss of life to the operator and damage to equipment.

If the boiler is generating 20,000 pounds of steam per hour, it must be supplied with 20,000 pounds of water per hour. Water weighs approximately 8.3 pounds per gallon, so the boiler needs about 2,410 gallons of water per hour (20,000 ÷ 8.3 = 2,410 gallons of water per hour).

The feedwater system has many components that must function in an orderly fashion to provide a normal operating water level (NOWL). See Figure 3-2. The condensate (1) returns from the system and enters the open feedwater heater (2). Oxygen and other noncondensable gases are separated and vented to the atmosphere (3). All of the steam does not return

to the feedwater heater as condensate. Some is lost because of leaks in glands and valves or lost in process work.

A float (4) opens a valve (5) located on a city water line (6) to add makeup water. To prevent the feedwater heater from becoming waterlogged, an internal overflow line (7) discharges to waste (8). The open feedwater heater is located above the feedwater pumps, so the water is supplied to the pumps through the suction line (9) at a slight pressure.

The feedwater pump (10) is an electric centrifugal pump and the second feedwater pump (11) is a steam-driven turbine centrifugal pump. This allows the plant to be flexible. Each feedwater pump has its own set of suction valves (12) and discharge valves (13). This allows either pump to be taken out of service for repairs.

Each feedwater pump also has its own check valve (14) to prevent water from backing up if the check valve located close to the boiler should fail. The feedwater leaves the pump through a feedwater discharge line (15) and enters the closed feedwater heater (16) where it is heated to a relatively high temperature.

The closed feedwater heater is equipped with an inlet valve (17) and an outlet valve (18). A bypass line and valve (19) are needed so the heater can be taken out of service without a shutdown.

After the closed feedwater heater, the main feedwater line has branch lines. Each boiler in the plant has a branch line. Each branch line has a main feedwater stop valve (20). To maintain a proper level in each boiler (21), an automatic feedwater regulator is used. It can be the thermoexpansion or the thermohydraulic type.

The control element (22) is located at the NOWL. The top of the control element is connected by a line (23) that goes to the highest part of the steam side of the boiler. There is a shutoff valve (24) so that the regulator may be taken out of service for repairs.

The bottom of the control element is connected to the boiler by a line (25) that is well below the NOWL. The shutoff valve (26) is also used when making repairs. The control ele-

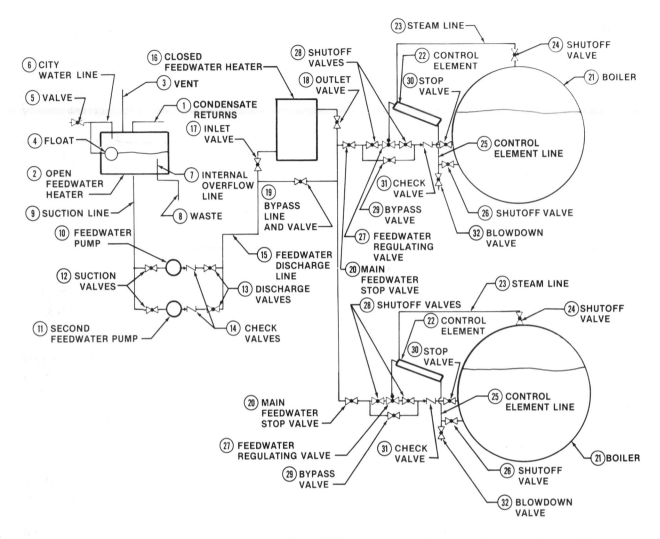

Figure 3-2. The feedwater system must supply sufficient water at the proper temperature and pressure to maintain a normal operating water level (NOWL).

ment is connected to a feedwater regulating valve (27) located in the feedwater discharge line.

The feedwater regulating valve has two shutoff valves (28) so the regulator may be taken out of service if it malfunctions. The water then goes through the bypass valve (29). Now the boiler does not have to be taken off-line because of a regulator failure.

A stop valve (30) and a check valve (31) are located on the feedwater line. The stop valve is located closest to the shell of the boiler so that the check valve can be repaired without draining (dumping) the boiler. The feedwater regulator is equipped with a blowdown valve

(32) to ensure that the water and steam lines are free of sludge and sediment.

FUEL SYSTEMS

Fuel systems used in steam boilers include gas, fuel oil, a combination of gas and fuel oil, or coal. The type of fuel used is governed by its availability, federal and local air pollution standards, and fuel cost. Fuel costs reflect purchase price, storage facilities, required auxiliary equipment, and boiler maintenance costs resulting from use of the specific fuel. For plant flexibility, it is advantageous to have the capability of burning more than one type of fuel in the boiler.

Gas Systems

Gas is a clean, nonpolluting fuel that requires no storage and is readily available in most areas. However, gas is very combustible and must be carefully controlled. Because of the possible danger of an explosion, gas leaks cannot be tolerated. Any indication of a gas leak must be promptly addressed.

Gas leakage must be determined by qualified in-plant personnel, or preferably, a gas company representative. Gas company officials should be notified immediately at the sign of any gas leak. A leak detector is used to locate the leak, the line is secured, and the repair is made. Personnel in the general area must be notified when repairs are made.

The pressure of the gas available at a given location can play an important part in determining the type of gas system used.

Low Pressure Gas System. A low pressure gas system is safer than a high pressure gas system because the possibility of gas leakage is minimized due to the lower pressures involved. The low pressure gas system has many components necessary to properly deliver fuel to the burner. See Figure 3-3.

The gas line (1) is fitted with a gas cock (2) that allows the boiler operator to close the gas off from the system when making repairs. The solenoid valve (3) controls gas to the pilot (4). The manual reset valve (5) is an electric valve that cannot be opened until the gas pilot is lighted. The pressure-reducing governor (6) reduces the pressure of the gas to 0 psi.

The line just before the pressure-reducing governor goes to the vaporstat (7). The vaporstat is a switch turned on by the gas pressure in the line or turned off when there is insufficient pressure. The main gas solenoid valve (8) opens at the proper time, allowing gas to be drawn down to the mixjector (9) where it is mixed with air.

The forced draft blower (10) sends air

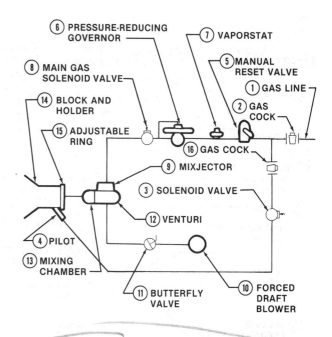

Figure 3-3. In a low pressure gas system, the rate of combustion is controlled by the amount of air supplied to the venturi.

through the butterfly valve (11). The air passes through a venturi (12) and draws the gas with it to the mixing chamber (13). The block and holder (14) is mounted on the boiler front, and as the air and gas mixture passes through the cage, it is ignited by the pilot. The cage has an adjustable ring (15) that controls the secondary air that enters so complete combustion occurs. A gas cock (16) found on the gas line to the pilot can be used to secure the gas to the pilot.

High Pressure Gas System. A high pressure gas burner system supplies gas to the burner at a set pressure. It mixes with the air on the inside of the burner register. See Figure 3-4.

In the high pressure gas system, the gas line (1) is fitted with a manually operated shutoff valve (2) and a pressure gauge (3). A gas pressure regulator (4) controls the desired set pressure at the burner.

The pressure gauge (5) shows the gas pres-

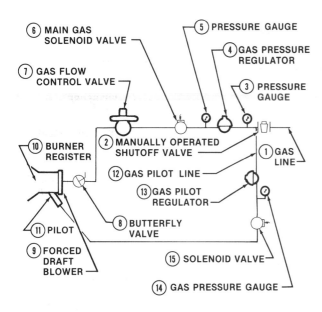

Figure 3-4. The basic controlling elements of a high pressure gas system are the gas pressure regulator, the main gas solenoid valve, and the butterfly valve.

sure on the downstream side of the regulator. The main gas solenoid valve (6) is used as an automatic shutoff gas valve. A gas flow control valve (7) gradually allows the gas to flow to the burner during start-up. A butterfly valve (8) controls the volume of gas to the burner.

A gas pilot line (12) supplies gas to the gas pilot regulator (13), the gas pressure gauge (14), and the solenoid valve (15). Air is supplied by a forced draft blower (9), and this air mixes with the gas in the burner register (10). The gas is ignited by the pilot (11).

Fuel Oil System

The purpose of any fuel oil system is to supply fuel oil to the burner at the proper temperature and pressure. The system must pump, heat, and regulate the flow of fuel oil before it reaches the burner. Once the fuel oil reaches the burner, it is the function of the burner to properly distribute the fuel oil into the com-

bustion chamber of the boiler. The fuel oil system consists of various parts. See Figure 3-5.

Most steam plants that use No. 6 fuel oil have two tanks (1). The size of the tanks depends on the number of gallons that a plant burns in an average day. No. 6 fuel oil must be heated in order to pump it. This is accomplished by a heating bell (coil) located in the fuel oil tank and controlled by a steam regulator (2). To indicate the temperature of the fuel oil coming from the tank, a thermometer (3) is located on the suction line.

Stop valves (4) isolate a tank when it is not in use. The duplex strainers (5) permit one strainer to be cleaned while the other is in service. The suction gauge (6) shows how much vacuum is on the suction side of the pump. The suction valves (7) and discharge valves (8), located before and after the fuel oil pumps, allow a pump to be isolated from the system.

The fuel oil pumps (9) increase the pressure while moving the fuel oil through the discharge line (10). It is good practice to have both an electrically driven and a steam-driven fuel oil pump in the system in case of a power failure. The relief valves (11) protect the system from excessive fuel oil pressure and discharge back to the fuel oil return line (12).

All fuel oil return lines return directly to the tank. A pressure gauge (13) indicates the fuel oil discharge pressure. The fuel oil is further heated by steam fuel oil heaters (14). Inlet valves (15) and outlet valves (16) allow a heater to be isolated for maintenance. Thermometers (17) indicate the temperature of the fuel oil leaving the heater.

The fuel oil then goes to an electric heater (18) where it is brought up to the temperature at which it is to be burned. A thermometer (19) shows the temperature of the fuel oil after it leaves the electric heater. A simplex strainer (20) collects any impurities or dirt left in the fuel oil.

A pressure gauge (21) indicates the pressure of the fuel oil at the burner (22), which is regulated by a back pressure valve (23). All of the fuel oil is not burned. Some fuel oil is recirculated through a return line. A thermometer

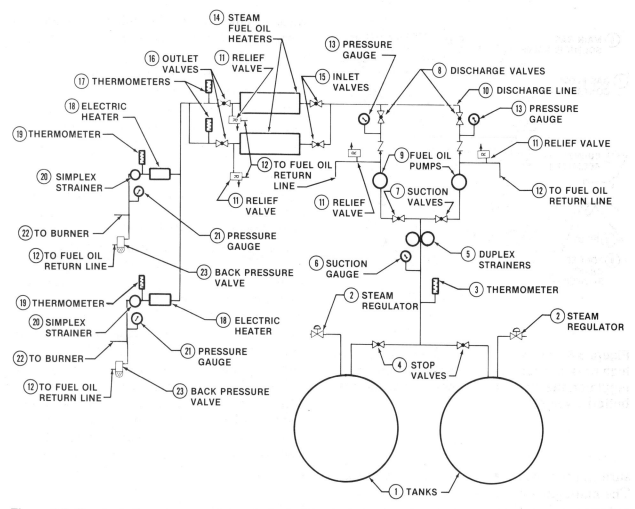

Figure 3-5. The fuel oil system must supply fuel oil to the burner at the proper temperature and pressure.

shows the fuel oil return temperature as the fuel oil returns to the storage tank.

Gas/Fuel Oil Systems

Combination gas/fuel oil burners are used in some boiler installations. These burners are actually two burners in one and are capable of burning gas or fuel oil. These combination burners have the advantage of being able to burn the cheapest or most available fuel, and during air pollution alerts, of burning non-polluting gas. See Figure 3-6.

The gas line (1) is fitted with a manually operated shutoff valve (2) and a pressure gauge (3). A gas pressure regulator (4) controls the

desired set pressure at the burner, shown on the pressure gauge (5).

The electrically operated solenoid valve (6) is used as an automatic shutoff gas valve. A gas flow control valve (7) gradually opens to allow the gas to flow to the burner slowly at start-up. A gas volume control (8) controls the volume of gas to the burner (10).

The fuel oil line (17) is fitted with a thermometer (18) to indicate the temperature of the fuel oil coming from the fuel oil tank. A set of duplex strainers (19) removes any foreign matter from the fuel oil. The suction gauge (20) shows how much pressure is on the suction side of the pump. The suction valve (21) and discharge valve (25), located before and after

Figure 3-6. Combination gas/fuel oil burners are capable of burning gas or fuel oil.

the fuel oil pump, are used to isolate a pump from the system.

The fuel oil pump (22) increases the pressure while moving the fuel oil through the discharge line. The relief valve (23) protects the system from excessive fuel oil pressure and discharges back to the fuel oil return line (38). A discharge pressure gauge (24) indicates the fuel oil discharge pressure.

The fuel oil is heated by a steam fuel oil heater (27). An inlet valve (26) and an outlet valve (29) are used to isolate the heater for maintenance. A thermometer (28) indicates the temperature of the fuel oil leaving the heater. Duplex strainers (31) collect any impurties or dirt left in the fuel oil. Pressure gauges (30 and 32) indicate dirty duplex strainers.

The fuel oil then goes to an electric heater (33) where it is brought up to the temperature

at which it will be burned. A thermometer (34) shows the temperature of the fuel oil after it leaves the electric heater. The electrically operated solenoid valve (35) is used as an automatic shutoff valve to the burner.

A pressure gauge (36) indicates the pressure of the fuel oil at the burner, which is regulated by a back pressure valve (37). All of the fuel oil is not burned. Some fuel oil is recirculated through the fuel oil return line. All fuel oil return lines return directly to the tank.

The gas pilot ignition system is common to both systems and consists of the following: a gas line (12) is fitted with a shutoff valve (16) that supplies gas to the gas pilot pressure regulator (13). The gas pressure is indicated by a pressure gauge (14). The solenoid valve (15) is used as an automatic shutoff valve.

Ignition of the gas or fuel oil occurs at the

burner by the pilot (11). Air is supplied by a forced draft blower (9) and mixes with the gas or fuel oil in the burner.

Coal Systems

Coal systems utilize stokers that are classified by the method the coal is fed into the boiler. The three general types of stokers are *underfeed, overfeed,* and *chain (traveling) grate.* Coal stokers and pulverized coal systems were developed because of the inefficiency of hand firing coal and the limitations of the size of a boiler that could be fired by hand.

Coal stokers feed coal continuously or intermittently to maintain constant steam pressure in the boiler. The stoker must be able to regulate the amount of coal that is fed to the boiler furnace. An increase in steam demand requires the stoker to feed more coal. If the steam load is reduced, the stoker decreases the amount of coal fed.

Coal stokers provide the means for igniting the coal as it enters the furnace. Underfeed and overfeed stokers ignite the coal from the coal bed. Chain grate stokers are equipped with ignition arches to ignite the coal as it enters the furnace.

Coal stokers also provide air distribution for the proper combustion of coal. Underfeed and overfeed stokers have primary air supplied under the grates and secondary air introduced over the fire.

The overfeed stoker requires a large amount of secondary air because some coal is burned while suspended in air. In chain grate stokers, primary air for combustion is supplied to the coal bed through windboxes under the traveling grates. Secondary air is introduced over the coal bed to ensure complete combustion. *NOTE*: The furnace grate surface upon which the fire rests is measured in square feet.

Coal stokers also provide for ash removal. In the underfeed and overfeed stoker, ash is either removed by hand or removed automatically by suction. In chain grate stokers, ash drops off into an ash hopper at the rear of the boiler. Ash removed from the boiler is stored. When sufficient quantities have been collected, ash is sold for use in the manufacture of cinder blocks.

Underfeed Stoker. The underfeed stoker supplies coal to the furnace from under the coal bed. See Figure 3-7. This stoker consists of a coal bunker (1) for the storage of coal. From the bunker, the coal is moved by the coal conveyor (2) to the coal scale (3).

When the coal scale has weighed a predetermined amount, it dumps into the hopper (4). The hopper supplies coal to the screw feed (5), which moves the coal against pusher blocks (6), distributing coal in the fuel retort (7). From the fuel retort, the coal moves on the grates (8). A fan supplies air to the windbox (9) and the air is distributed through the grates to the coal bed (10).

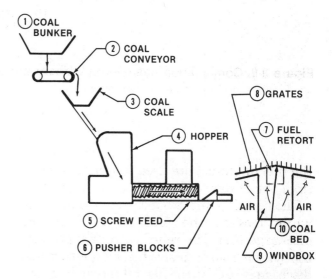

Figure 3-7. The underfeed stoker feeds coal to the furnace, mechanically obtaining a higher rate of combustion efficiency than is possible with hand firing.

Overfeed Stoker. The overfeed stoker is also known as a spreader stoker. See Figure 3-8. The overfeed stoker has a coal bunker (1) where the coal is stored before being moved

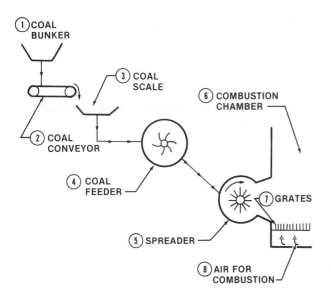

Figure 3-8. The overfeed (spreader) stoker allows some of the coal to be burned in suspension.

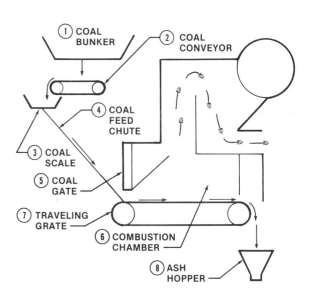

Figure 3-9. The development of the chain (traveling) grate stoker was instrumental in building boilers with large steam capacities.

by the coal conveyor (2) to the coal scale (3). The coal is weighed and then passes to the coal feeder (4) that regulates the flow of coal going to the spreader (5).

The spreader throws or sprinkles the coal into the combustion chamber (6). Some of the coal is burned in suspension and the remainder falls to the grates (7) where the combustion process is completed. Air for combustion (8) is supplied below the grates and controls the rate of combustion.

Chain (Traveling) Grate Stoker. The chain (traveling) grate coal stoker is an example of a cross-feed stoker. Because of its ability to feed coal at a greater rate, it is used with larger capacity steam boilers. See Figure 3-9.

In this system, a coal bunker (1) supplies coal to a coal conveyor (2). The conveyor fills a coal scale (3) that weighs the coal before dumping it into the coal feed chute (4).

A coal gate (5) controls the amount of coal that is going onto the traveling grate (7). Combustion is completed in the combustion chamber (6) before the fuel reaches the end of

the traveling grate. An ash hopper (8) stores ashes until they are removed as required.

Pulverized Coal System. Coal is pulverized for the same reason fuel oil is atomized (broken up). Pulverizing allows closer contact between the coal and the oxygen in the air, facilitating complete combustion. Coal is pulverized so it is the consistency of talcum powder and is then introduced into the combustion chamber, where it is burned in suspension.

Because of the explosive properties of pulverized coal, special precautions must be taken when handling it. See Figure 3-10. In the basic pulverized coal system, the coal bunker (1) stores the coal before it flows onto the coal conveyor (2). The coal drops into the coal scale (3) and is weighed before being dumped into the coal chute (4) that leads to the coal feeder (5).

The coal feeder controls the flow of coal entering the pulverizer (6), which is driven by a motor drive (7). The pulverizer grinds the coal to a fine powder. Hot air (8) enters the pulverizer and mixes with the coal powder before passing to the exhauster (9). The ex-

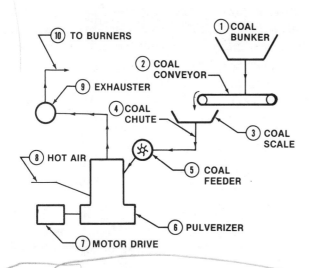

Figure 3-10. Pulverized coal is burned in suspension and requires special precautions when handling because of its explosive properties.

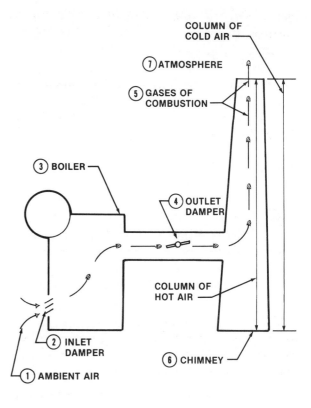

Figure 3-11. The height of the chimney affects the amount of natural draft produced.

hauster discharges the mixture of coal and air to the burner (10).

DRAFT SYSTEMS

Draft is the difference in pressure that causes air or gases to flow. In order to burn a fuel in a furnace, sufficient quantities of air at the correct pressure must overcome all resistance while passing through the boiler. Draft is classified as *natural* or *mechanical*. The type of draft system used will depend on the requirements of the steam plant.

Draft systems contribute to the overall efficiency of the steam plant. Without the proper draft, complete combustion of fuels cannot be achieved.

Natural Draft

Natural draft is produced only by a chimney. The hot gases inside the chimney rise and are replaced by cooler air outside the chimney. The amount of available draft is dependent on the difference in temperature of the column of gas inside the chimney and of the column of air outside the chimney. See Figure 3-11.

In the natural draft system, the flow of ambient (surrounding) air (1) into the boiler (3) is controlled by the inlet damper (2). The combustion process takes place in the boiler and the flow of the gases of combustion is controlled by the outlet damper (4). The gases of combustion (5) flow into the chimney (6), and then rise to the atmosphere (7).

The disadvantages of natural draft are:

1. the rate of combustion (amount of fuel burned per hour) is limited,

2. high chimneys are required to produce the necessary draft,

3. the operator has less control over the combustion process.

Mechanical Draft

Mechanical draft utilizes fans and/or blowers to produce the flow of air for combustion.

Because of the limitations of natural draft, mechanical means were developed to supply the required air flow in larger boilers.

When compared with natural draft, mechanical draft allows increased rates of combustion. Mechanical draft also offers greater control of the combustion process. The three types of mechanical draft are *forced draft, induced draft,* and *combination forced and induced draft.*

Forced Draft.

The forced draft system overcomes disadvantages of the natural draft system by using a fan to provide air for the combustion process. See Figure 3-12.

The ambient air (1) is pulled into the inlet damper (2), which controls the amount of air entering the forced draft fan (3). Discharge air from the fan passes into the boiler (4), in which combustion occurs. The gases of combustion (5) leave the boiler through the breeching (6), where their flow is controlled by the outlet damper (7). The gases then pass into the chimney (8) and out into the atmosphere (9).

Induced Draft.

Induced draft systems produce pressure in the furnace slightly below atmospheric pressure. See Figure 3-13. In this system, the ambient air (1) is pulled through the inlet damper (2) into the boiler (3).

After the combustion process is completed, the products of combustion flow through the outlet damper (4) into the induced draft fan (5). The induced draft fan is located in the breeching (6) and discharges the gases of combustion (7) into the chimney (8). From the chimney, the gases of combustion pass to the atmosphere (9).

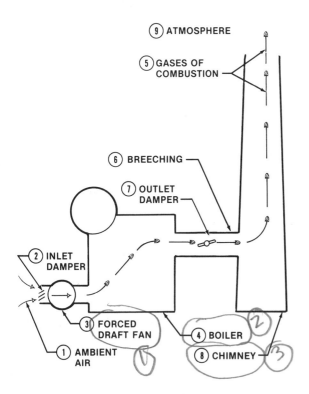

Figure 3-12. Mechanical draft overcomes the shortcomings of natural draft.

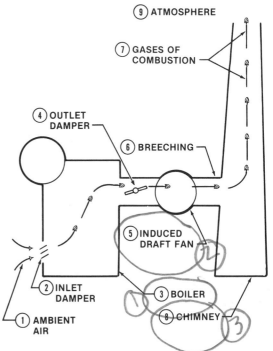

Figure 3-13. Induced draft produces a pressure below the atmospheric pressure to create air flow in the furnace.

Combination Forced and Induced Draft.
Combination forced and induced draft systems
are often used in large steam plants. See
Figure 3-14. In this system, ambient air (1) is
drawn through the forced draft fan (2) and is
discharged into the boiler (4). The rate of air
flow is controlled by the inlet damper (3).

The products of combustion leave the boiler
through the outlet damper (5) and enter the
intake of the induced draft fan (6). The induced
draft fan is located in the breeching (7) and
discharges into the chimney (8). The gases of
combustion (9) then pass up the chimney and
into the atmosphere (10).

Pressurized Furnace

Pressurized furnaces operate at slightly above
atmospheric pressure. This prevents the infiltration of excess air into the combustion process
which results in greater combustion efficiency.
In addition, pressurized furnaces provide
greater control of the amount of air introduced
to the furnace. Pressurized furnaces operate
with forced or forced and induced draft. See
Figure 3-15. Ambient air (1) is drawn through
the forced draft fan (2) and is discharged
through the inlet damper (3) into the boiler (4).
The pressure in the furnace is slightly above atmospheric pressure and is controlled by the outlet damper (5). Gases of combustion (6) pass
through the breeching (7) into the chimney (8)
and exits into the atmosphere (9). **WARNING:
Pressurized furnace boilers should be
checked periodically for leakage. Any leaks in
a pressurized furnace boiler can result in
toxic gases of combustion leaking into the
boiler room.**

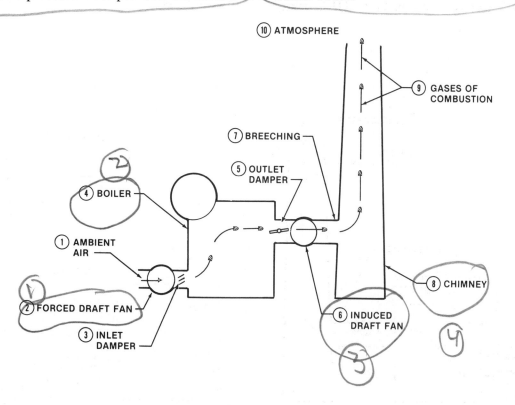

Figure 3-14. Combination forced and induced draft allows more effective control of combustion for
maximum efficiency in large plants.

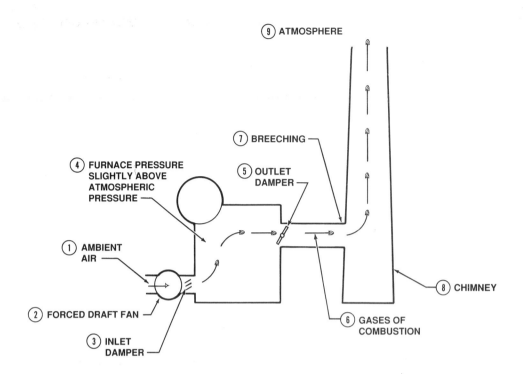

Figure 3-15. In a pressurized furnace, excess air introduced into the furnace is minimized.

Key Words

chain (traveling) grate stoker
coal system
combination forced and induced draft
draft system
extraction steam
feedwater system
forced draft
fuel system
fuel oil system
gas/fuel oil system

high pressure gas system
induced draft
low pressure gas system
mechanical draft
natural draft
overfeed stoker
pressurized furnace
pulverized coal system
steam system
underfeed stoker

TECH CHECK ✓ 3

Name _____ Date _____

C **1.** The four systems required to operate a steam boiler are _____.
   A. steam, exhaust, condensate, and return
   B. fuel, condensate, air, and return
   C. steam, feedwater, fuel, and draft
   D. steam, condensate, fuel, and draft

C **2.** In order to produce one pound of steam, it is necessary to evaporate _____.
   A. 144 Btu's
   B. 970.3 Btu's
   C. one pound of water
   D. three pounds of water

B **3.** Steam that has lost its heat and has turned back into water is _____.
   A. returned steam
   B. condensate
   C. exhaust steam
   D. reclaimed steam

C **4.** Water from an open deaerating feedwater heater flows _____.
   A. to a closed feedwater heater
   B. to the boiler
   C. to the feedwater pump
   D. directly to the sewer

A **5.** A safe and efficient boiler plant should include _____ pump(s).
   A. one steam and one electric feedwater
   B. two steam feedwater (reciprocating)
   C. one steam turbine and one steam reciprocating
   D. two electric high-capacity feedwater

C **6.** When steam is superheated it has _____.
   A. a higher pressure, thus producing more work
   B. a large volume
   C. more heat energy, thus producing more work
   D. a higher temperature and pressure

A/ D **7.** Steam is extracted from the turbine after it has passed through some of the turbine stages to _____.
   A. reduce back pressure
   B. increase back pressure
   C. prevent excessive speed within the turbine
   D. be used for process work and heating

D **8.** A surface condenser has water _____.
   A. and steam mixed together to create a vacuum
   B. passed around the tubes with steam inside the tubes to create a vacuum
   C. and air mixed to create a vacuum
   D. passed through tubes to cause steam to condense, causing a vacuum

(handwritten: A)

9. The vacuum on the exhaust side of the turbine _____.
   A. reduces back pressure and water rate
   B. reduces back pressure and increases water rate
   C. prevents excessive speed within the turbine
   D. vacuum is never allowed on a turbine

(handwritten: C)

10. A boiler generating 20,000 pounds of steam per hour must be supplied with at least _____.
   A. 1½ times its MAWP
   B. 10,000 pounds of water per hour
   C. 20,000 pounds of water per hour
   D. 20,000 pounds of water per shift

(handwritten: C)

11. Oxygen and other noncondensable gases are separated from the feedwater _____.
   A. in the closed feedwater heater
   B. in the economizer
   C. in the open feedwater heater
   D. by using steam traps

(handwritten: A)

12. The open feedwater heater is located *PREFERABLY* _____.
   A. above the feedwater pump(s)
   B. below the feedwater pump(s)
   C. after the closed feedwater heater
   D. none of the above

(handwritten: B)

13. On the feedwater line near the boiler is a check valve and a stop valve. The valve closest to the shell of the boiler is the _____ valve.
   A. check
   B. stop
   C. automatic nonreturn
   D. no valves are allowed on this line

(handwritten: C)

14. On a boiler burning low pressure gas, the volume (amount) of gas burned is controlled by the _____.
   A. pressure-regulating valve
   B. pressure-reducing governor
   C. volume of air passing through the venturi tube
   D. manual reset valve

(handwritten: D)

15. The blower on a low pressure gas system will not start until the _____.
   A. operator pushes the start button
   B. manual reset valve is disengaged
   C. butterfly valve is closed
   D. vaporstat senses gas up to the pressure-reducing governor

(handwritten: B)

16. On the fuel oil system, the purpose of the duplex strainers on the suction line between the tank and fuel oil pump is to _____.
   A. isolate the system in the event of fire
   B. allow one strainer to be cleaned without securing the boiler
   C. make sure the fuel oil is clean
   D. prevent return flow to the tank

_D_ **17.** Coal stokers were developed because _____.
   A. all grades of coal could be burned
   B. coal is easy to burn
   C. coal has less sulfur than fuel oil or gas
   D. hand firing was inefficient in larger-sized boilers

_B_ **18.** Pulverized coal has the consistency of talcum powder so that it _____.
   A. can be stored easier
   B. can come in closer contact with the oxygen for complete combustion
   C. can burn better on the grates
   D. is easier to hand fire

_A_ **19.** Draft is defined as a difference in pressure that causes _____.
   A. air or gases to flow
   B. a balance of pressure
   C. a back pressure
   D. none of the above

_C_ **20.** Natural draft is produced by a _____.
   A. forced draft fan
   B. induced draft fan (used in larger plants)
   C. difference in temperature of a column of gas inside the chimney from a column of air outside the chimney
   D. clean coal bed

_B_ **21.** Air is mixed inside of the burner register in a _____ gas system.
   A. low pressure
   B. high pressure
   C. equalizing
   D. fuel oil

_C_ **22.** A draft fan located between the boiler and chimney is used in a _____ draft system.
   A. natural
   B. forced
   C. induced
   D. combination

_C_ **23.** Pulverized coal is burned in _____ in the furnace.
   A. the scale
   B. the grates
   C. suspension P r58
   D. large particles

_D_ **24.** Gas leaks must be located and repaired by a _____.
   A. boiler operator
   B. shift foreman
   C. fuel superintendent
   D. gas company representative

7.48 GALLONS PER CUBIC FT.

_____ C _____   **25.** Water weighs approximately _____ pounds per gallon.
  A. 2
  B. 6.4
  C. 8.3   *62.4 LBS PER CUBIC FT*
  D. 10

Identify the parts of the induced draft system.

_____ A _____   **26.** Gases of combustion
_____ B _____   **27.** Induced draft fan
_____ C _____   **28.** Inlet damper
_____ D _____   **29.** Ambient air

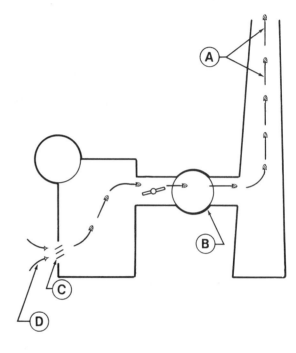

Identify the parts of the forced draft system.

_____ D _____   **30.** Forced draft fan
_____ C _____   **31.** Outlet damper
_____ B _____   **32.** Chimney
_____ A _____   **33.** Breeching

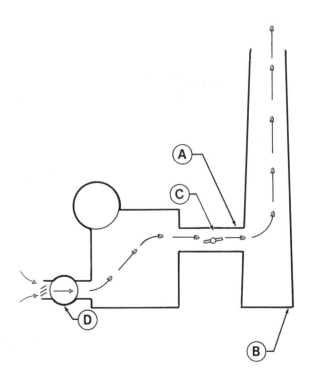

Chapter 4

STEAM AND WATER ACCESSORIES

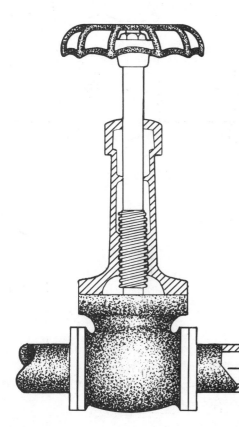

Accessories are pieces of equipment not directly attached to the boiler, but which are necessary for its safe and efficient operation. Feedwater heaters, feedwater pumps, condensate tanks with booster pumps, main feedwater lines, steam traps, desuperheaters, and pressure-reducing stations are accessories required for the operation of boilers.

Accessories are used to heat and store water, automatically add city water makeup, remove fuel oil or grease returning into the system, and vent oxygen and other noncondensable gases. Pumps are used to deliver water to boilers at the proper pressure. Feedwater regulators maintain a constant water level.

Steam traps increase the efficiency of plant operation. Desuperheaters reduce the temperature of steam to be used by auxiliary equipment. Pressure-reducing stations reduce high pressure steam for process.

KEY TO ARROWHEAD SYMBOLS			
△ - Air	▲ - Water	▲ - Fuel Oil	⌂ - Air to Atmosphere
⚠ - Gas	△ - Steam	⚠ - Condensate	⚠ - Gases of Combustion

FEEDWATER HEATERS

One of the main functions of feedwater heaters is to heat the boiler feedwater before it enters the boiler drum. The raw water entering the feedwater heater contains varying degrees of scale-forming salts. At approximately 150°F, these salts begin to settle.

When a feedwater heater is used, some scale caused by the salts will settle in the feedwater heater rather than the boiler. This benefits plant operation since scale is more easily removed from the feedwater heater than from the boiler.

The location of feedwater heaters in the system will vary, depending on the types used. Feedwater heaters can be located on the suction side or discharge side of the boiler feedwater pump or in the breeching. They may be heated by live steam, exhaust steam, or by gases of combustion. The two basic types of feedwater heaters are the *open feedwater heater* and the *closed feedwater heater*.

Open Feedwater Heater

An open feedwater heater is a steel vessel that is designed so steam and water come into direct contact (mix) with each other. Internally it contains a feedwater distributing line, a set of steel or cast iron trays, and a filter bed.

The external connections consist of a float-controlled valve on the city water line, a condensate return line, an atmospheric vent line, and a low pressure steam line. Other connections include an outlet line to the feedwater pump, an overflow connection, and in some cases, an oil-separating device on the steam line. See Figure 4-1.

Steam enters the open feedwater heater, filling it internally. At the same time, feedwater and condensate flow onto the trays, where the water passes through small openings before dropping to the filter bed below. In this manner, the water is broken up into small droplets and comes into close contact with the steam, thereby increasing the temperature of the feedwater.

The primary reason for using an open feed-

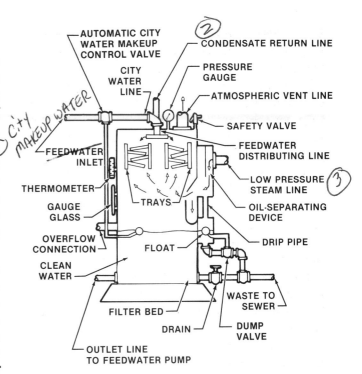

Figure 4-1. The open feedwater heater, located above the feedwater pump on its suction side, supplies water to the pump at a slight pressure.

water heater is to reduce the thermal shock to the steam boiler as water enters the drum. In addition, the open feedwater heater

1. removes oxygen that causes pitting of the boiler drum,
2. acts as a reservoir for available feedwater,
3. increases boiler plant efficiency when exhaust steam is used.

A rule of thumb is that for every 10°F rise in feedwater temperature, there is a 1% fuel savings. This is only true when heating with exhaust steam or heat from the gases of combustion.

The open feedwater heater is located above the feedwater pump and is connected to the suction side of the pump. The location of the heater above the pump gives the suction side of the feedwater pump a *positive pressure* caused by gravity. Positive pressure is pressure more than the atmospheric pressure.

With a higher positive pressure on the suction side of the feedwater pump, it is possible to have a higher feedwater temperature. An increase in pressure will increase the boiling point of the water.

An automatic city water makeup control valve is usually used to maintain a constant water level in the heater. The valve is controlled by a float mechanism that is actuated when insufficient condensate is returned to the heater and the water level starts to drop. The heater is equipped with a safety valve, pressure gauge, and thermometer. All are necessary for efficient and safe operation. The correct water temperature and level must be maintained when operating an open feedwater heating system.

Water Temperature. The correct water temperature must be maintained in a feedwater heater. Water that is too hot will cause the feedwater pump to become steambound, resulting in the water flashing into steam within the pump casing.

If this occurs, the pump will not discharge feedwater to the boiler, resulting in a dangerously low water level in the boiler. Feedwater temperatures that are too low will not remove the oxygen from the water, which causes pitting of the boiler drum. ↑150°

Water Level. The correct water level must be maintained in a feedwater heater. A low water level can cause a loss of suction pressure on the feedwater pump. This results in the feedwater pump becoming steambound. The heater should not be flooded.

Water can enter the steam or condensate lines and cause water hammer. The internal overflow in the feedwater heater controls this condition with a float that opens only when water enters its chamber. The water raises a float that opens a dump valve, which discharges to the sewer.

Deaerating Feedwater Heater

A deaerating feedwater heater is similar to an open feedwater heater. See Figure 4-2. The basic difference between the deaerating feedwater heater and the open feedwater heater is that the deaerating type has a vent condenser that separates oxygen and other gases from the steam before releasing the gases into the atmosphere. The vent condenser is a shell-and-tube type of vessel located at the top of the heater.

The vent condenser functions in the following manner. Steam and noncondensable gases enter the shell of the condenser. Condensate and city water makeup pass through the tubes. The end result is that the water passing through the tubes condenses the steam and increases in temperature before entering the heater.

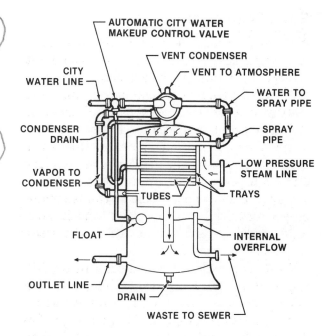

Figure 4-2. Because of its vent condenser, the deaerating feedwater heater does a more effective job of removing oxygen and other noncondensable gases from the steam than an open feedwater heater.

The condensed steam drops back into the heater, leaving behind noncondensable gases that are vented into the atmosphere. This continuous process removes harmful gases without excessive loss of steam or heat.

The deaerating feedwater heater is more efficient than an open feedwater heater. Deaerating feedwater heaters can also be horizontal in configuration. See Figure 4-3. Horizontal deaerating feedwater heaters are used where there is minimal headroom.

Closed Feedwater Heater

The closed feedwater heater is another type of feedwater heater found in some feedwater systems. See Figure 4-4. The closed feedwater heater is basically a steel shell containing a large number of small tubes secured into two tube sheets.

Closed feedwater heaters are designed for vertical or horizontal operation made in single or multiple passes. The manufacture and in-stallation of a closed feedwater heater must allow for expansion and contraction of the shell and tubes.

In this type of heater, steam and water do not come into direct contact. The steam enters the shell and feedwater passes through the tubes. The heat in the steam is transferred to the water, which raises the water temperature. As the latent heat is removed from the steam, it condenses into water and falls to the bottom of the shell, where it is removed by a steam trap.

This heater must be equipped with a safety valve on the shell and a relief valve on the feedwater side to protect the shell and heads from excessive pressure. A bypass piping arrangement is normally used to assist in taking the heater out of service for cleaning or repairs.

The closed feedwater heater is located on the discharge side of the feedwater pump and therefore has a higher pressure on the feedwater than the open feedwater heater.

This higher pressure allows a higher water temperature without the water flashing into

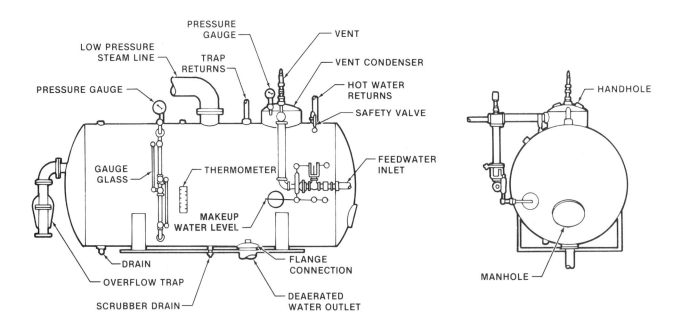

Figure 4-3. The horizontal deaerating feedwater heater is used when headroom is a problem. (*The Permutit Co., Inc.*)

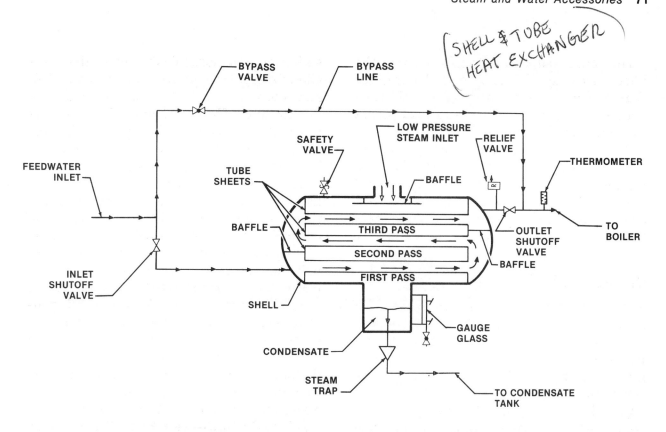

SHELL & TUBE HEAT EXCHANGER

Figure 4-4. The closed feedwater heater is <u>located on the discharge side of the feedwater pump.</u> Unlike the open feedwater heater, the closed feedwater heater does not mix steam and water.

steam. The temperature of the water leaving the feedwater heater is determined by two factors, which are

1. the rate at which feedwater is passing through the heater,
2. the steam pressure in the shell of the heater.

The purpose of the closed feedwater heater is to reduce thermal shock on the boiler metal. Correct feedwater temperature will reduce boiler metal failure. In addition, plant efficiency is increased with the use of a closed feedwater heater when steam that is bled or extracted from a steam turbine is used.

Economizer

Another type of feedwater heater, which is found on larger water tube boilers, is an economizer (fuel saver). It is located in the breeching between the outlet damper and the chimney where gases of combustion make their last pass in the boiler. With this heater, the feedwater is heated by the gases of combustion as they leave the boiler.

Economizer heaters are a unit type, which is outside the boiler casing, or an integral type, which is within the casing. These heaters have the gases of combustion passing around tubes, through which the feedwater flows. See Figure 4-5.

The increase in boiler efficiency can be substantial when using an economizer. Heat that would normally be lost is reclaimed directly from the gases of combustion.

Sufficient draft is needed to overcome resistance caused by the economizer tubes. Induced draft fans are usually used to create this necessary draft. The economizer surface must be

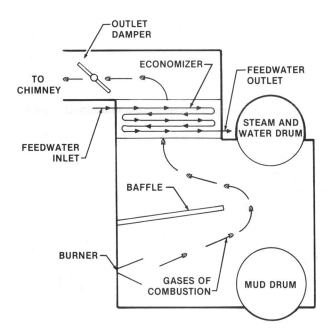

Figure 4-5. Gases of combustion are used to raise boiler feedwater temperature . For every 10°F rise in boiler feedwater temperature, there is approximately a 1% savings in fuel.

kept free of soot. Soot retards heat transfer because it insulates the surface of the economizer.

The temperature of the gases leaving the economizer must be maintained at a level high enough to prevent the tubes from sweating. When moisture and soot come together in the economizer, the end result is corrosion of the metal surfaces.

An economizer becomes a necessity on boilers with operating steam pressures in excess of 450 psi where the temperature of gases leaving the boiler is in excess of 600°F. An economizer or some other form of heat recovery equipment reduces the temperature of gases leaving the boiler.

Feedwater economizers must be inspected for leakage periodically, and repairs made when signs of leakage occur. This is essential not only because of the loss of feedwater, but because of the boiler metal corrosion when water and soot combine.

FEEDWATER PUMPS

The heart of any boiler feedwater system is the feedwater pump. Its purpose is to remove water from the open feedwater heater and develop sufficient pressure to overcome boiler pressure. The pump must deliver the quantity of water necessary to main a NOWL in the boiler.

Feedwater pumps may be driven by steam or electricity. Plant safety and flexibility require one feedwater pump to be steam-driven and the other electric-driven.

The ASME code states that boilers having over 500 square feet of boiler heating surface must have at least two means of supplying feedwater to the boiler. Boilers fired with solid fuel (coal) must have one steam-driven feedwater pump. Boilers having large furnace settings (brickwork) that continue to radiate heat and generate steam after the fuel has been secured must also have at least one steam-driven feedwater pump.

Feedwater pumps may be *reciprocating*, *centrifugal*, or *turbine* type, with each having its advantages and disadvantages.

Reciprocating Feedwater Pump

A reciprocating feedwater pump may be simplex (single cylinder) or duplex (double cylinder). The duplex reciprocating feedwater pump is a simple type of steam-operated pump that runs at a slow speed. See Figure 4-6. It is reliable, but does lose efficiency rather quickly when the steam valves or water valves are worn.

The exhaust steam from this type of pump may be used for heating the feedwater in the open feedwater heater. Because of oil contamination from the pump cylinder, however, it must first be passed through an oil separator.

Reciprocating pumps are positive displacement pumps. A specific amount of water is discharged when the piston moves through each stroke. The quantity of water delivered depends upon the size of the piston and the length of its stroke.

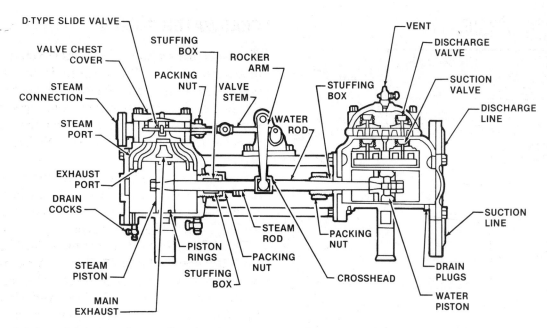

Figure 4-6. In a duplex-reciprocating feedwater pump, the steam piston must be 2 to 2½ times larger in area than the water piston.

The discharge valve must be open whenever the pump is running to prevent excessive pressure. It is good practice to have a safety relief valve installed between the pump and discharge stop valve to limit the pressure on the discharge side of the pump.

In order for a reciprocating pump to be used as a feedwater pump, the steam piston must be two to two-and-a-half times larger in area than the water piston. This design allows sufficient pressure to develop on the water side, which will overcome boiler pressure while using the steam pressure from the boiler to operate the pump. A nameplate mounted on each reciprocating pump gives three numbers (in inches) that determine

1. size of the pump,
2. steam and discharge pressure,
3. gallons per minute the pump can discharge.

These three numbers refer to the diameter of the steam piston, the diameter of the water piston, and the length of the pump stroke.

A 4 × 2 × 4 reciprocating pump indicates a steam piston diameter of 4″, a water piston diameter of 2″, and a pump stroke length of 4″. Using these numbers, the steam pressure required to develop a specific water pressure on the discharge side of the pump can be found.

(*NOTE*: Total force of the steam piston equals total force of the water piston, or $TF_s = TF_w$. Also, total force is equal to pressure times area, or $TF = P \times A$.) After finding the steam pressure, the water pressure that the pump is capable of producing can be determined by using the following formula.

$$P_s \times d^2_s = P_w \times d^2_w$$

The following steps are taken to arrive at this formula.

$$P_s \times A_s = P_w \times A_w \quad \text{where}$$

P_s = steam pressure in psi
A_s = area of steam piston in square inches
P_w = water pressure in psi
A_w = area of water piston in square inches
(*NOTE*: Area equals .7854 times diameter ^{2}, or
$A = .7854 \times d^2$)

Substitute A_s and A_w with $.7854 \times d^2$ to arrive at:

$$P_s \times (.7854 \times d^2_s) = P_w \times (.7854 \times d^2_w)$$

(*NOTE*: Divide both sides by .7854 to simplify.)

$$P_s \times \frac{.7854}{.7854} \times d^2_s = P_w \times \frac{.7854}{.7854} \times d^2_w$$

This gives the formula:

$$P_s \times d^2_s = P_w \times d^2_w \quad \text{where}$$

P_s = steam pressure in psi

d^2_s = diameter^2 of steam piston in square inches

P_w = water pressure in psi

d^2_w = diameter^2 of water piston in square inches

Example: A boiler has an operating pressure of 200 psi. A $4 \times 2 \times 4$ reciprocating feedwater pump is available. How much water pressure is this pump capable of producing?

Given: P_s = 200 psi

$\quad\quad d^2_s$ = 4″

$\quad\quad d^2_w$ = 2″

Find: P_w

Solution: $P_s \times d^2_s = P_w \times d^2_w$

$\quad\quad\quad 200 \times 4^2 = P_w \times 2^2$

OR: $\quad\quad P_w \times 2^2 = 200 \times 4^2$

(*NOTE*: Divide both sides by 2×2 to simplify.)

$$P_w \times \frac{\overset{1}{\cancel{2}} \times \overset{1}{\cancel{2}}}{\underset{1}{\cancel{2}} \times \underset{1}{\cancel{2}}} = 200 \times \frac{\overset{2}{\cancel{4}} \times \overset{2}{\cancel{4}}}{\underset{1}{\cancel{2}} \times \underset{1}{\cancel{2}}}$$

$$P_w = 200 \times 2 \times 2$$
$$P_w = 800 \text{ psi}$$

Use the following formula to find the gallons per minute a reciprocating pump can discharge.

$$G.P.M. = \frac{L \times A \times N \times E}{231} \quad \text{where}$$

$G.P.M.$ = gallons per minute

L = length of pump stroke in inches

A = area of water piston in square inches

N = number of pump strokes per minute

E = pump efficiency

231 = number of cubic inches in a gallon

[*NOTE*: A duplex reciprocating pump has two cylinders. Therefore, it has two pumping strokes. (50 strokes per minute = 100 pumping strokes)]

Example: Find the G.P.M. a duplex reciprocating pump can deliver given the following information. The pump is $6 \times 4 \times 8$, making 50 double strokes per minute. The pump is 80% efficient.

Given: $L = 8″$

$\quad\quad A = .7854 \times 4^2$

$\quad\quad N = 50$

$\quad\quad E = 80\%$

$\quad\quad 231$ = number of cubic inches in a gallon

Find: *G.P.M.*

Solution: $G.P.M. = \dfrac{L \times A \times N \times E}{231}$

$$G.P.M. = \frac{8 \times (.7854 \times 4 \times 4) \times (50 \times 2) \times .80}{231}$$

$$G.P.M. = 34.816 \text{ gallons per minute}$$

The disadvantage of using reciprocating pumps is that they are limited in capacity and therefore are used mainly with small boilers. Reciprocating pumps do not work well in conjunction with feedwater regulators and are limited to moderate discharge pressures because of reduced capacity and excessive leakage. Many boiler rooms use these pumps for reserve or back-up units in the event of an electrical power failure.

A reciprocating feedwater pump may fail to supply sufficient water to a steam boiler if

1. the open or deaerating feedwater heater has no water in it (loss of condensate return or automatic city water makeup valve closed or not functioning),

2. the suction or discharge stop valve is closed or partly closed.

3. the suction and/or discharge pump valves are worn or are not seating correctly,

4. the feedwater temperature is too high, resulting in the water cylinder becoming steambound,

5. the water plunger rings are worn and leaking,

6. the steam admission valves are worn or improperly set,

7. the steam piston rings are worn or broken,
8. the steam cylinder is worn excessively.

Boiler operators may not have control over the maintenance work performed on a pump. However, the boiler operator must maintain the correct water level and temperature in the open feedwater heater to reduce the possibility of a sudden pump breakdown.

Centrifugal Feedwater Pump

The centrifugal feedwater pump is the most widely used feedwater pump today. In a centrifugal pump, the centrifugal force of a rotating element is convertible into pressure. See Figure 4-7. Centrifugal pumps can be driven by an electric motor or by steam. These pumps have few moving parts.

Many different types of centrifugal pumps are used on boilers. Generally, the two main types used are the single-stage type and the multiple-stage type. Single-stage centrifugal pumps are used for low to medium pressure steam boilers. Multiple-stage pumps are de-

signed for higher pressure steam boilers. See Figure 4-8.

The basic parts of a centrifugal pump are the casing, impeller, impeller shaft, shaft bearings, and packing glands or mechanical seals. The casing is the outer part of the pump that directs the flow of water from the pump. The impeller is the rotating element that imparts centrifugal force to the liquid.

The impeller shaft supports the impeller and transmits rotational force to the impeller from the drive. Shaft bearings support the impeller and shaft in a fixed axial and radial position. The packing glands or mechanical seals prevent leakage of liquid between casing and shaft.

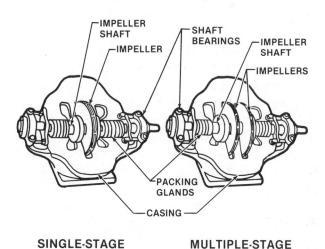

SINGLE-STAGE
CENTRIFUGAL
FEEDWATER PUMP

MULTIPLE-STAGE
CENTRIFUGAL
FEEDWATER PUMP

Figure 4-8. The two most common centrifugal feedwater pumps are the single-stage and multiple-stage types.

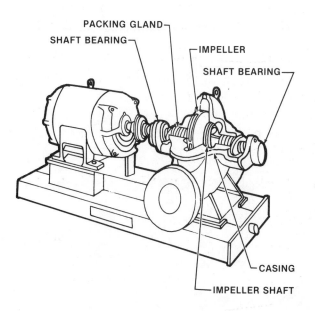

Figure 4-7. In a centrifugal pump, the centrifugal force of the impeller produces pressure.

Centrifugal Pump Operation. Water enters the rotating impeller at the center and builds up centrifugal force as it moves toward the outer edge of the impeller. Once the water leaves the impeller, the casing guides it to the discharge line. The discharge pressure depends upon the centrifugal force that was built up by the impeller.

In a multiple-stage centrifugal pump, the discharge from the first impeller enters the suction of the second impeller and increases the pressure even more. As many as four impellers may be on a single shaft when higher pressures are needed. Each stage of a multiple-stage pump has a single impeller.

Centifugal pumps will fail to supply sufficient water to a steam boiler if the water temperature is too high, if not enough water is supplied to the pump, and/or if the pump has a mechanical failure.

The mechanical failure could be caused by the impeller shearing from the shaft, the bearings wearing excessively, the coupling that connects the pump and drive shearing off, or the mechanical seal badly wearing or breaking. Repairs to centrifugal pumps must be made by skilled personnel.

Turbine Feedwater Pumps

A turbine feedwater pump should not be confused with a centrifugal feedwater pump. See Figure 4-9. Although they may look alike, the basic difference between the centrifugal feedwater pump and the turbine feedwater pump is in their design for discharging water.

The centrifugal pump uses the shape of the casing to direct the discharge. The turbine pump uses a diffusing ring and casing. The axial clearance between the impeller and casing are smaller in the turbine pump than in the centrifugal pump.

Turbine pumps are positive displacement pumps. They cannot be started with the discharge valve closed. Centrifugal pumps, however, can be started with the discharge valve closed.

Turbine pumps must be equipped with a relief valve on the discharge line to protect the pump from excessive pressure. Turbine pumps have a higher operating efficiency than centrifugal pumps. However, both turbine and centrifugal pumps maintain high efficiencies with minimal maintenance.

CONDENSATE TANK AND PUMP UNIT

In many steam boiler plants, condensate that is uncontaminated is pumped back to the open feedwater heater. The condensate is usually a considerable distance from the boiler room and cannot gravitate back. The condensate tank and pump are installed at the lowest point in each building where steam is being used for heating or process. See Figure 4-10.

The condensate tank collects the condensate from the heating or process condensate return lines. A pressure buildup in this tank is prevented by an atmospheric vent line. Although the condensate tank is vented, it is possible to have a pressure buildup caused by

Figure 4-9. Turbine feedwater pumps are positive displacement pumps and require an open discharge valve when starting. (*Aurora Pump*)

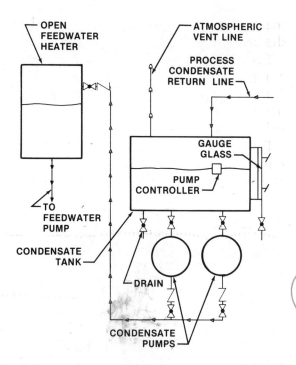

Figure 4-10. Condensate pumps are used to return all possible condensate from various parts of the plant to the open feedwater heater.

leaking steam traps. When this occurs, it is necessary to trace back, locate, and repair or replace any faulty steam traps.

Condensate pumps take condensate from the tank and discharge it to the open feedwater heater. A float feedwater regulator, also referred to as a pump controller, is used to operate the pump. A gauge glass is attached to the tank to indicate condensate level when adjusting the pump controller.

MAIN FEEDWATER LINE

The pipeline going from the discharge side of the feedwater pump to the steam boiler is the main feedwater line. This line must have a check valve and a stop valve located near the shell of the boiler. See Figure 4-11.

The stop valve could be a gate or globe valve. The stop valve is the closest valve to the boiler. When a globe valve is used, it must be installed so that the pressure from the feedwater pump is under the seat of the valve.

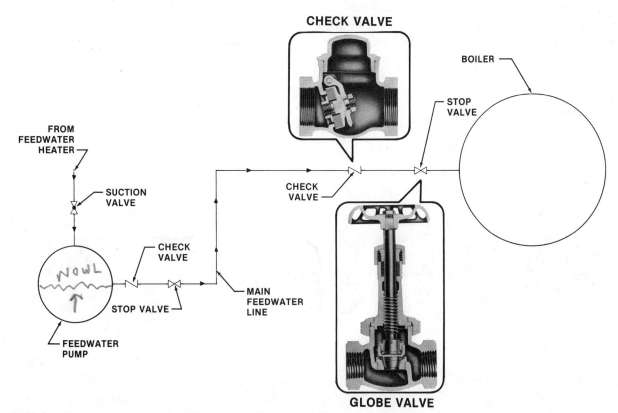

Figure 4-11. The main feedwater line utilizes check and stop valves to control water flow. The stop valve may be a gate or globe valve. (*Jenkins Bros.*)

The stop valve is required in case the check valve should fail and require repair or replacement. Without a stop valve, the boiler would have to be taken off-line for repair or replacement of the check valve. When two or more boilers are fed from a common source, a globe valve is installed on each branch line between the check valve and the main line. See Figure 4-12.

The globe valve on the branch feedwater lines can be used to regulate the flow of feedwater if the feedwater regulator fails or malfunctions. All valves and piping used on the feedwater lines must conform to the pressures and temperatures at which they will be operated.

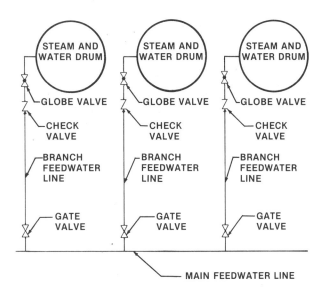

Figure 4-12. When a feedwater pump feeds more than one boiler, each boiler should be isolated with a globe valve.

FEEDWATER REGULATORS

To increase the overall efficiency and safety of a steam boiler, it is necessary to control the amount of feedwater that is going into the boiler. By maintaining a consistent water level, fuel consumption and thermal shock to boiler metal can be reduced.

Feedwater regulators reduce the possibility of water carryover into the steam header or a low water level condition that could lead to overheating of the boiler. All feedwater regulators, regardless of their make or design, should maintain a NOWL. Sensing elements for feedwater regulators must be located at the NOWL.

Basic types of feedwater regulators are *thermoexpansion*, *thermohydraulic*, and *float regulators*. Thermoexpansion and thermohydraulic feedwater regulators are found on larger water tube boilers where feedwater pumps run continuously. The float regulators are found on package fire tube or water tube boilers where feedwater pumps run intermittently.

Thermoexpansion Feedwater Regulator

The thermoexpansion feedwater regulator is connected to the boiler and the main feedwater line. See Figure 4-13. The thermostat is located at the NOWL and is connected to the steam

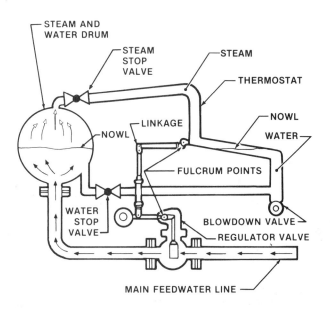

Figure 4-13. A thermoexpansion feedwater regulator is used on large boilers with a fairly constant load.

and water side of the boiler. If the water level drops, the steam space within the thermostat increases. This increases the temperature in the thermostat, causing it to expand.

The increase in the length of the thermostat moves the mechanical linkage, which opens the regulator valve. As the regulator valve on the main feedwater line opens, water enters the boiler, raising the water level. The opposite result occurs if the boiler water level is high. The thermostat contracts and the linkage moves the regulator valve toward the closed position.

For closer control of the water level in a boiler with a superheater, a thermoexpansion feedwater regulator can be equipped with a steam-flow sensing element. The element consists of a diaphragm assembly on the top part of the regulator valve. This type of regulator is known as a two-element feedwater regulator. See Figure 4-14.

By connecting the top and bottom of the diaphragm across the superheater, the diaphragm moves when pressure drops. This movement indicates steam flow. Movement of the diaphragm is amplified through mechanical linkage, which moves the regulator valve.

For optimum efficiency the line connections to the thermostat and diaphragm should be blown down once a month. When blowing down, the regulator must be removed from service. The procedure for blowing down line connections to the thermostat and diaphragm follows:

1. Close stop valves to top and bottom diaphragm connections.
2. Open equalizing line valve between connections.
3. Blow down the saturated and superheater steam lines.
4. Close steam connection to thermostat.
5. Blow down line that connects water side to thermostat.
6. Open steam connection to thermostat and close the water side.
7. Blow down steam line through thermostat.
8. Allow the thermostat to stabilize and the diaphragm connections to fill with condensate. This will take about one hour.
9. Open water and steam line to thermostat.
10. Open top connection to diaphragm and close equalizing line valve.
11. Open bottom connection to diaphragm.

The regulator is now back in service.

Thermohydraulic Feedwater Regulator

A thermohydraulic feedwater regulator consists of a regulating valve, bellows, generator, and stop valves. See Figure 4-15. The control element is the generator, which is a tube within a tube. The generator is located at the NOWL and the inner tube is connected to the steam and water side of the boiler. Stop valves are used to isolate steam and water to the generator.

A blowdown valve is used to keep the inner generator tube free of sludge and sediment. The outer tube of the generator is connected to the bellows with copper tubing and is filled with condensate. When the level of the boiler water drops, the inner tube of the generator has a large steam space.

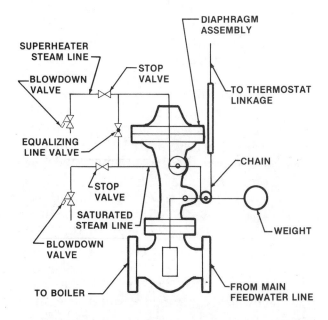

Figure 4-14. For closer control of the water level, a two-element feedwater regulator is used.

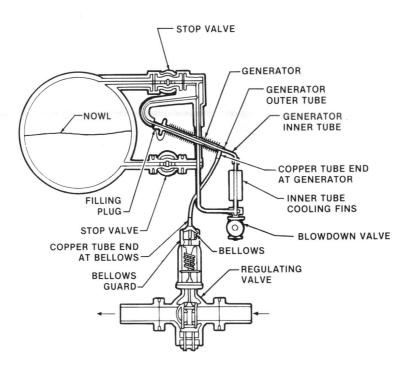

Figure 4-15. A thermohydraulic feedwater regulator operates when boiler water level increases or decreases.

The heat from the steam in that space is given up to the condensate in the outer tube. The condensate within the bellows expands, which moves the regulating valve toward the open position.

When the water level in the boiler rises, the reverse action takes place. The connection to the steam and water side of the boiler should be blown down once a month to remove any sludge or sediment. After blowing down the regulator, allow approximately one hour for the regulator to stabilize before returning it to service.

Float Feedwater Regulator

A float feedwater regulator is used most often on small package boilers. The regulator consists of a float chamber, a float, and mercury switch or a microswitch. See Figure 4-16. The float chamber is connected to the steam and water side of the boiler. It is located at the NOWL. A blowdown line and valve are installed to remove any accumulation of sludge and sediment from the float chamber.

When the boiler water level drops, the float in the float chamber drops and mechanically moves the mercury switch. The mercury switch is connected electrically to a feedwater pump starter relay that energizes the pump motor. The pump will continue to run until the float rises and moves the mercury switch in the opposite direction.

Frequently, a *low water fuel cutoff* is used in conjunction with this type of regulator. The low water fuel cutoff is a safety device that shuts off the fuel going to the burner if a low water condition occurs. With float controls, it is essential that the float chambers be blown down once every shift in order to prevent any sludge or sediment from accumulating.

This blowdown should be done with the burner firing, thereby testing the low water fuel cutoff operation. It is also recommended that the low water fuel cutoff be tested not less than once a month. This involves cutting off the feedwater, allowing the water level in the boiler to drop by evaporation. *NOTE:* The boiler operator must be present during this test to monitor the safety of the boiler. Float feed-

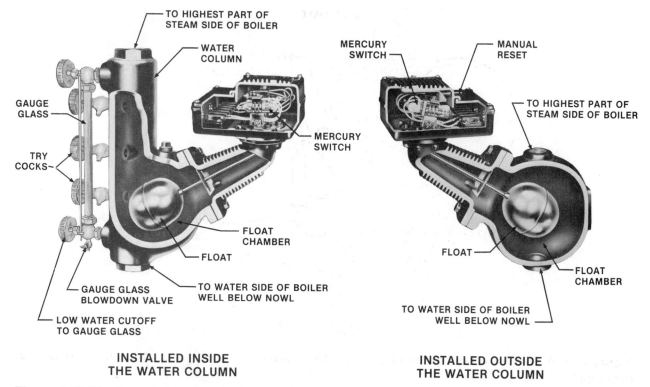

Figure 4-16. Float regulators may be installed inside or outside the water column, depending on their design. (*McDonnell-Miller*)

water regulators should be opened once a year for cleaning and inspection.

STEAM TRAPS

Steam traps are automatic devices that increase the overall efficiency of a steam plant by removing air and condensate from steam lines and heat exchangers without the loss of steam. If condensate is not removed from the steam lines and heat exchangers, it could lead to water hammer or cause the heat exchangers to become waterlogged, thus reducing the heat transfer rate. Water hammer is caused by mixing steam and water and could lead to a line rupture.

The main steam header in the boiler room must be equipped with a steam trap. A steam trap must also be installed at the base of a steam riser. Heat exchangers such as fuel oil heaters, hot water heaters, radiators, and steam jackets require steam traps if the condensate is to be reclaimed.

Steam traps are located as necessary to achieve the most efficient removal of condensate. See Figure 4-17. Several types of steam traps are available. These operate in different ways, yet they all perform the function of removing unwanted condensate and air from steam lines and heat exchangers. A steam trap should have a steam strainer installed on the inlet line. This will prevent scale or other solid particles from entering the trap.

Thermostatic Steam Trap

The thermostatic steam trap consists of a body, a valve, a valve seat, and a bellows-type element. See Figure 4-18. When steam is in contact with the element, it causes the element to expand and the valve to close. If air or condensate surrounds the element, it contracts

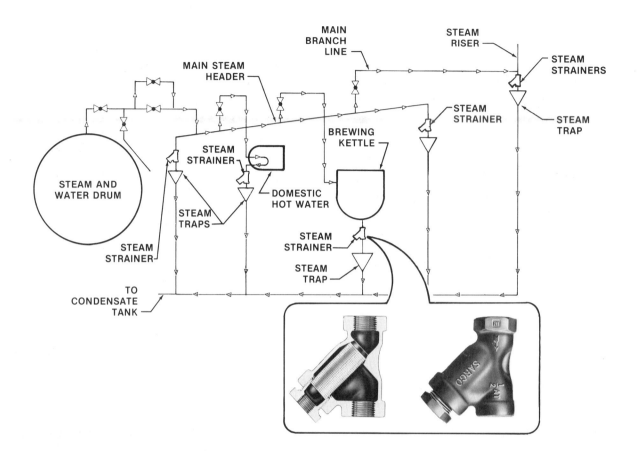

Figure 4-17. Steam traps are located in the system wherever steam releases its heat and condenses. Steam strainers are installed before steam traps. (*Sarco Co., Inc.*)

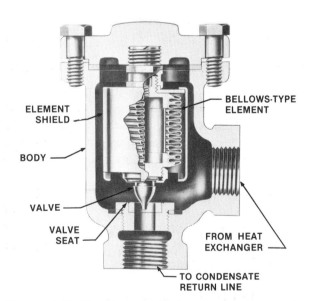

Figure 4-18. The thermostatic trap can be used with both high and low pressure steam. (*Sarco Co., Inc.*)

and the valve opens to allow the air or condensate to pass into the condensate return line.

The bellows are usually filled with an alcohol and water solution to increase the sensitivity of the trap. The thermostatic steam trap is used in low pressure plants. It can also be modified for use in plants with pressures up to 250 psi.

Float Thermostatic Steam Trap

The float thermostatic steam trap has a body, a float that controls a valve, and a thermostatic element. See Figure 4-19. When condensate enters the body of the trap, the float is raised and the valve opens to allow the condensate to flow into the condensate return line. If

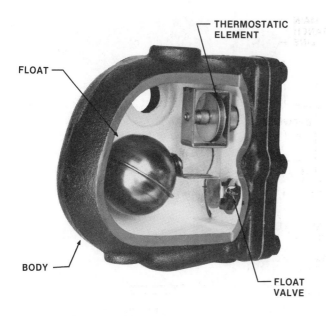

Figure 4-19. The float thermostatic trap removes air and other noncondensable gases as well as condensate. (*Sarco Co., Inc.*)

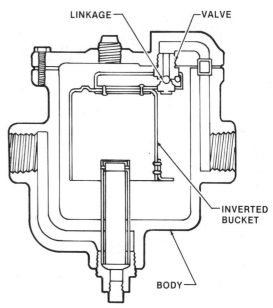

Figure 4-20. Inverted bucket steam traps are used when large quantities of condensate must be removed.

there is no condensate in the body, the valve will close.

The thermostatic element opens only if there is a temperature drop around the element caused by air or noncondensable gases in the body of the trap. When steam enters the body of the trap, the thermostatic element expands and closes.

In this type of trap, the thermostatic element opens and closes to discharge only air and noncondensable gases. The float opens and closes the valve to discharge condensate. These traps are generally used in plants up to 125 psi.

Inverted Bucket Steam Trap

The main parts of an inverted bucket steam trap are the body, an inverted bucket, a valve, and linkage that connects the valve and bucket. See Figure 4-20. Steam and condensate enter the trap from the bottom of the inverted bucket. If only steam enters the trap, the bucket will become buoyant and the valve will close.

When condensate enters the trap, the bucket sinks and the valve opens. A small hole at the top of the bucket removes air that becomes trapped in the bucket. Air and condensate leave the body of the trap when the valve opens.

Impulse Steam Trap

The impulse steam trap consists of a body, a piston, and a valve. The opening and closing of the valve in this trap depend on a pressure differential across the piston. When condensate or air enters this trap, a pressure drop occurs above the piston, opening the valve. Air and condensate enter the return line until steam enters the trap, increasing the pressure above the piston and closing the valve.

Another type of impulse steam trap is the thermodynamic steam trap. In this type of steam trap, a pressure differential is created across a disc. These traps are used primarily in medium pressure plants.

Variable Orifice Steam Trap

The variable orifice steam trap consists of a body, a series of compartments, a gauge glass, and a manual valve. The steam and condensate enter the body and pass through a series of compartments that reduce the pressure. In the first compartment, the condensate level can be seen with the gauge glass. The manual orifice is adjusted to maintain a constant condensate level in the glass.

Selection and Maintenance of Steam Traps

Each type of steam trap is made to perform a specific function. When selecting a steam trap, size and application are extremely important. If in doubt as to what type to use, it is always advisable to contact a reliable manufacturer for information.

Steam traps are often neglected in both high and low pressure steam plants. A regular maintenance schedule should be set up to check each trap to make sure it is operating properly. A steam trap that is stuck closed will lead to a waterlogged line and could cause water hammer.

On the other hand, a steam trap that is stuck open will cause steam to blow through. If steam were allowed to enter the return line, it would result in a loss of plant efficiency. All steam traps must be in proper working order for maximum plant efficiency.

DESUPERHEATING AND PRESSURE-REDUCING STATION

The desuperheating and pressure-reducing station is usually found in a plant that has superheater-equipped steam boilers. Superheated steam is essential for use with turbines that are designed to use superheated steam to achieve maximum efficiency. Auxiliaries such as reciprocating pumps, saturated steam turbines, and heat exchangers are designed for saturated steam. Process steam is also saturated.

Desuperheaters

In plants requiring superheated and saturated steam, having one boiler for superheated steam and another for saturated steam is impractical. It is much easier to draw off some superheated steam, desuperheat it, and then send it to the auxiliaries or process lines.

Drum Desuperheater. To desuperheat superheated steam, enough heat must be removed to bring the steam back to the saturation point. One method of desuperheating steam, which is used in marine boilers, is to route steam back through coils of submerged piping within the steam and water drum. See Figure 4-21.

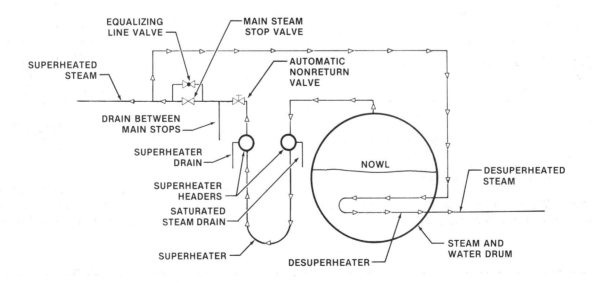

Figure 4-21. Drum desuperheaters are used primarily on marine boilers.

The coil is known as the drum desuperheater. The superheated steam gives up some of its heat to the boiler water, which is at the saturation temperature. The steam leaves the coil at or near the temperature of the saturated steam.

Line Desuperheater. Another type of desuperheater is a line (spray) type. It is used in conjunction with a pressure-reducing station. See Figure 4-22. The desuperheater functions as follows:

1. A chamber in the steam line is fitted with one or more nozzles.

2. The nozzles deliver a fine spray of feedwater into the superheated steam, thus reducing the temperature.

3. The quantity of steam increases when the feedwater changes state after absorbing the superheat.

4. A thermostat is placed in the line on the saturated steam side of the desuperheater. This controls the feedwater supply valve to the nozzles.

5. If the temperature of the steam rises, the feedwater supply valve to the nozzles will begin to open.

6. If the temperature of the steam falls, the feedwater valve will start to close.

Reducing Steam Pressure

Steam pressure is reduced through a pressure-reducing valve, which is controlled by a positioning controller. This system of desuperheating and pressure-reducing is used most frequently with a steam turbine that has extraction lines used for process work. See Figure 4-23.

When a low load condition exists on the turbine, not enough steam can be extracted. This requires the use of a desuperheating and pressure-reducing station. For this station to function properly, the nozzles must be inspected and cleaned periodically to prevent any buildup of deposits.

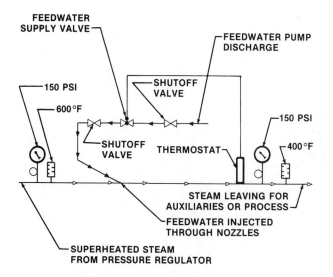

Figure 4-22. The quantity of steam increases with the use of a line desuperheater.

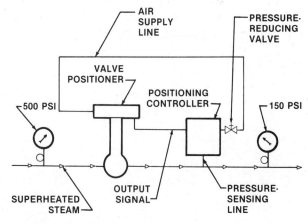

Figure 4-23. Plants often require steam at different pressures. Steam at the required pressure is supplied by using pressure-reducing stations.

Key Words

centrifugal feedwater pump
closed feedwater heater
condensate tank and pump
deaerating feedwater heater
desuperheater
drum desuperheater
economizer
feedwater heater
feedwater pump
feedwater regulator
float feedwater regulator
float thermostatic steam trap
impulse steam trap

inverted bucket steam trap
line desuperheater
low water fuel cutoff
main feedwater line
open feedwater heater
reciprocating feedwater pump
steam trap
thermoexpansion feedwater regulator
thermohydraulic feedwater regulator
thermostatic steam trap
turbine feedwater pump
variable orifice steam trap

Name _____ Date _____

___B___ 1. The automatic city water makeup valve found on an open feedwater heater is used to _____.
A. add city water to the boiler if returns are low
B. maintain a water level in the feedwater heater if there are insufficient condensate returns
C. start and stop the feedwater pump on boiler demand
D. never found on open feedwater heaters

___C___ 2. Too high a water temperature in the feedwater heater could cause _____.
A. oxygen pitting in the boiler
B. thermal shock to the boiler
C. the feedwater pump to become steambound
D. the feedwater pump to become waterbound

___A___ 3. Too low a water temperature in the feedwater heater could cause _____.
A. oxygen pitting in the boiler
B. the feedwater pump to become steambound
C. the feedwater pump to become waterbound
D. no problem; extra heat would be made up in the combustion chamber

___D___ 4. The three numbers found on the data plate attached to a reciprocating feed-water pump indicate the _____.
A. area of steam piston, area of water piston, and length of pump stroke
B. area of water piston, area of steam piston, and length of pump stroke
C. diameter of water piston, diameter of steam piston, and length of pump stroke
D. diameter of steam piston, diameter of water piston, and length of pump stroke.

___B___ 5. A reciprocating feedwater pump must have a safety relief valve located between the _____.
A. pump discharge valve and the boiler
B. pump and the discharge valve
C. pump and the open feedwater heater
D. because the reciprocating feedwater pump is a positive displacement pump, no safety relief valve is needed

___C___ 6. An economizer is used in large boiler plants to heat _____.
A. fuel oil using flue gas temperature
B. air for combustion
C. feedwater using gases of combustion
D. steam before it enters the superheater

___A___ 7. A(n) _____ draft fan must be used to overcome resistance caused by gases of combustion leaving the boiler when an economizer is used.
A. induced
B. forced
C. natural
D. natural and forced

_B_

8. The theory of operation of a centrifugal pump is that the centrifugal force of a rotating element _____.
    A. will overcome kinetic energy
    B. is converted into pressure
    C. will be less than potential energy
    D. total force equals total force

_C_

9. Centrifugal feedwater pumps can be started with their discharge valves _____.
    A. open
    B. partly open
    C. open or closed
    D. they have no discharge valve

RECIPRICATING OPEN?

_B_

10. A turbine feedwater pump differs from a centrifugal feedwater pump in that it is a _____.
    A. nonpositive displacement pump
    B. positive displacement pump
    C. pump that can only be steam driven
    D. straight mechanical drive pump

_A_

11. To protect the turbine pump from excessive pressure, a(n) _____.
    A. safety relief valve must be installed on the discharge line
    B. bypass line is installed
    C. pump governor is installed
    D. overspeed trip is installed

_C_

12. The feedwater stop valve on the feedwater line is located closest to the shell of the boiler so that the _____.
    A. operator can reach it
    B. boiler can be taken off-line
    C. check valve can be repaired without taking the boiler off-line
    D. no valves are allowed between the boiler and the feedwater pump

_D_

13. The purpose of a feedwater regulator is to _____.
    A. shut down the boiler in the event of low water
    B. prevent a furnace explosion
    C. control water level in the feedwater heater
    D. maintain a consistent water level in the boiler

_D_

14. Feedwater regulator sensing elements are located _____.
    A. on the steam line
    B. on the water line
    C. on the blowdown line
    D. at the NOWL

_D_

15. By maintaining a constant water level in a boiler, it is possible to reduce _____.
    A. fuel consumption
    B. thermal shock to boiler metal
    C. the chance of high or low water in the boiler
    D. all of the above

Chapter 5

FUEL BURNING EQUIPMENT

Fuel burning equipment is required for the release of heat energy in fuel. The four main types of fuel burning equipment are fuel oil burners, gas burners, stokers (coal burners), and pulverized coal burners.

The type of fuel burned determines the fuel burning equipment required. In addition, different fuels require specific storage and handling procedures. All fuels are combustible and can be dangerous if necessary safety precautions are not followed.

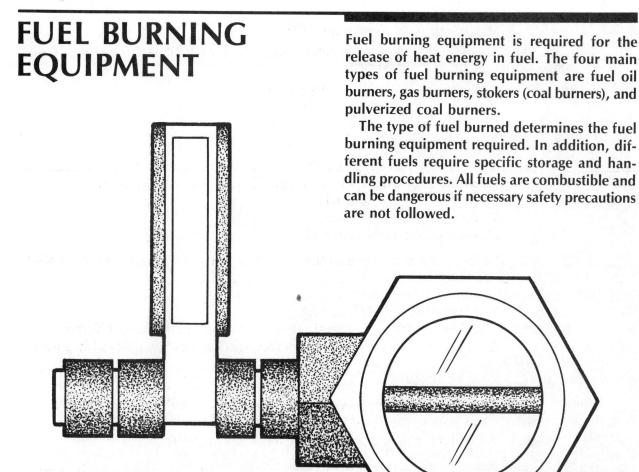

KEY TO ARROWHEAD SYMBOLS			
△ - Air	▲ - Water	▲ - Fuel Oil	⌂ - Air to Atmosphere
⚠ - Gas	△ - Steam	⚠ - Condensate	⚠ - Gases of Combustion

FUEL OIL BURNERS

Fuel oil burners deliver fuel oil to the furnace in a fine spray, which mixes with air to provide efficient combustion. Different types of fuel oil burners utilize various methods to produce the fine spray of fuel oil necessary for combustion.

The size of the plant determines the type of fuel oil burner used. The types of fuel oil burners commonly used in industrial plants today include *rotary cup burners, pressure atomizing burners,* and *steam and air atomizing burners.* These burner types differ in their accessories, fuel oil pressure, and how they utilize steam and air to function.

The type of fuel oil burned is also a factor in the type of burner used. Rotary cup burners burn No. 4 or No. 6 fuel oil at temperatures ranging from 100 °F to 180 °F. Pressure atomizing burners can burn unheated No. 2 and No. 4 fuel oil. No. 6 ("bunker C") fuel oil can be burned at temperatures ranging from 180 °F to 220 °F.

In comparison, steam or air atomizing burners can burn No. 6 fuel oil at lower temperatures. The fuel oil temperatures identified are approximate. Contact your local supplier to determine the proper temperatures to store and burn fuel oil.

Rotary Cup Burners

The rotary cup burner can burn a wide range of fuel oil at low temperatures and pressures. It is ideal for completely automatic operation. The rotary cup burner atomizes fuel oil using a spinning cup and high velocity air. See Figure 5-1.

NOTE: The numbers in the following step-by-step explanations correspond to the numbers in the circles on the figures. The solenoid valve (1) controls the flow of oil through the fuel tube (2). Fuel oil flows onto the spinning cup (3), which is rotating, and forms a thin film. The spinning cup increases the velocity of the fuel oil as it moves toward the end of the cup.

The primary air fan (4) produces high velocity air (5) that atomizes the fuel oil as it leaves

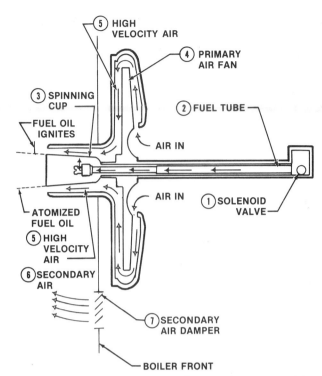

Figure 5-1. The rotary cup burner burns a wide range of fuel oil and is readily adaptable to automatic operation.

the spinning cup. Air used to atomize fuel oil is primary air. The secondary air damper (7) regulates secondary air (6), which controls combustion efficiency.

The air to fuel ratio to the burner must be regulated to obtain complete combustion, thus reducing the amount of smoke produced. Regulation of the air to fuel ratio is maintained by the modulating pressure control, the modulating motor and mechanical linkage controlling the fuel oil valve, and the primary air fan and secondary air dampers.

Pressure Atomizing Burners

The two types of atomizers used in pressure atomizing burners are the *plug-and-tip* type and the *sprayer plate* type. Both types of atomizers require fuel oil pressures of 100 psi or higher for atomization. See Figure 5-2.

The fuel oil enters the burner tube (1) and is forced through the plug channel (2) or the sprayer plate channel (2). In both cases, the

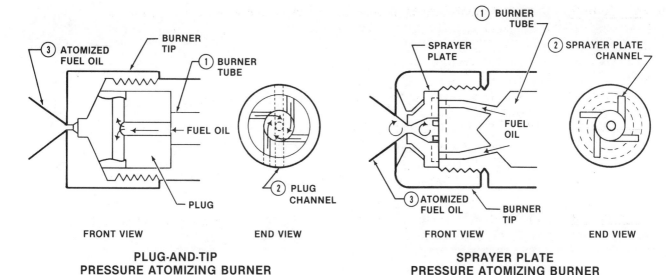

Figure 5-2. The pressure atomizing burner requires high temperatures and pressures to atomize the fuel oil.

atomized fuel oil (3) leaves the tip at a high velocity and is rotating.

The amount of fuel oil going to the burner is controlled by pressure on the fuel oil and the size of the orifice in the burner tip. Small changes in boiler load are compensated for by increasing or decreasing the fuel oil pressure. Changes in steam demand require a change in the size of the burner tip. The amount of air going to the furnace is controlled by a damper or by the speed of the forced draft fan.

A diffuser located at the end of the burner tube controls the flame pattern developed. An improper flame pattern will cause fuel oil impinging (hitting) on the furnace walls, resulting in a buildup of carbon deposits.

Steam and Air Atomizing Burners

The two basic types of steam atomizing burners are the *outside mixing* and *inside mixing* types. In the outside mixing steam atomizing burner, fuel oil and steam mix outside the burner. In the inside mixing steam atomizing burner, fuel oil and steam mix inside the burner. See Figure 5-3.

The purpose of the steam is to atomize the fuel oil. The fuel oil is supplied to the burner at a pressure of 50 psi and a temperature of

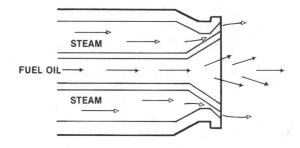

**OUTSIDE MIXING
STEAM ATOMIZING BURNER**

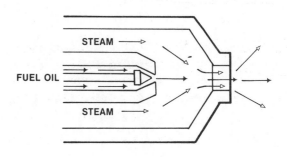

**INSIDE MIXING
STEAM ATOMIZING BURNER**

Figure 5-3. Steam is used to atomize fuel oil and can mix with the fuel oil outside or inside the burner.

120-150°F. Steam at a pressure 20 psi higher than the fuel oil pressure is required for atomization.

Steam and fuel oil do not come into contact with each other until the steam is directed across the path of the fuel oil flowing outside or inside the burner nozzle, depending upon the type of atomizer. Air is supplied in the same manner as in the pressure atomizing burner.

For efficient operation of the steam atomizing burner, the pressure of the fuel oil and steam must be regulated at all times. The difference in pressure between the fuel oil and steam must be maintained during the changes in steam flow rates.

Live steam (steam obtained directly from the boiler) that is used for atomization of the fuel oil is obtained from the highest point of the steam and water drum. This live steam is saturated.

Air atomizing burners are inside mixing and use air instead of steam to atomize fuel oil. Air atomizing burners must have an air compressor (air pump) to supply the air needed for atomization. This type of burner is primarily used in smaller installations.

Fuel Oil Accessories

Fuel oil accessories are supporting components necessary for the safe and efficient operation of the fuel oil burner. Fuel oil accessories store, clean, control the temperature of, and regulate the pressure of fuel oil.

Variations in the purity of the fuel oil may cause buildup of foreign matter in the lines of the burner, resulting in restricted flow or inefficient combustion. Maintaining the proper fuel oil pressure is essential for proper atomization of the fuel oil. The temperature required for efficient combustion will vary according to fuel oil grade.

Fuel Oil Tanks. Fuel oil tanks are used to store fuel oil in specific quantities as required. The construction, installation, and location of the fuel oil storage tank must conform with local and state regulations. See Figure 5-4.

The tank has a covered opening (manhole)

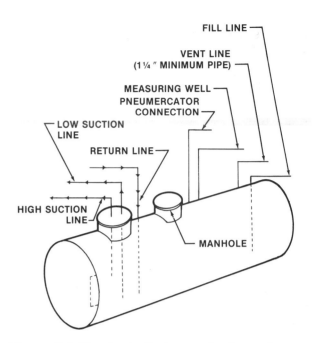

Figure 5-4. The fuel oil storage tank must conform to local and state regulations. (*Babcock and Wilcox Co.*)

used as an entrance for inspection and cleaning. Either a fuel oil heater within the tank or a pipeline heater heats the fuel oil so it can be pumped.

The fill line is located on top of the tank. A required vent line is installed on the tank with a minimum pipe size of 1¼″. The vent line prevents pressure buildup when filling the tank and prevents a vacuum from developing in the tank when fuel oil is removed.

Other openings on the tank are for the pneumercator connection and the measuring well. The pneumercator is used to measure the level of fuel oil in the tank, which is indicated on a gauge away from the tank.

A measuring stick (dipstick) dipped into the measuring well is also used to determine the fuel oil level in the tank. A chart is used to convert inches on the measuring stick into gallons present in the fuel oil tank.

Fuel Oil Lines. Different fuel oil lines are required to connect the various parts of a fuel oil system. High or low suction lines can be used to supply the burner from the tank, but the low suction line is used under normal conditions. However, if water or sludge is found in the fuel oil, the high suction line is used until the tank is pumped out and the cause of the problem is identified.

The fuel lines and equipment located on the discharge side of the fuel oil pump must be protected against excess fuel oil pressure by relief valves. The relief valves discharge excess fuel oil bypassing the burner to return lines feeding into the tank. Return lines are used to circulate fuel oil that is being heated or fuel oil that bypasses the burner.

Fuel Oil Strainers. Fuel oil, although it has been refined, still has impurities present in it. If not removed, these impurities will settle on the fuel oil heater. This can cause retarded heat transfer, restricted flow, and clogged burner tips, all resulting in boiler downtime.

Two sets of duplex type fuel oil strainers are used to remove foreign matter in a fuel oil system. See Figure 5-5. The first set is located on the suction side of the fuel oil pump. It consists of a machined casting that houses a coarse, mesh basket screen.

To gain access to the basket screens, the covers of the duplex strainer must be removed. The selector lever controls a plug valve, allowing the use of one strainer while the other is removed from service for cleaning. The fuel oil

Figure 5-5. Duplex strainers allow the operator to keep the boiler on-line while cleaning one strainer. *(The Kraissl Co., Inc.)*

enters the top of the basket and passes through the screen before entering the suction line to the fuel oil pump.

The second set of strainers is located close to the fuel oil burner on the discharge side of the fuel oil pump. In this set, the mesh of the basket screen is finer, thus removing additional foreign matter from fuel oil before passing through the pump.

Fuel Oil Pressure Gauges. Fuel oil pressure gauges indicate any drop or rise in fuel oil pressure. Fuel oil pressure gauges are located on both sides of all strainers. The gauges will indicate any pressure drop caused by restriction in the strainer, alerting the operator to change over and/or clean the strainer.

Pressure gauges are also located on the suction and discharge side of the fuel oil pump and at the fuel oil burner inlet. The suction pressure gauge changes with the fuel oil level in the tank and with the fuel oil temperature. The pressure at the discharge side does not vary much in the normal operation of the burner.

The fuel oil burner inlet pressure varies depending on the type of fuel oil burner being used. Inlet pressures of 8 to 10 psi are required for rotary cup burners. Pressure atomizing burners require pressures ranging from 100 to 250 psi. Steam and air atomizing burners require inlet pressure ranging from 8 to 20 psi. *NOTE:* The pressures listed are approximate. Check with the equipment manufacturer for specific recommendations.

Fuel Oil Heaters. Most industrial steam plants that burn fuel oil use No. 6 fuel oil. No. 6 fuel oil must be heated before it can be pumped or burned. To permit adequate flow for transport of fuel oil, No. 6 fuel oil tanks are equipped with heaters.

The two types of tank heaters commonly used are the *coil* type and the *bell* type. The coil heater is a round pipe coil heated with steam. The fuel oil suction line passes through the center of the coil. This arrangement makes it unnecessary to heat all the fuel oil in the tank. The bell heater functions the same except that it uses a closed bell-shaped vessel instead of coils. Fuel oil in the storage tank is only heated high enough to permit adequate flow.

WARNING: Fuel oil heated above its flash point can result in a fire in the tank.

Fuel oil heaters are also used to heat fuel oil to its firing point. Fuel oil heaters are located on the discharge side of the fuel oil pump and heat fuel oil for efficient use in the burner. The two types of fuel oil heaters used for this purpose are *steam fuel oil heaters* and *electric fuel oil heaters*. See Figure 5-6.

The steam fuel oil heater is of shell-and-coil or shell-and-tube construction. In both types of heaters, the fuel oil passes through the tubes while steam and condensate are in the shell.

The electric fuel oil heater consists of a shell with one or more electric heating elements inserted into the shell. The fuel oil enters at the lower section of the shell and leaves from the top. Both steam and electric fuel oil heaters are equipped with automatic temperature regulators. See Figure 5-7.

A safety relief valve is installed after the fuel oil heater to protect against excessive fuel oil pressure. See Figure 5-8. The discharge from the safety relief valve is connected to the return line going to the tank. If the inlet and outlet valves on the heater are closed and steam is left on the heater, the fuel oil will expand, causing a pressure increase within the shell of the heater.

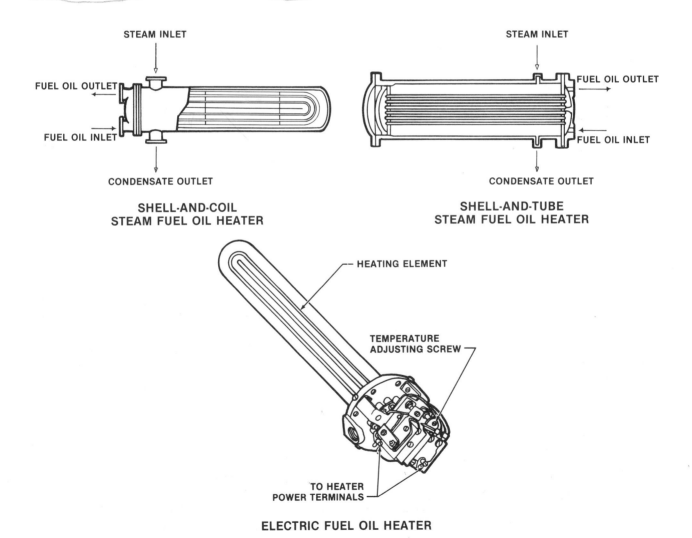

Figure 5-6. Fuel oil heaters are used to heat fuel oil so it can be pumped or burned.

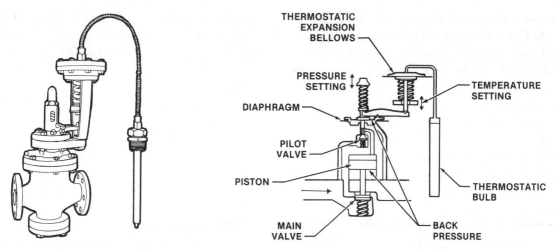

Figure 5-7. The automatic temperature regulator controls the fuel oil temperature and steam pressure. (*Lawler Automatic Control, Inc.*)

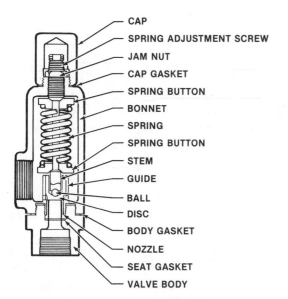

Figure 5-8. Because fuel oil pumps are positive displacement pumps and produce a constant discharge of fuel oil, safety relief valves must be installed between the fuel oil pump and discharge valve. (*Teledyne Farris Engineering*)

Fuel Oil Pumps. Fuel oil pumps move fuel oil through the system, delivering fuel oil to the burner under pressure. Reciprocating or gear-type pumps are commonly used. See Figure 5-9. Because fuel oil pumps are positive displacement pumps that produce a constant discharge of fuel oil, safety relief valves are required.

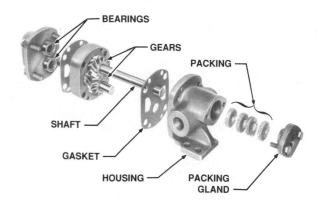

Figure 5-9. The gear-type fuel oil pump is used in small- to moderate-size boiler plants. (*Worthington Pump*)

Not all of the fuel oil is delivered to the burner. The safety relief valve is located on the discharge line from the pump and discharges fuel oil to the return line, which goes back to the fuel oil tank. The amount of fuel oil returned to the fuel oil tank depends upon the rate of combustion and the pressure-regulating device at the fuel oil burner that works to maintain a constant pressure.

GAS BURNERS

Gas burners may be either high pressure or low pressure burners, depending on the gas service available. Gas burners supply the proper mixture of air and gas to the furnace so complete combustion is achieved. Components required to provide the proper gas flow include gas regulators, solenoid valves, control valves, blowers, and control mechanisms that maintain the proper air to gas ratio. Both high and low pressure boilers can use either type of gas burner.

WARNING: Gas used as a fuel is highly explosive and the boiler operator must take extreme care when firing it.

High Pressure Gas Burners

Gas is supplied to high pressure gas burners at a set pressure. Gas mixes with air on the inside of the burner register. See Figure 5-10.

Larger plants and plants using combination gas/fuel oil burners commonly use high pressure gas burners. In combination burners, the gas system is separate and includes components such as gas pressure regulators, solenoid valves, pressure gauges, and gas flow control valves.

However, a forced draft fan supplies the necessary primary and secondary air to both the gas and the fuel oil systems. When larger quantities of gas at higher pressures are required, gas booster compressors are sometimes used.

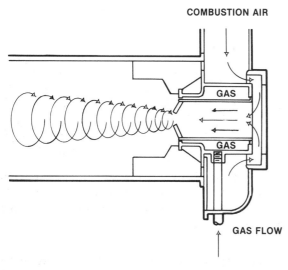

Figure 5-10. The high pressure gas burner must be supplied with gas at a set pressure.

Gas Lines and Controls. The gas supply line to the burner must be large enough to prevent excessive pressure drop through the line. It is fitted with a Bourdon tube pressure gauge that is calibrated with two scales. The first scale reads in inches of water column and the second in ounces per square inch.

The gas line is also fitted with a manually operated shutoff valve. It is a plug cock valve that can be opened or closed with a quarter turn of the lever.

To prevent the system from operating when the gas pressure is low, a vaporstat is connected to the gas line. The vaporstat is an electrical switch actuated by the gas pressure acting on the diaphragm. See Figure 5-11. During normal operation, the switch is closed. If a gas pressure drop occurs, the switch opens and secures the system.

A gas pressure regulator controls the desired set pressure at the burner. See Figure 5-12. The regulator consists of a diaphragm connected to a globe valve with an opposing adjustable spring. By adjusting the spring tension, the pressure at the burner can be changed.

An electrically operated solenoid valve is used as an automatic shutoff gas valve. It is a direct-acting valve that opens when the coil is energized electrically and produces an electromagnetic field.

An iron core connected to the disc of the valve is attracted to the magnetic field. When the iron core moves toward the magnetic field, the valve opens. The valve closes when the coil is de-energized.

The gas flow control valve gradually allows gas to flow to the burner at start-up. This valve prevents a large volume of gas from going into the furnace before lightoff (ignition) has taken place. The gas flow control valve is basically a solenoid-operated diaphragm valve. When the solenoid valve opens, the gas pressure on top of the diaphragm is gradually released. The high pressure gas under the diaphragm now moves the valve toward the open position.

The gas control valve, commonly known as a butterfly valve, controls the volume of gas going to the burner. This valve modulates to

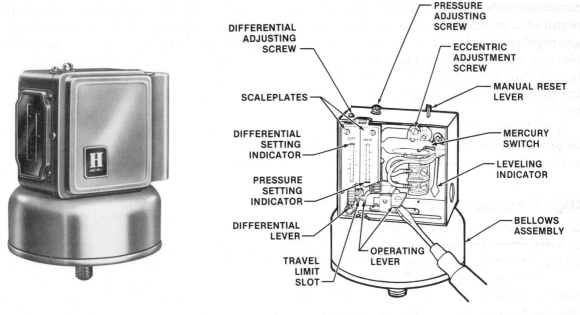

Figure 5-11. The vaporstat prevents the system from operating when the gas pressure is too low. *(Honeywell, Inc.)*

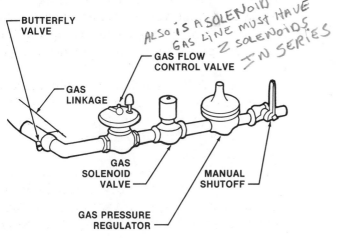

ALSO IS A SOLENOID GAS LINE MUST HAVE 2 SOLENOIDS IN SERIES

Figure 5-12. The gas pressure regulator supplies the burner with the proper pressure of gas.

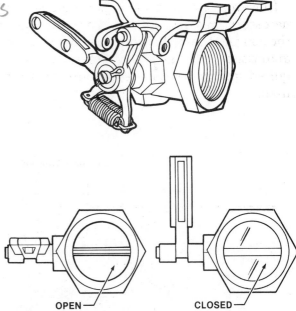

Figure 5-13. The butterfly valve controls the volume of gas going to the burner. The valve modulates to maintain the proper ratio of air to gas. *(Honeywell, Inc.)*

maintain the correct air to gas ratio. See Figure 5-13.

The valve consists of a body, a circular disc, and a pin. The pin passes through the body and circular disc. When the pin turns, it moves the valve toward the open or closed position for accurate gas flow control.

The gas entering the furnace is ignited by a gas pilot flame. The gas pilot flame is sup-

plied with gas from a line connected to the main gas line. See Figure 5-14. On the gas pilot line is a gas shutoff cock, a direct-acting

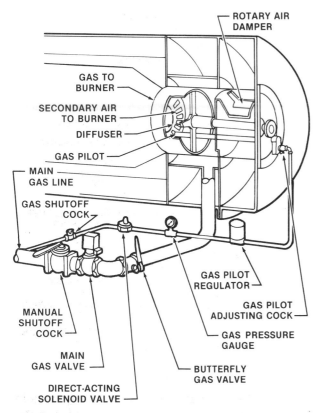

Figure 5-14. The line supplying gas to the pilot is connected to the main gas line before the manual shutoff cock. *(Cleaver-Brooks)*

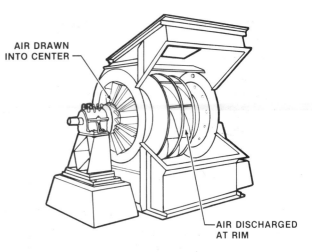

SQUIRREL CAGE BLOWER

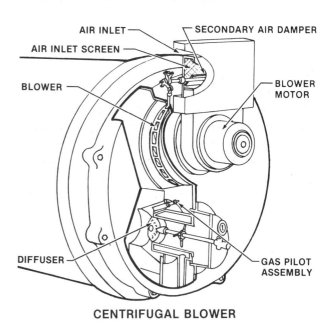

CENTRIFUGAL BLOWER

Figure 5-15. Air for combustion is supplied by either a squirrel cage blower or a centrifugal blower. Both are types of forced draft blowers. *(top—Babcock and Wilcox Co.; bottom—Cleaver-Brooks)*

solenoid valve, a gas pressure gauge, and a gas pilot regulator.

Blowers for High Pressure Gas Burners.

Air for combustion is supplied by a forced draft blower. The two types of blowers are the *squirrel cage blower* and the *centrifugal blower*.

The squirrel cage blower consists of a wheel that has blades attached at the rim and rotates in a housing. When the blower is running, air is drawn into the center and discharges at the rim of the wheel. The centrifugal blower also has a rotating impeller in a housing. The centrifugal blower pulls air in at the center and discharges the air at the outer edge of the impeller. See Figure 5-15.

In both blowers, air flow can be controlled by inlet or outlet dampers. The correct air to gas ratio is maintained by mechanical linkage

between the air damper, the butterfly valve, and the operating control mechanism.

Low Pressure Gas Burners

Low pressure gas burners are used primarily in smaller plants. Using a low pressure gas system reduces the possibility of gas leaks, making it safer than a high pressure gas system.

Gas leaks in a low pressure system usually occur up to the zero-reducing governor. Although leaks are not as common in low pressure systems as in high pressure systems, all leaks must be identified and repaired. The main components of a low pressure gas system are the manual reset valve, air blower, mixing chamber, regulator, solenoid valves, and air control valve. Low pressure gas burner systems supply gas to the mixing chamber at 0 psi gauge pressure. The gas and primary air mix together outside of the combustion chamber and are forced along to the gas nozzle by the blower.

Gas Lines and Controls. A shutoff cock is required on the gas line in case the operator has to secure the system. A vaporstat is also installed to ensure that there is gas pressure in the supply line.

The most important valve on a low pressure gas system is the manual reset valve. The manual reset valve is located on the gas line to the burner and shuts off the gas supply if the pilot flame goes out or a low water condition exists. The manual reset valve is a solenoid valve that remains open as long as the electrical coil is energized.

When the coil is de-energized for any reason, the valve will close. To reset the valve, a manual lever must be lifted into position. Before the manual lever can be lifted, a pilot flame is needed.

The gas pressure reducing valve is a diaphragm valve that functions in the same manner as the reducing valve found in the high pressure system. The valve reduces the gas pressure to 0 psi. See Figure 5-16.

The main gas solenoid valve controls the gas supply to the burner. It opens fully when energized and closes tightly when de-energized. From the solenoid valve, the gas is drawn into the mixing chamber. See Figure 5-17.

The mixing chamber functions when air from the blower is forced through a nozzle and creates a venturi effect. Gas enters the stream

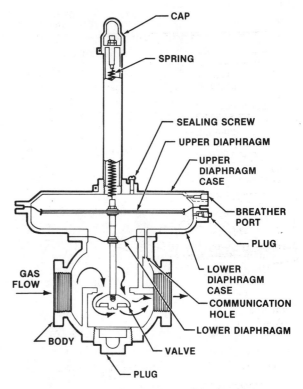

Figure 5-16. The gas pressure reducing valve in the low pressure gas burner system reduces the gas pressure to 0 psi.

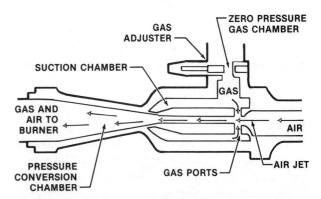

Figure 5-17. Air and gas combine in the mixing chamber of the low pressure gas burner system.

of air through the gas ports, and the air and gas mix. The mixture of air and gas leaves the nozzle, then entering the furnace.

The air flow from the blower to the mixing chamber is controlled by a butterfly valve. This valve allows the ratio of primary air to gas to be varied for different firing rates.

The mixture of air and gas is ignited by a pilot flame. Secondary air, which is necessary to complete the combustion process, is controlled by an adjustable ring on the burner front.

COMBINATION GAS/FUEL OIL BURNERS

Combination gas/fuel oil burners are used in some installations. A combination gas/fuel oil burner is essentially the same as having a high pressure gas burner system and a fuel oil burner connected together at the burner throat. The parts of the combined system are the same as they would be if the systems were separate. See Figure 5-18.

Combination gas/fuel oil burners are designed to use a high pressure gas burner in conjunction with either a rotary cup burner or a pressure atomizing burner. Using two types of fuel allows for flexibility in operation because the operator can change from one fuel to another in the event of a mechanical failure in the system.

In addition, using a combination gas/fuel oil burner makes it possible to burn the fuel that is least expensive at a particular time of year. Larger, more sophisticated plants can burn gas and fuel oil at the same time for maximum efficiency and minimal air pollution.

STOKERS (COAL BURNERS)

The three kinds of stokers in use today are the *underfeed stoker*, the *spreader stoker*, and the *chain (traveling) grate stoker*. The properties of the coal burned determine the type of stoker used. Soft coal, which has a high volatile content, cannot be burned in the same furnace as hard coal, which has a high fixed carbon content.

The type of stoker, the type of grate, and the furnace volume are designed to accommodate the type of coal being burned. The amount of ash produced by burning coal varies with the type of coal.

The ash from the type of coal burned serves to protect grates in some stokers from excessive furnace temperatures. This minimizes the possibility of the cast iron grates warping.

The type of coal, depth of the coal bed, and

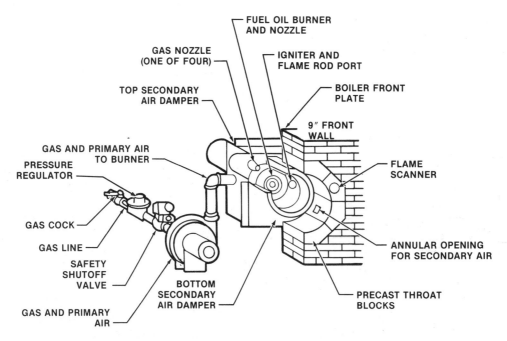

Figure 5-18. Boilers equipped with combination gas/fuel oil burners are more flexible because they can burn either gas or fuel oil. *(Cleaver-Brooks)*

the size of the boiler are all factors in determining the type of stoker to be used. In addition, the boiler must be designed to provide the proper distribution of air for combustion

Underfeed Stokers

The different types of underfeed stokers each utilize the same principle of operation. See Figure 5-19. Coal is fed into a hopper and is pulled down to a coal ram (feeder) by gravity. The coal ram forces the coal into a retort chamber.

Pusher blocks move the coal forward and upward, distributing and leveling coal over the entire grate surface. Green (fresh) coal is continuously fed under the fire. Ash is removed from the ash pit either automatically or by hand.

The lateral movement of the moving grate bars slowly moves the burned-out refuse toward the dump grates. The lateral movement of the grates in the firebox makes it look as if the fuel bed is breathing.

The underfeed stoker can be designed for automatic operation. The rate that the coal is fed, the rate that the air for combustion is supplied to the furnace area, and the rate that the gases of combustion are removed are all contingent upon the steam load. Underfeed stokers are generally used in small to medium-sized plants.

Air for combustion that is supplied to the underfeed stoker is provided by a blower that forces air into the air chamber directly under the retort. From the air chamber, the air moves through the grate openings and fuel bed. Combustion takes place from the top of the fuel bed down.

Underfeed stokers are capable of burning either anthracite or bituminous coal. Because bituminous coal has a high volatile gas content, *overfire air*, which is additional air introduced above the fire, is required to prevent smoking.

When bituminous coal is heated, the gases are driven off and burned above the fuel bed. Overfire air is taken from the main air chamber and its flow is controlled by a damper.

With the proper distribution of air, high combustion efficiency is achieved and low maintenance costs are obtained. Load changes are controlled by adjusting the speed of the feeder block and amount of air supplied.

Spreader Stokers

Spreader (sprinkler) stokers are designed for firing small pieces of bituminous coal. The coal is sprinkled (showered) on the grates. Fine particles of coal burn in suspension above the grates.

Larger particles of coal ignite while in suspension but fall to the grate to complete the

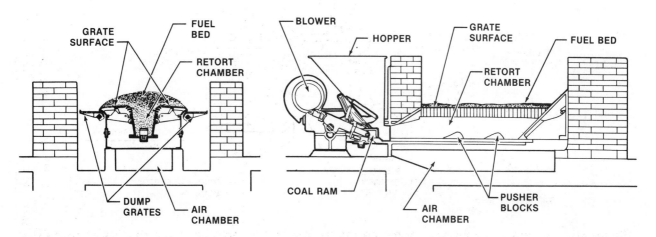

Figure 5-19. The underfeed stoker is well adapted to smaller boilers. (*Babcock and Wilcox Co.*)

combustion process. This method prevents the grates from being covered with green coal, thus keeping the fuel bed hot.

The main parts of the spreader stoker are the coal conveyors, the coal hopper, the coal feeder (distributor), and the overthrow unit. The two types of coal feeders used in spreader stokers are the reciprocating type and the conveyor type. See Figure 5-20. Both types function similarly. The conveyor moves the coal from the coal bunker to the coal scale. When the correct amount of coal is on the coal scale, the conveyor stops and the scale dumps the coal into the coal hopper.

From the coal hopper the coal drops into the coal feeder. The coal is then fed into the overthrow unit, which throws the coal out in a sprinkled form to be burned in suspension or on the grates.

Air for combustion is supplied to spreader stokers by a forced draft blower. Air is forced through the fuel bed from under the grates. See Figure 5-21. Overfire air is also supplied to complete combustion of particles in suspension.

The rate of combustion is controlled by the speed of the drive on the coal feeder as well as by the overfire and underfire air supplied. Spreader stokers can use all grades of bituminous coal and operate with a very thin fuel bed.

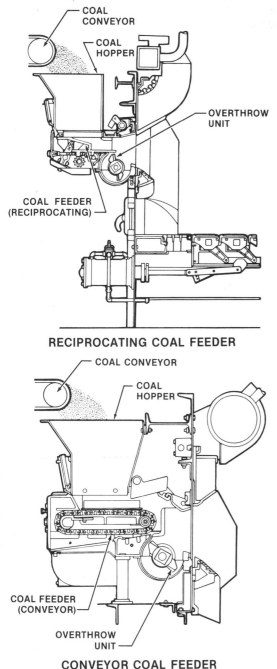

Figure 5-20. Smaller particles of coal will burn in suspension using the spreader stoker. (*Babcock and Wilcox Co.*)

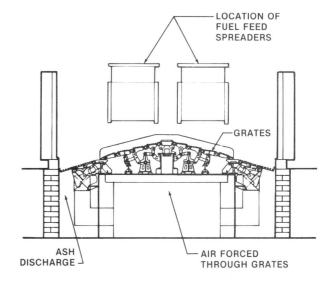

Figure 5-21. Air is forced through the fuel bed from under the grates of a spreader stoker, which helps to cool the grates. (*Babcock and Wilcox Co.*)

Chain (Traveling) Grate Stokers

Chain (traveling) grate stokers are used for larger steam boilers. See Figure 5-22. Parts on

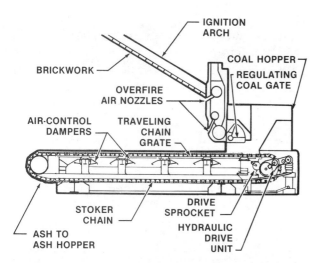

Figure 5-22. The regulating coal gate controls the thickness of the fuel bed in a chain grate stoker. (*Babcock and Wilcox Co.*)

a chain grate stoker include the coal conveyor, coal hopper, regulating coal gate, traveling chain grate, hydraulic drive unit, and ash hopper.

The coal conveyor and coal hopper on the chain grate stoker function as in the spreader stoker. The regulating coal gate controls the thickness of the fuel bed by raising or lowering the sliding gate at the back of the hopper.

The chain grate is formed by a chain that runs around two sprockets, one of which is attached to a variable-speed drive. Coal is deposited on the front of the grate and travels past the ignition arch that starts the combustion process.

The ignition arch is formed from the refractory, which absorbs radiant heat from the combustion process and then radiates the heat back to the incoming green coal. Combustion must be completed before the coal reaches the end of the grate. Ash falls off the grate into the ash hopper.

Coals best suited for the chain grate stoker are noncaking coals with relatively high ash content. The high ash content helps protect the grate from overheating.

A forced draft blower supplies air, which is fed through a windbox under the grates. The amount of coal burned on the chain grate stoker is regulated by the thickness of the fuel bed, the rate of grate travel, and the amount of air supplied.

The air supplied under the grates is controlled so that burning coal is continuously blown toward the front of the traveling grate. This ensures that the coal is burned completely, so the ash is dumped into the hopper rather than on the burning green coal. The boiler operator must regulate the air to prevent the air from blowing holes through the fuel bed.

Pulverized Coal Burners

Pulverized coal is highly explosive so care must be taken when burning it. A flame must be maintained in the furnace at all times. Also, the furnace must have a *negative pressure* (less than atmospheric pressure). If the pressure in the furnace becomes positive, the flame could travel back to the pulverizer and cause an explosion.

Pulverized coal systems are most suitable for use with bituminous coals. The main parts of a pulverized coal system are the overhead coal bunker, coal conveyor, coal scale, coal feeder, pulverizing mill, and exhauster. See Figure 5-23.

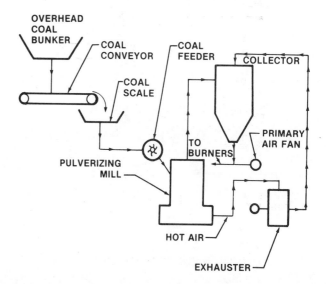

Figure 5-23. Pulverized coal is highly explosive, so the operator must be alert to prevent an explosion in the furnace or pulverizing mill.

In a pulverized coal burner, coal is stored in an overhead bunker to allow the coal to flow by gravity to the opening at its base. This movement of the coal is necessary to prevent spontaneous combustion from occurring within the bunker.

The belt conveyor at the base of the coal bunker moves the coal to the coal scale. The position of the scale controls the belt conveyor. When the scale is in an up position, the conveyor will run until the scale is filled with the correct amount of coal.

When the scale moves down to the dump position, the conveyor stops. From the coal scale, the coal moves to the feeder. The speed of the rotating blade of the coal feeder controls the amount of coal being delivered to the pulverizing mill. See Figure 5-24.

Once the coal is in the pulverizing mill, it is ground using steel balls or rollers rotating around the bowl. The coal is crushed as it passes between the surfaces, which results in the coal having the consistency of face powder.

Warm air is introduced into the pulverizing mill to dry the coal and prevent caking. Air mixes with powdered coal and passes into the exhauster. Coal and air are discharged from the exhauster to the burner throat, and then into the furnace. Coal is burned in suspension and requires a furnace temperature of approximately 3000°F to maintain complete combustion.

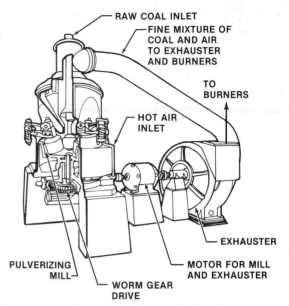

Figure 5-24. The pulverizer grinds the coal into the consistency of face powder before it enters the firebox. *(Combustion Engineering)*

Combustion Air for Pulverized Coal Burners.

A forced draft blower supplies air for the pulverizing mill and windbox. Air from the windbox enters the furnace around the outer edge of the burner throat. Air introduced into the pulverizing mill is primary air. Air from the windbox is secondary air. Steam boilers that burn pulverized coal are usually equipped with an air preheater to supply warm air for the pulverizing mill and windbox.

Key Words

centrifugal blower
chain (traveling) grate stoker
combination gas/fuel oil burner
electric fuel oil heater
fuel oil burner
fuel oil heater
fuel oil line
fuel oil pressure gauge
fuel oil pump
fuel oil strainer
fuel oil tank
high pressure gas burner

inside mixing burner
live steam
negative pressure
outside mixing burner
pressure atomizing burner
pulverized coal burner
rotary cup burner
spreader stoker
squirrel cage blower
steam and air atomizing burner
steam fuel oil heater
underfeed stoker

TECH CHECK ✓ 5

___C___   **1.** Burning a fuel releases _____.
- A. solar energy
- B. hydrogen gas
- C. heat energy
- D. none of the above

___B___   **2.** A clogged vent line on a fuel oil tank being filled with fuel oil could result in a _____.
- A. loss of suction
- B. pressure buildup, which would cause an oil spill
- C. loss of pressure
- D. no vents are allowed on fuel oil tanks

___C___   **3.** A high suction line on a fuel oil tank is used when _____.
- A. the tank is full
- B. the tank is low on fuel
- C. signs of sludge and water are evident in the tank
- D. changing over tanks

___D___   **4.** The purpose of the fuel oil return line is to _____.
- A. circulate fuel oil during warm-up
- B. return fuel oil that bypasses the burner
- C. return fuel oil from the relief valve
- D. all of the above

___A___   **5.** The pneumercator is used to _____.
- A. indicate gallons of fuel oil in the tank
- B. supply primary air to the burner
- C. indicate fuel burned in a 24-hour shift
- D. indicate gallons of makeup used

___A___   **6.** An indication of a dirty fuel oil strainer would be _____ across the strainer.
- A. a large pressure drop
- B. an equalizing of pressure
- C. a slight pressure drop
- D. no change in pressure

___C___   **7.** Duplex strainers are found on _____ of the fuel oil pump.
- A. the suction side
- B. the discharge side
- C. both the suction and discharge sides
- D. none of the above

___D___   **8.** Fuel oil heaters must be used when burning No. _____ fuel oil.
- A. 1
- B. 2
- C. 4
- D. 6

_____ C

9. Fuel oil heaters must be protected from excessive fuel oil pressure because they are located _____ the fuel pumps.
   A. above
   B. on the suction side of
   — C. on the discharge side of
   D. they need no protection due to internal bypass

_____ B

10. The rotary cup burner atomizes fuel oil using _____.
    A. pressure
    B. a spinning cup   P. 90
    C. a spinning cup and an air nozzle
    D. an air nozzle

_____ A

11. In a pressure atomizing burner, atomization is accomplished by _____.
    A. the burner tube
    B. the sprayer plate and air   B 2.
    C. air or steam
    D. low temperature and high pressure

_____

12. In both steam and air atomizing burners, atomization is accomplished by _____.
    A. live steam and air
    B. high fuel oil pressure
    C. the sprayer plate
    D. low temperature, high pressure fuel oil

_____ D

13. To prevent the gas system from operating when the gas pressure is low, a(n) _____ is used.
    A. pressure control
    B. zero-reducing governor
    C. diaphragm solenoid valve
    D. vaporstat

_____ B

14. A gas pressure regulator is used to control the _____.
    A. flow of gases of combustion
    B. desired pressure at the burner
    C. air flow going to the burner
    D. mixture of air and gas

_____ C

15. A solenoid valve is a direct-acting valve in the gas system and is used _____.
    A. to regulate the flow of gas to the burner
    B. to regulate the flow of air to the burner
    C. as an automatic gas shutoff valve
    D. as a gas return valve

_____ D

16. The volume of gas to the burner is controlled by a _____ valve.
    A. solenoid
    B. manual reset
    C. check
    D. butterfly

_A_

17. Blowers are used in a high pressure gas system to _____.
A. supply air for combustion
B. remove gases of combustion
C. regulate the flow of gas
D. cool the combustion chamber

_B D_

18. The air to gas ratio is maintained by a(n) _____.
A. air damper
B. butterfly valve
C. modulating motor and linkage
D. all of the above

_A_

19. The gas pressure reducing valve in the low pressure gas system reduces the gas pressure to _____ psi.
A. 0
B. 5
C. 10
D. 15

_D C_

20. The amount of gas being supplied to the burner in the low pressure gas system is controlled by the _____.
A. manual reset valve
B. check valve
C. amount of air passing through the venturi tube
D. flow control valve

CHECK THIS ONE?

_B_

21. Boilers are equipped with a combination gas/fuel oil burner for _____.
A. greater efficiency ?
B. more flexible operation
C. safer operation
D. higher rates of combustion

_C_

22. The underfeed stoker can burn _____.
A. only anthracite coal
B. only bituminous coal
C. anthracite or bituminous coal
D. only coal with a highly volatile content

_C_

23. Spreader stokers burn coal _____.
A. only in suspension
B. only on grates
C. in suspension and on grates
D. in retorts

_A_

24. To achieve complete combustion in a spreader stoker, air is introduced _____.
A. under and over the fuel bed
B. only under the fuel bed
C. only over the fuel bed
D. using an induced draft fan

_____D_____ 25. The thickness of the fuel bed on a chain grate stoker is regulated by a coal _____.
    A. conveyor
    B. scale
    C. hopper
    D. gate

_____B_____ 26. Pulverized coal burns _____.
    A. on inclined grates
    B. in suspension
    C. in suspension and on grates
    D. in the pulverizer

_____C_____ 27. To prevent caking and to dry the coal entering the pulverizer, _____.
    A. heating coils are used
    B. electric pipe heaters are used
    C. warm air is used
    D. dryers are used

Identify the parts of the high pressure gas burner.

_____B_____ 28. Butterfly gas valve
_____A_____ 29. Gas pressure gauge
_____D_____ 30. Gas pilot
_____C_____ 31. Manual shutoff cock

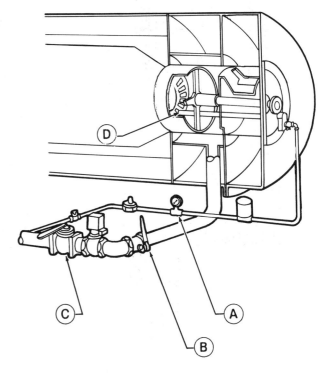

Chapter 6

DRAFT

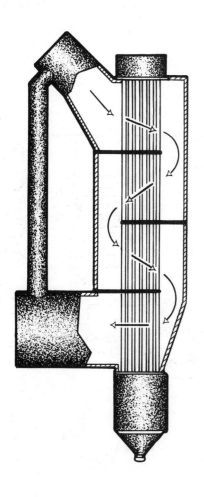

Every boiler has a draft system. Draft is the difference in pressure between two points that causes air or gases to flow. This difference in pressure, although quite small, is measured as more than or less than atmospheric pressure. Draft is necessary to complete the combustion process in a steam boiler. Air is supplied to the furnace, and the products of combustion are removed, passing through the boiler and up the chimney.

Boiler rooms must be designed to permit the proper flow of outside air to the furnace for combustion. If the boiler room is airtight, a vacuum is created that starves the furnace of air for combustion. Many plants are designed to draw outside air over the top of the boiler through skylights. This air passes by the heated boiler and is warmed prior to entering the furnace, which aids the combustion process.

A sufficient quantity of air at the correct pressure is required to burn fuel completely. Approximately 15 pounds of air are required to burn one pound of fuel. Draft is necessary to overcome the resistance caused by baffles, tube passes, dampers, economizers, air heaters, superheaters, and breeching.

KEY TO ARROWHEAD SYMBOLS			
△ - Air	▲ - Water	▲ - Fuel Oil	⌂ - Air to Atmosphere
◭ - Gas	△ - Steam	◬ - Condensate	▨ - Gases of Combustion

MEASUREMENT OF DRAFT

Draft is measured in inches or tenths of an inch of a vertical water column. The *manometer* and the *diaphragm* are the two types of draft gauges commonly used.

Manometer draft gauges are portable and use a liquid to measure draft. Manometer gauges are used primarily when measuring higher pressures. Diaphragm draft gauges are stationary and are usually mounted on the panel board. Diaphragm gauges are mechanically operated and are used primarily for measuring lower pressures.

The boiler operator must be familiar with the correct draft readings required at various locations within the boiler system. Improper draft pressure in the boiler furnace could indicate a malfunctioning outlet damper, which would result in gases of combustion leaking into the boiler room through the boiler setting.

Manometer Draft Gauge

The manometer draft gauge can be a U-tube or inclined-tube type gauge. Both types use liquid to indicate pressure. When both columns are open to the atmosphere, the liquid in the columns is at the same level.

To measure draft, one column of the manometer is open to the atmosphere, and the other column is connected to the point of measurement. The point of measure could be the furnace, the last pass of the boiler, the breeching (connection between the boiler and the chimney), or the windbox (plenum chamber), which is the chamber that supplies forced draft to the furnace. See Figure 6-1.

Pressure on the surface of the liquid in one column of the manometer causes the liquid to rise in the other column. The distance the liquid rises varies with the amount of pressure applied. The amount of draft is determined by the difference in liquid level in both columns

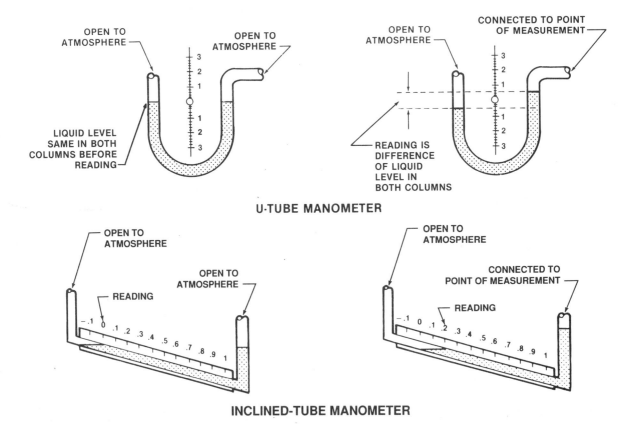

Figure 6-1. Manometer draft gauges use liquid in a tube to measure draft.

and is expressed in inches or tenths of inches on the manometer scale.

Diaphragm Draft Gauge

The diaphragm draft gauge consists of a diaphragm, linkage, and a pointer with a scale calibrated in inches or fractions of an inch of water pressure. See Figure 6-2. The top and bottom of the diaphragm are permanently connected to the two points to be measured, one of which must be connected to the atmosphere. Any difference in pressure between the two points causes the diaphragm to move. The diaphragm is attached to linkage that causes movement of the pointer to indicate a reading on the scale.

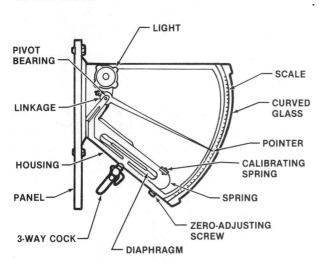

FURNACE UPTAKE

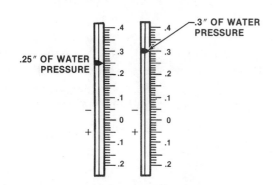

SCALE OF DIAPHRAGM PRESSURE GAUGE

Figure 6-2. A diaphragm draft gauge is mounted permanently on a panel board and is mechanically operated.

The scales used on diaphragm gauges vary from hundredths of an inch to several inches of water pressure. The diaphragm gauge scale used is determined by the location of the measurement. For example, furnace pressure is low and requires a different scale than windbox pressure, which is high.

NATURAL DRAFT

Natural draft is the oldest form of draft. It is produced only by a chimney, without the use of fans. Natural draft is created by the difference in weight between a column of hot gas inside a chimney and the cooler, outside air at the same height.

The amount of draft produced by a chimney depends on the height of the chimney and the difference in temperature between the outside air and the *flue gas*. Flue gases are gases of combustion located in the chimney. Flue gases rise because they are lighter than the outside air. The heavier, outside air replaces the gases of combustion leaving the furnace area of the boiler. See Figure 6-3.

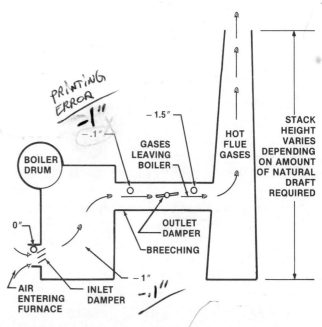

Figure 6-3. Natural draft is the result of the difference in weight between hot and cold air. Draft readings are expressed in inches of water.

The amount of natural draft available can be determined by measuring the difference in pressure between two points such as the atmosphere and the inside of the boiler setting. Air leaks in the boiler setting, breeching, or side walls dilute the flue gases. Air leaks cause an increase in the gas volume, lower the temperature of the gas, and thus lower draft efficiency.

Natural draft is controlled by the use of dampers. The flow of air to the burners is regulated by an inlet damper. The gases of combustion leaving the boiler setting are regulated by an outlet damper. The average draft pressures within a natural draft system are at

1. atmospheric pressure before the inlet damper,
2. $\frac{1}{10}$" of water pressure below atmospheric pressure inside the furnace area,
3. 1" of water pressure below atmospheric pressure before the outlet damper,
4. $1\frac{1}{2}$" of water pressure below atmospheric pressure on the chimney side of the outlet damper.

NOTE: Atmospheric pressure is measured with a barometer.

A furnace draft pressure maintained at a constant value is a *balanced draft system*. Draft pressure is controlled by the positioning of the outlet damper in a balanced draft system.

Natural draft chimneys cannot be used in all applications. Modern boilers are designed to permit higher rates of heat transfer, which in turn produce less draft. Therefore, a higher chimney is required to produce the necessary amount of draft. Since higher chimneys are often physically and economically impractical, mechanical draft was developed to produce the amount of draft needed for efficient combustion.

MECHANICAL DRAFT

Mechanical draft is produced by power-driven fans. The two types of mechanical draft are *forced* and *induced*. These two types may be combined in a *combination forced and induced* mechanical draft system. See Figure 6-4.

Correct air to fuel ratios must be maintained for clean and efficient combustion. To accomplish this, the draft going through the boiler must be controlled at all times, even when load conditions are changing. Mechanical draft is controlled by the speed of the forced and/or induced draft fans and by the use of inlet and outlet dampers.

Forced Draft

Forced draft was developed to provide sufficient air for combustion that was required by the increased firing rates of coal stokers, and of pulverized coal, fuel oil, and gas-fired furnaces. Forced draft is produced by a fan or blower located in front of the boiler setting that forces (pushes) air into a furnace. A relatively high chimney is still required when using forced draft.

The amount of draft is controlled by an inlet and an outlet damper, and a variable-speed forced draft fan. Draft pressures are the same as in the natural draft system except that higher pressure is present at the discharge side of the forced draft fan. The pressure at the discharge side is normally 2" to 3" of water pressure above atmospheric pressure.

Forced draft fans supply *primary air*, which is air used to control the quantity of fuel burned, as well as *secondary air*, which is air used to control how efficiently the fuel is burned. Large forced draft blowers can supply air to more than one boiler through the use of windboxes and tunnels. Small forced draft blower units, which are used on rotary cup burners, supply air to only one burner.

Induced Draft

Induced draft is produced by a fan or blower located between the boiler and chimney that removes (pulls) gases of combustion from the boiler and discharges them into the chimney. With this system, the chimney can be relative-

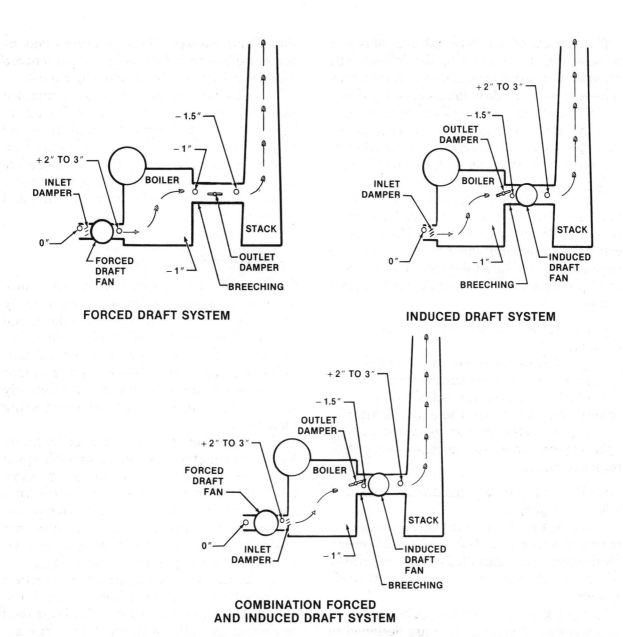

Figure 6-4. The three types of mechanical draft are forced, induced, and combination forced and induced.

ly short. The amount of draft is controlled by the inlet and outlet dampers and the speed of the fan.

Induced draft fans remove gases of combustion from the boiler and breeching and prevent back pressure from developing. Poor draft conditions caused by a faulty chimney can be compensated for by the induced draft fan. Architects, concerned with the aesthetic appearance of a building, indirectly promote the use of induced draft fans by specifying short chimneys on new buildings.

Combination Forced and Induced Draft

Combination forced and induced draft uses both forced and induced draft fans. Large industrial and utility plants require both forced and induced draft to allow for heat recovery equipment such as economizers, air heaters, and superheaters, which are located in the path of the gases of combustion.

In addition to overcoming air and gas flow resistance caused by heat recovery equipment, combination forced and induced draft is necessary to maintain high combustion rates within the boiler. The amount of draft is controlled in the same manner as it would be if the systems were separate.

Care must be taken to maintain a balance between the two fans. The induced draft fan must be larger than the forced draft fan because of the greater volume of gases of combustion it must handle. In addition, induced draft fans must be designed to withstand increased wear caused by *fly ash* (solid particles) in the gases of combustion. Fly ash is created in the combustion process.

AIR HEATERS

In recent years the increase in fuel costs has created a demand for improved plant efficiency. When the heat in flue gas goes up the chimney, the steam boiler loses efficiency. Economizers and air heaters are used to reclaim some of the lost heat and to reduce flue gas temperature.

The air heater is located between the boiler and the chimney. Once flue gases leave the boiler, any residual heat is lost to the atmosphere. Installing air heaters increases combustion efficiency by supplying warm primary and secondary air to the furnace. In addition, air heaters prolong the life of the firebrick and furnace refractory. Cold air entering the furnace causes spalling (hairline cracks) in the brickwork. The two basic types of air heaters are the *convection* type and the *regenerative* type.

Convection Air Heater

The convection air heater may be of *tubular* or *plate* design. See Figure 6-5. The tubular heater consists of tubes through which the flue gas passes. Air flows over the outside of the

tubes. The air makes several passes across the tubes to increase the transfer of heat.

The plate heater uses plates instead of tubes. The plates are assembled and spaced in a structural steel frame. The plates form air and gas chambers. Heat transfer occurs as the air and flue gas move past each other on opposite sides of the plate.

Both types of convection air heaters employ a counterflow principle in that the flue gas and air flow in different directions. This results in greater heat transfer as the hotter gases of combustion pass by the warmer air leaving the heater. Some convection heaters are designed with bypass dampers so part of the air can be bypassed around the heater for more accurate control of the air and flue gas temperature.

Regenerative Air Heater

A regenerative air heater is used primarily in larger boiler installations. The number of moving parts found in regenerative air heaters requires more care and maintenance than other types of air heaters.

The regenerative air heater consists of a round casing divided into three zones: the *gases of combustion zone*, the *sealing zone*, and the *air zone*. A slow-moving rotor consisting of a honeycomb plate element rotates through the three zones of the air heater casing. See Figure 6-6.

When the plate element rotates through the gases of combustion zone, the plate element absorbs heat and reduces the temperature of the gases of combustion. After passing through the plate element, the gases of combustion go through the induced draft fan and out the chimney.

The plate element continues to rotate through the sealing zone. In the sealing zone of the air heater casing, gases of combustion are prevented from mixing with the air for combustion.

When the plate element rotates through the air zone, the plate element releases heat and is cooled as the air for combustion is heated. The air for combustion is forced through the

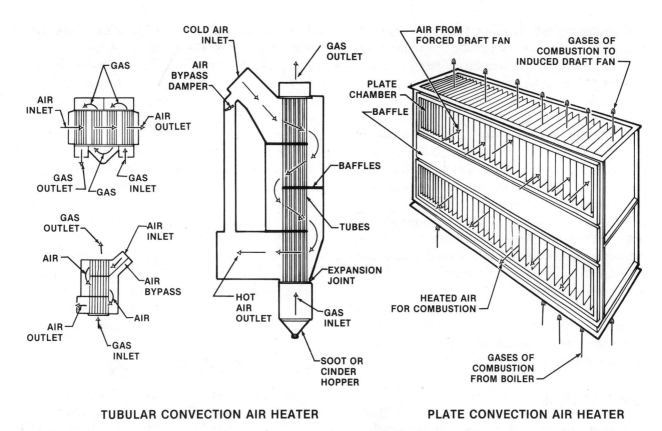

Figure 6-5. Convection air heaters remove heat from gases of combustion before the gases enter the chimney.

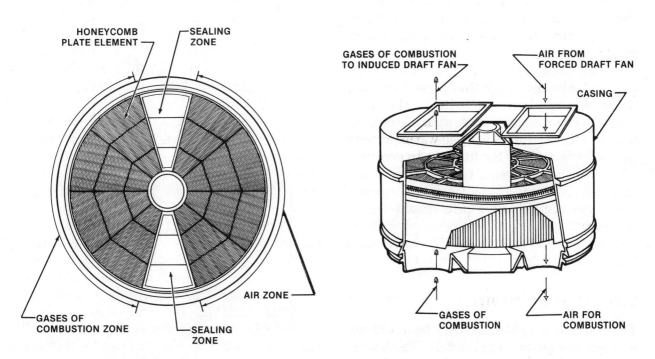

Figure 6-6. The plate element in the regenerative air heater rotates to absorb and release the heat from the gases of combustion.

air heater to the furnace by the forced draft fan.

The plate element rotates continuously during the air heating process. The counterflow principle is used in this heater, as in the convection air heater, for greater efficiency.

Care of Air Heaters

All air heaters are made of steel and must be externally insulated to prevent heat loss. The temperature of the air entering the heater must be monitored. If the temperature gets too low, the gas side of the heater will sweat, resulting in corrosion when soot and moisture combine.

Since air heaters are located in the direct path of the gases of combustion, they are continuously bombarded with soot and fly ash. Air heaters are cleaned with soot blowers. Air heaters must be examined at least once a year for signs of corrosion. If the tubes or plates are corroded, some of the air will mix with flue gas leaving the chimney. This loss of air for combustion could lead to incomplete combustion of the fuel and create smoke.

In addition, heat could be lost, resulting in lower boiler efficiency. Air heaters can be used most successfully in plants with a fairly constant steam load.

GAS AND FUEL OIL DRAFT SYSTEM

The gas and fuel oil draft system consists of a forced draft fan, an air heater, a windbox at each burner, and an induced draft fan. See Figure 6-7. The forced draft fan takes air from the boiler room and forces it through a metal duct to the air heater. As the air passes through the heater, its temperature increases. The air then moves through an insulated duct to the windbox.

From the windbox, the air, which is mixed with fuel oil or gas, enters the furnace. Combustion is completed within the furnace. The gases of combustion then pass through the boiler before entering the air heater.

As the flue gas passes through the air heater, the temperature of the gas drops. The flue gas leaves the air heater to enter the suction of the induced draft fan. The induced draft fan then discharges the flue gas to the chimney.

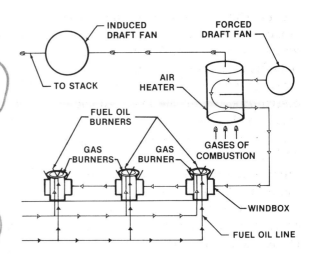

Figure 6-7. The forced draft fan of gas and fuel oil draft system supplies the heated air for combustion to a windbox (plenum chamber) before it mixes with the fuel being burned.

CHAIN (TRAVELING) GRATE STOKER DRAFT SYSTEM

The chain (traveling) grate stoker draft system consists of a forced draft fan, an air heater, a windbox under the chain grate, an economizer, and an induced draft fan. See Figure 6-8. In this system, the forced draft fan pulls air from the boiler room and forces the air through the air heater. The air temperature increases as it passes through the air heater.

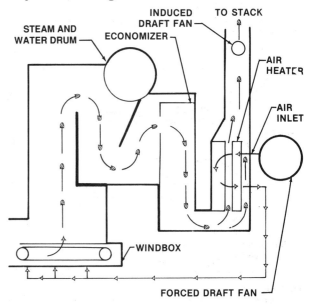

Figure 6-8. The air supplied for combustion in a chain grate stoker is uniformly distributed under the grates to the fuel bed.

From the heater, the air passes to the windbox under the chain grate stoker. The air flow, which is necessary for combustion, is also beneficial in preventing the grates from warping because of overheating. The air is distributed under the grate so that it passes through the fuel bed uniformly.

Gases of combustion pass through the boiler and economizer. After leaving the economizer, the flue gases enter the air heater. Heat from the flue gas is released into the incoming air. After it leaves the air heater, the flue gas enters the suction of the induced draft fan and is discharged to the chimney.

PULVERIZED COAL DRAFT SYSTEM

The pulverized coal draft system consists of a forced draft fan, an air heater, a dust collector, an air tempering damper, a pulverizing mill, an exhauster, and a dust collector. See Figure 6-9.

A forced draft fan takes air from the boiler room and discharges it into the air heater. Heated air flows from the air heater through an insulated duct toward the windbox and the air tempering damper. At the windbox, the air is ready to mix with the incoming pulverized coal.

The air that flows to the air tempering damper blends with air from the boiler room to maintain an air temperature of 200°F. This air is primary air, whereas the air at the windbox is secondary air. The primary air enters the pulverizing mill. Its purpose is to dry the coal and carry the pulverized coal in suspension.

The primary air and pulverized coal are removed from the pulverizing mill by the exhauster. The exhauster discharges the air

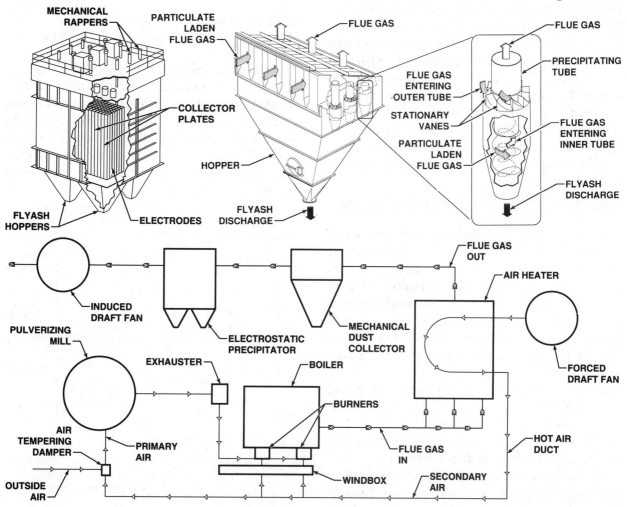

Figure 6-9. Heated primary air carries pulverized coal to the burner, where it mixes with secondary air for efficient combustion.

and coal mixture through a pipe to the burners. Coal is burned in suspension with sufficient secondary air to achieve complete combustion. The gases of combustion then pass through the boiler and enter the air heater.

From the air heater, the flue gas, which contains a considerable amount of flyash and dust, enters the dust collector and/or electrostatic precipitator. The mechanical dust collector separates flyash particles (particulates) from the flue gas using centrifugal force. Flue gas is directed in a circular path in the outer tubes of the precipitating tubes. The swirling motion causes the flyash to be discharged with the clean flue gas exiting through the inner tubes to the atmosphere. Flyash removed collects in a hopper below the tubes.

The electrostatic precipitator removes finer flyash particulates from the flue gas using electricity. Collector plates are grounded, and the flue gas is passed through an electrically charged grid between electrodes. The flyash particulates become charged as they pass through the grid and are attracted to the collector plates. The particulate dust collects on the collector plates and is shaken off by mechanical rappers into flyash hoppers.

After passing through the mechanical dust collector and electrostatic precipitator, the flue gas enters the induced draft fan and is discharged to the chimney. Devices used in the removal of flyash will affect the draft of the furnace and must be considered when operating the plant.

SCRUBBER

A scrubber removes undesirable gaseous elements from the flue gas. Mechanical dust collectors and electrostatic precipitators remove solid particles from flue gas. Scrubbers remove acidic chemical compounds which cause air pollution. Sulfur dioxide and carbon dioxide are the most common acidic chemical compounds produced in the combustion process. Sulfur dioxide and carbon dioxide are removed through intimate contact with an alkaline solution. See Figure 6-10. Flue gas is directed through a spray of alkaline solution. The alkaline solution is further dispersed by diffusing packing and falls through the flue gas traveling upward. The neutralized flue gas is then discharged through the chimney.

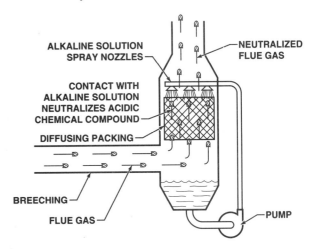

Figure 6-10. Scrubbers neutralize acidic chemical compounds in flue gas to reduce air pollution.

Key Words

air heater
balanced draft system
combination forced and induced draft
convection air heater
diaphragm draft gauge

draft
electrostatic precipitator
flue gas
fly ash

forced draft
induced draft
manometer draft gauge
mechanical draft
mechanical dust collector
natural draft
plate air heater
regenerative air heater
scrubber
tubular air heater

TECH CHECK ✓ 6

_C_ 1. In order to burn one pound of fuel, approximately _____ pounds of air are needed.
A. 8.3
B. 14.7
C. 15
D. 32.5

_B_ 2. Draft is measured in _____.
A. pounds per square inch
B. inches or tenths of an inch of a vertical water column
C. inches or tenths of an inch of mercury
D. ounces per square inch

_✗A_ 3. Draft in the boiler is measured between two points such as the _____ and _____.
A. atmosphere, inside the boiler setting
B. chimney, breeching
C. breeching, firebox
D. boiler's first pass, chimney

_A_ 4. The furnace of boilers using forced draft can register (an) _____ draft pressure.
A. slightly negative
B. atmospheric   P.112
C. no pressure
D. balanced

_C_ 5. To reduce the heat loss of flue gases going to the chimney, boilers are equipped with _____.
A. open feedwater heaters
B. superheaters
C. economizers and air heaters
D. baffles in uptakes

_C_ 6. The convection air heater employs a counterflow principle in which the gases of combustion _____.
A. move down while air goes up
B. and air move in the same direction
C. move up while the air goes down
D. and air mix together

_D_ 7. Both air and flue gas temperatures are controlled by _____.
A. increasing the firing rate
B. decreasing the firing rate
C. balancing the plant load
D. the use of bypass dampers

_A_   **8.** If the temperature of air entering the heater gets too low, it will cause
_____.
   A. sweating on the gas side of the heater
   B. thermal shock to the heater
   C. incomplete combustion
   D. oxygen pitting

_C_   **9.** Air heaters must be cleaned to ensure good heat transfer by _____.
   A. wire brushing monthly
   B. reversing air and gas flow
   C. using soot blowers
   D. having high pressure water used on the gas side

_B_   **10.** Air heaters can be most successfully used in plants that _____.
   A. have a fluctuating steam load
   B. have a fairly constant steam load
   C. have high chimneys
   D. burn only coal or fuel oil

_A_   **11.** If air supplied for combustion mixes with gases of combustion, it could lead
to _____.
   A. a loss of air for combustion and lower boiler efficiency
   B. an increase in chimney temperature
   C. an increase in combustion air temperature
   D. higher boiler efficiency

_C_   **12.** A diaphragm draft gauge is calibrated in _____.
   A. pounds per square inch
   B. feet of water
   C. inches of water
   D. inches of mercury

_A B_   **13.** The amount of draft available in a natural draft system is dependent on the
_____.
   A. diameter of the chimney
   B. height of the chimney
   C. fly ash in the gases of combustion
   D. types of fans used

_A_   **14.** The gases of combustion leaving a boiler that has natural draft are
controlled by _____.
   A. outlet dampers
   B. inlet dampers
   C. higher firing rates
   D. an induced draft fan

_C_   **15.** Mechanical draft is produced by the _____.
   A. height of the chimney
   B. diameter of the chimney
   C. power-driven fans
   D. steam jets

_D_ 16. Mechanical draft can be classified as _____.
- A. pressurized
- B. natural
- C. regenerative
- D. forced or induced

_A_ 17. The induced draft fan is located _____.
- A. between the boiler and the chimney
- B. at the base of the chimney
- C. at the burner
- D. in the first pass of the gases of combustion

_P_ 18. Mechanical draft is used when burning _____.
- A. fuel oil
- B. coal
- C. gas
- D. all of the above

_C_ 19. Larger steam boilers, which are equipped with air heaters and/or economizers, must use _____.
- A. forced draft fans only
- B. induced draft fans only
- C. both forced and induced draft fans   P 114
- D. natural draft only

_C_ 20. When using mechanical draft, it is possible to _____.
- A. increase the boiler steam pressure
- B. reduce thermal shock to the boiler
- C. increase the rate of combustion
- D. increase the mechanical efficiency

_D_ 21. Draft pressure maintained at a constant pressure is called a _____ draft system.
- A. secondary
- B. primary
- C. forced
- D. balanced

_B_ 22. The oldest form of draft used in a boiler is _____ draft.
- A. mechanical
- B. natural
- C. forced
- D. combination

_D_ 23. Solid particles created in the combustion process are called _____.
- A. gases of combustion
- B. pulverized particles
- C. induced carbon
- D. fly ash

Identify the parts of the diaphragm draft gauge.

_____ B   **24.** Pointer
_____ A   **25.** Scale
_____ D   **26.** Diaphragm
_____ C   **27.** Zero-adjusting screw

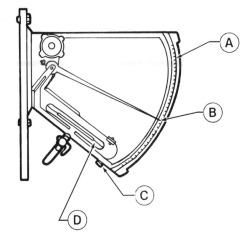

Identify the parts of the tubular convection air heater.

_____ A   **28.** Hot air outlet
_____ C   **29.** Cold air inlet
_____ D   **30.** Tubes
_____ B   **31.** Baffles

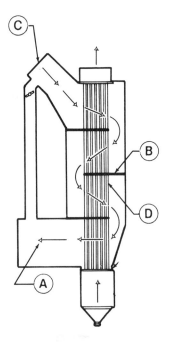

Identify the parts of the regenerative air heater.

_____ D   **32.** Gases of combustion to induced draft fan
_____ A   **33.** Air from forced draft fan
_____ C   **34.** Gases of combustion
_____ B   **35.** Air for combustion

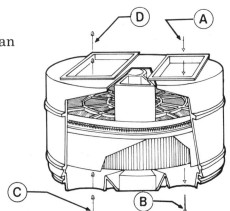

Chapter 7

COMBUSTION

Combustion of a fuel is required to generate the heat necessary to produce steam in a boiler. Combustion is the rapid union of oxygen with an element or compound that results in the release of heat. Fuels commonly used to sustain combustion in a steam boiler include coal, fuel oil, and natural gas. Each fuel is capable of producing a given amount of heat.

In addition, each fuel requires special consideration in storage, handling, and combustion procedures. Specific safety precautions for each fuel used must be followed. The combustion efficiency and the type of fuel used determines the products of combustion. The products of combustion are monitored to comply with local, state, and federal laws.

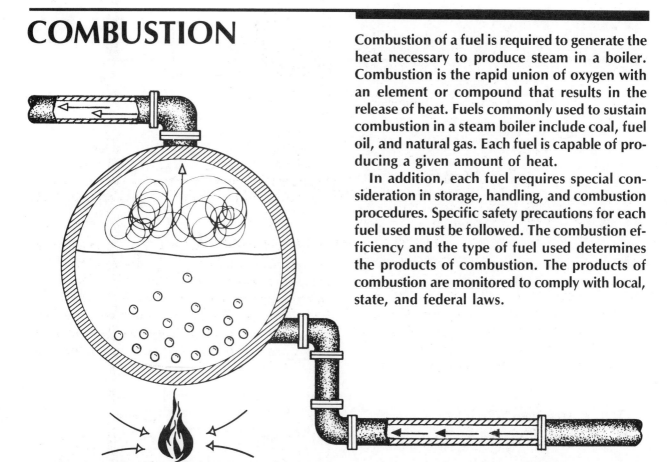

KEY TO ARROWHEAD SYMBOLS			
△ - Air	▲ - Water	▲ - Fuel Oil	⌂ - Air to Atmosphere
⚠ - Gas	△ - Steam	⚠ - Condensate	⚠ - Gases of Combustion

FUELS FOR COMBUSTION

The three types of fuels commonly used for combustion are coal, fuel oil, and natural gas. All of these fuels are taken from the ground. Coal, fuel oil, and natural gas are called fossil fuels because they are composed of organic materials and were formed under great pressures. This process, which spanned millions of years, trapped these fuels within the crust of the earth.

When the type of fuel to be used in a particular boiler application is chosen, factors to be considered include the design of the boiler, the price and availability of the fuel, and the sulfur content of the fuel.

An additional consideration in choosing a fuel is *heating value*. The heating value of a fuel is expressed in British thermal units (Btu's). A Btu is the quantity of heat required to raise the temperature of one pound of water 1°F. The Btu rating of a fuel indicates how much heat it can produce.

Coal

Coal is classified according to *grade* and *rank*. Grade identifies the size, heating value, and ash content of the coal. Rank identifies how hard the coal is. Coals used in boilers include lignite, bituminous, and anthracite coal.

Lignite coal has a low heating value and a high moisture content. Lignite coal is rarely used in boilers as a fuel for combustion. Bituminous coal is a soft coal with a high volatile content. Anthracite coal is a hard coal with a high carbon content.

Coal is further classified by grade. Bituminous coal comes in grades based on size, including (from largest to smallest) run of the mine, lump, egg, nut, stoker, and slack. Anthracite coal also comes in grades based on size, including (from largest to smallest) broken egg, stove, nut, pea, buckwheat, rice, and barley.

To determine the coal suited to a particular plant, the characteristics of the coal must be identified. To identify the characteristics of a particular type of coal, a *proximate* or an *ultimate* analysis is required. A proximate analysis is used to determine the amount of moisture, volatile matter, fixed carbon, and ash in a coal specimen. An ultimate analysis is used to determine the elements present in the specimen.

Elements commonly found in coal include nitrogen, oxygen, carbon, sulfur, and hydrogen. The amount of each element present in the coal specimen determines the heating value, which is expressed in Btu's per pound (Btu's/lb). The Btu content of coal will range from 12,000 to 18,000 Btu's/lb, depending on the grade of coal.

Fuel Oil

Crude oil from the well is distilled into individual products, producing gasoline, diesel fuel, lubricating oils, and fuel oil. Fuel oil consists primarily of carbon, hydrogen, and moisture. Sulfur, nitrogen, arsenic, phosphorous, and silt are also present in fuel oil. Many states have passed laws limiting the amount of sulfur contained in fuel oil. Characteristics of fuel oils include *viscosity*, *flash point*, *fire point*, and *pour point*.

Viscosity is the internal resistance of the fuel oil to flow. The viscosity of fuel oil is lowered by raising its temperature. Lowering the viscosity allows the fuel oil to be pumped and transported more easily.

Flash point is the temperature at which fuel oil gives off a vapor that flashes when exposed to an open flame. Fuel oils with low flash points can be dangerous and require special precautions when handling. Fire point is the temperature at which fuel oil gives off a vapor that burns continuously. Pour point is the lowest temperature at which fuel oil flows as a liquid.

Fuel oil is classified by grades into No. 1, No. 2, No. 3, No. 4, No. 5, or No. 6 fuel oil. The American Society for Testing Materials is responsible for establishing standards for grading fuel oils.

The fuel oils most commonly used in high pressure boilers are No. 2 fuel oil, No. 4 fuel oil, No. 5 fuel oil, and No. 6 fuel oil. No. 2 fuel oil is a *distillate* (not mixed with other grades) with a heating value of approximately 141,000 Btu's/gal. No. 2 fuel oil does not have to be preheated, and it is usually burned using a high or low pressure atomizing burner.

No. 4 fuel oil is heavier than No. 2 fuel oil and has a heating value of approximately 146,000 Btu's/gal. In many locations it is not available as a straight distillate, but only as a blend with No. 2 fuel oil and heavier fuel oils.

No. 4 fuel oil normally does not require preheating. However, in colder climates it may be necessary to preheat the fuel oil, which will lower its viscosity to facilitate pumping. If the fuel oil is not properly blended, it may stratify (separate) in the tank.

No. 5 fuel oil is divided into hot No. 5, which requires preheating, and cold No. 5, which can be burned as it comes from the tank. No. 5 fuel oil has a heating value of approximately 148,000 Btu's/gal. In colder climates, tank heaters may be required to lower the fuel oil viscosity so pumping is easier.

No. 6 fuel oil, commonly referred to as "bunker C" fuel oil, is a residual fuel oil (containing heavy elements from the distillation process) with a Btu content of approximately 150,000 Btu's/gal. Tank heaters and line heaters must be used to bring No. 6 fuel oil up to the required temperature for combustion.

No recommended standard temperatures exist for burning the various grades of fuel oil. The fuel oil temperature required depends on the type of burners used in the plant, and whether a straight distillate fuel oil or a blend of fuel oils is used. For the best results, obtain the pour point, flash point, and firing point of the fuel oil from the fuel oil supplier. A rule of thumb is to burn No. 4 fuel oil at 100°F, No. 5 fuel oil at 150°F, and No. 6 fuel oil at 220°F.

Specific gravity (S.G.) is another characteristic of fuel oil that is measured. The S.G. of fuel oil is the ratio of the weight of a given volume of fuel oil to the weight of the same volume of water at a standard temperature of 60°F. The API gravity is determined using the S.G. and the following formula.

$$\text{API Gravity}° = \frac{141.5}{\text{S.G. at 60°F}} - 131.5$$

NOTE: API is used in preference to specific gravity by the petroleum industry. The heating value of fuel oil is usually expressed in Btu's/gal, although occasionally it is expressed in Btu's/lb. Heavier, higher numbered fuels produce more Btu's/gal than lighter, lower numbered fuel oils. However, by weight, lighter fuel oils produce more Btu's/lb than heavier fuel oils. See Figure 7-1.

FUEL OIL CHARACTERISTICS	No. 1 Fuel Oil	No. 2 Fuel Oil	No. 4 Fuel Oil	No. 5 Fuel Oil	No. 6 Fuel Oil
Type	Distillate Kerosene	Distillate	Very Light Residual	Light Residual	Residual
Color	Light	Amber	Black	Black	Black
American Petroleum Institute (A.P.I.) 60°F	40	32	21	17	12
Specific Gravity	.8250	.8654	.9279	.9529	.9861
Lbs/U.S. Gal	6.87	7.206	7.727	7.935	8.212
Btu's/Gal	137,000	141,000	146,000	148,000	150,000
Btu's/Lb	19,850	19,500	19,100	18,950	18,750

Figure 7-1. Heavier, higher numbered grades of fuel oil have a higher Btu content per gallon than lighter, lower numbered grades of fuel oil.

Natural Gas.   Natural gas is a product of nature and is found in oil fields and coal fields. Natural gas consists of methane, minute quantities of ethylene, and smaller amounts of other gases. It burns cleaner, causing less pollution than other fuels. Natural gas is being used more and more to comply with antipollution laws.

Natural gas has a Btu content that ranges from 950 to 1,050 Btu's per cubic foot (Btu's/cu.ft.). Because the Btu content of natural gas varies, heating values are expressed using a standard measurement called a *therm*. A therm has 100,000 Btu's. The heating value of natural gas is determined by using a gas calorimeter or by chemical analysis of the gas.

Storage and Handling of Fuels

The type of fuel used dictates the proper storage and handling procedures. Federal, state, and local laws may require specific handling procedures that the operator must follow. In addition, the boiler operator is responsible for detecting any potential hazards.

WARNING: Because of their flammable nature, fuels to be used for combustion must be treated with caution. Safety equipment is required in case of fire. Established emergency procedures must detail what procedures must be followed in an emergency.

Coal.   When coal is used as the fuel for combustion, it must be stockpiled to meet plant needs. Anthracite coal is safer to stockpile because it is not as susceptible as bituminous coal is to *spontaneous combustion*, which is a fire initiated without ignition. Bituminous coal, having a higher volatile content, must be carefully monitored when stockpiling to prevent spontaneous combustion.

Rotating coal in the stockpile reduces the chance of spontaneous combustion. From the stockpile, coal is transported into overhead bunkers. The possibility of spontaneous combustion also exists in the coal bunker. In addition, the gases given off from the coal bunker are extremely toxic and explosive. The operator should make sure the coal stays dry, because wet coal can produce sulfuric acid that corrodes the plates of the coal bunker.

WARNING: Heat built up in stockpiled coal can cause spontaneous combustion. Proper safety masks must be worn when entering the coal bunker. Only explosion-proof lights should be used in a coal bunker.

Fuel Oil.   Fuel oil presents different storage and handling problems. Heavier fuel oils must be heated to lower their viscosity when pumping for transport. Care should be taken not to overheat fuel oil. As overheated fuel oil becomes hotter, the sludge, sediment, and other impurities settle in the fuel oil tank. When residue builds up, the tank must be opened for cleaning. In addition, if the fuel oil is too hot, it can reach its flash point, which could lead to a fire.

When receiving a fuel oil delivery, care must be taken to prevent spills. Some fuel oil tanks are filled using gravity. Pumping fuel oil into fuel oil tanks is faster. However, the tank vent line must be clear to prevent a pressure buildup that could result in fuel oil being blown out of vent and fill lines.

Boiler rooms with furnaces that burn fuel oil must have the proper type of fire extinguishers placed in strategic locations. Foam, carbon dioxide, or dry chemical extinguishers should be used on fuel oil fires. Buckets of sand should be available for use in case of spills or small fires. When a fuel oil spill occurs, it should be cleaned up immediately and all fuel oil rags should be disposed of.

WARNING: Never use water to put out fuel oil fires because it will disperse the fire. Always use the recommended type of fire extinguisher for the type of fire.

Natural Gas.   Natural gas, although not stored, is very explosive and toxic. Natural gas received from the supplier must be regulated for use in either low pressure or high pressure gas burners. All natural gas lines and controls should be tested for leaks by using a liquid soap solution or leak detectors. Vent lines from regulators, reducing valves, or governors should be piped out of the boiler room to an area where they can be discharged safely.

WARNING: Any natural gas odor must be checked out immediately. Natural gas that is allowed to build up and mix with air can result in an explosion.

COMBUSTION OF FUELS

The combustion of fuels occurs when elements in coal, fuel oil, or natural gas combine with oxygen to produce heat. The three types of combustion are *perfect, complete,* and *incomplete.*

Perfect combustion occurs when all the fuel is burned using only the theoretical amount of air. Perfect combustion cannot be achieved in a boiler. It is only possible in a laboratory setting where the combustion process can be carefully controlled. The theoretical amount of air is the amount of air used to achieve perfect combustion in a laboratory.

Complete combustion occurs when all the fuel is burned using the minimum amount of air above the theoretical amount of air needed to burn the fuel. Complete combustion is the boiler operator's goal. If complete combustion is achieved, the fuel is burned at the highest combustion efficiency with minimum pollution. Incomplete combustion occurs when all the fuel is not burned, resulting in the formation of soot and smoke.

Air is necessary for the combustion of fuel. Air contains approximately 20% oxygen and 79% nitrogen. Oxygen will support combustion, but it is not a *combustible* (will not burn without the introduction of other elements). Nitrogen is not a combustible, nor will it support the combustion process.

The air used in the combustion process is classified into three types: *primary air, secondary air,* and *excess air.* Primary air controls the rate of combustion, thus determining the amount of fuel that can be burned. Secondary

air controls combustion efficiency by controlling how completely the fuel is burned. Excess air is air supplied to the boiler that is more than the theoretical amount needed to burn the fuel.

Carbon, hydrogen, and sulfur are the combustibles in fuel that combine with oxygen in the air to form compounds. This reaction takes place in the furnace during the combustion process. When carbon combines with oxygen, it forms a compound of carbon monoxide or carbon dioxide. Combustion occurs when the following chemical reactions take place:

1 carbon atom + 2 oxygen atoms produces
  1 carbon dioxide molecule + heat

$$C + O_2 = CO_2 + heat$$

Hydrogen combines with oxygen to form water vapor.

4 hydrogen atoms + 2 oxygen atoms produces
  2 molecules of water + heat

$$2H_2 + O_2 = 2H_2O + heat$$

When sulfer combines with oxygen, it forms sulfer dioxide.

1 sulfur atom + 2 oxygen atoms produces
  1 sulfur dioxide molecule + heat

$$S + O_2 = SO_2 + heat$$

When firing a boiler, the operator's goal is to achieve complete combustion. This involves burning all fuel using the minimum amount of excess air. To obtain complete combustion, the proper mixture of air and fuel, proper atomization, proper temperature of fuel, and enough time to complete combustion are required.

This can more easily be remembered by thinking of the letters *MATT. M* stands for mixture of air and fuel. The proper ratio of air and fuel must be maintained at all firing rates. High firing rates burn the maximum amount of fuel and require more air than low firing rates.

A represents the atomization of fuel. Atomization is the breaking up of fuel into small particles so that it can come into closer contact with the air to improve combustion.

T stands for temperature. The proper temperature of the air, fuel, and furnace zone must be maintained to achieve complete combustion.

The second *T* stands for the time needed to achieve complete combustion. The combustion process must be completed before the gases of combustion come in contact with the heating surface.

Combustion of Coal. The two methods of burning coal are on a grate or in suspension. Anthracite coal is burned on grates in a fuel bed 2″ to 5″ deep. Air is introduced under the fuel bed and is forced through it. Combustion is completed just above the fuel bed. Combustion efficiency is reduced if holes are allowed to form in the fuel bed, which allow air to pass through without combining with the fuel.

Bituminous (soft) coal requires a much thicker fuel bed than hard coal when burned on grates. Air required for combustion must be introduced over the fire as well as under it. Because of the large amount of gases leaving the fuel bed and the combustion that is taking place over the bed, a much larger air space is needed over a soft coal fire than over a hard coal fire. The proper temperature must be maintained in both cases to obtain complete combustion.

When burning bituminous coal in suspension, the coal must be pulverized into a fine dust. The dust is mixed with heated air as it passes through the pulverizer, where it is blown into the furnace to burn in suspension. Sufficient secondary air is introduced to complete combustion. Temperatures are relatively high in this furnace. If combustion is not completed before reaching the first pass, slag could build up on the tubes. *NOTE*: Slag is formed as molten ash cools when it contacts the heating surface of the boiler.

Combustion of Fuel Oil. The combustion efficiency of fuel oil in a furnace depends on the burner delivering the correct quantity of properly atomized fuel oil at the correct temperature for burning. The air is introduced in a rotary fashion so that it mixes with the fuel oil in sufficient quantities for complete combustion.

The furnace temperature must be high enough (usually 2500°F) to allow complete combustion to occur. *NOTE*: All fuel oil must be burned in suspension. The fuel oil must not be allowed to hit the furnace walls or the boiler heating surface. Any impingement of fuel oil will cause carbon deposits to form, thus interfering with the combustion process.

Combustion of Natural Gas. The two types of natural gas burners used to fire a boiler are the high pressure gas burner and the low pressure gas burner. In the high pressure gas burner, air mixes with gas on the inside of the burner register. In the low pressure gas burner, air mixes with gas outside the combustion chamber and is forced into the burner using a blower. Both types require the proper air to gas ratio.

Correct furnace temperature is necessary to achieve complete combustion. Burning natural gas produces a minimum of harmful by-products. Natural gas is a clean fuel that mixes readily with air. When burning natural gas, a minimum amount of excess air is required, which results in a cleaner and more efficient boiler.

Furnace Volume

Furnace volume is the space, measured in cubic feet, required to burn fuel completely before the fuel comes in contact with the boiler heating surface. The design, shape, and size of a furnace depend on the type of fuel being burned. Other factors considered in determining the furnace volume required include

1. natural or mechanical draft,
2. refractory or water-cooled furnace,
3. rate at which heat is released from the fuel.

In all cases and under all load conditions, the fuel must achieve complete combustion within the furnace volume.

Coal burned using a stoker with a refractory furnace requires a furnace volume of 2.25 cubic feet per rated boiler horsepower, compared to a furnace with completely water-cooled walls, which requires a volume of 1.5 cubic feet. These figures are average values for the many types of stokers in use. However, pulverized coal systems without a water-cooled furnace require 2.5 cubic feet per rated boiler horsepower, compared with 1.4 cubic feet for such a system with a water-cooled furnace.

When fuel oil is fired under natural draft conditions, 1 cubic foot of furnace volume is needed per rated boiler horsepower. Only .75 feet of furnace volume is required when mechanical draft is used. The volume of the furnace must be large enough to achieve complete combustion of all the fuel before it enters the first pass or touches the heating surfaces of the boiler.

A natural gas furnace requires 1.75 to 2.00 cubic feet of furnace volume per rated boiler horsepower. Furnace efficiency is affected by furnace volume and the amount of heat that can be released within that volume per hour. The volume of the furnace must be large enough to allow complete combustion of the fuel before the first pass or before the fuel touches any heating surface.

Products of Combustion

In the combustion process, elements in the fuel combine with oxygen to form heat and products of combustion. This reaction results in the formation of products of combustion such as carbon monoxide, carbon dioxide, sulfur dioxide, and water. In addition, soot, steam, smoke, and fly ash are discharged with the gases of combustion.

The operator is responsible for ensuring the most efficient combustion of the fuel in the boiler. By controlling the combustion process, the operator can eliminate soot and smoke discharged by the chimney. Fly ash is controlled by dust collectors (fly ash precipitators) that trap and hold ash so it may be disposed

of properly. The products of combustion will vary based on the efficiency of the fuel burned.

Combustion Gas Analysis. Combustion gas analysis is used to determine boiler combustion efficiency. Carbon dioxide (CO_2) in flue gas indicates complete combustion. Carbon monoxide (CO) in flue gas indicates incomplete combustion. Oxygen (O_2) in flue gas indicates the presence of excess air. *Fyrite analyzers*® are used to measure the percentage of carbon dioxide and oxygen in the flue gas. See Figure 7-2. The following steps are taken when measuring carbon dioxide using a Fyrite analyzer.

1. A sample of flue gas is drawn into the analyzer from the breeching as close to the boiler outlet as possible.

2. The analyzer is inverted so the sample can readily mix with the carbon dioxide-absorbing solution.

3. The absorption of the gas into the solution increases the volume of the solution and gives a direct reading of the percentage of carbon dioxide.

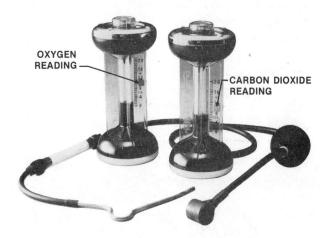

Figure 7-2. Fyrite analyzers are used to measure the percentage of oxygen and carbon dioxide in the flue gas. (*Bacharach, Inc.*)

If the percentage of carbon dioxide present and the temperature of the flue gas are known, the combustion efficiency can be computed using the slide rule calculator supplied with the analyzer. See Figure 7-3.

When using an *oxygen analyzer* to measure oxygen in the flue gas, follow the same procedure as when using the Fyrite analyzer. An oxygen analysis indicates the amount of excess air being used.

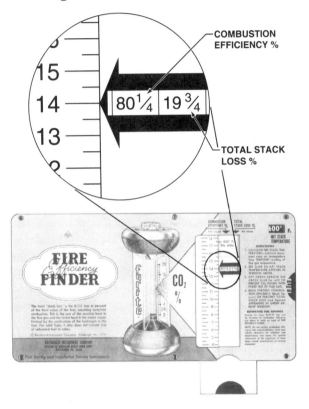

Figure 7-3. A slide rule calculator used with a Fyrite analyzer can determine the combustion efficiency of the boiler. (*Bacharach, Inc.*)

A more complete gas analysis can be achieved with the *Orsat analyzer*. The Orsat analyzer measures carbon dioxide, carbon monoxide, and oxygen. See Figure 7-4. The following steps are taken when using an Orsat analyzer to perform a gas analysis.

1. A sample of flue gas is taken into a burette (graduated glass tube) and the volume is carefully measured.

2. The flue gas is then brought into contact with the carbon dioxide-absorbing chemical that removes the carbon dioxide from the sample.

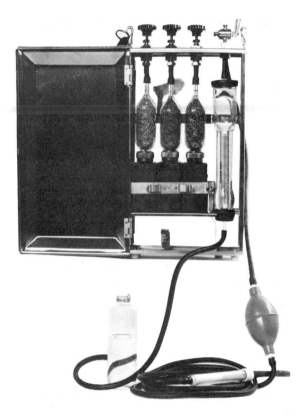

Figure 7-4. The Orsat analyzer measures the percentage of carbon dioxide, oxygen, and carbon monoxide in the flue gas. (*Hays Republic Corporation*)

3. The remaining amount of flue gas is then measured. The difference in volume is the amount of carbon dioxide that was present in the flue gas sample. For example:

Volume of flue gas sample	100 cc
Volume of flue gas sample after contact with carbon dioxide-absorbing chemical	− 87 cc
Amount of carbon dioxide in flue gas sample	13 cc or 13%

4. The next chamber contains an oxygen-absorbing chemical that removes oxygen from the flue gas sample. The flue gas sample is allowed to pass through while the oxygen is absorbed.

5. The flue gas sample is again measured

to determine the amount of oxygen present. For example:

Volume of flue gas sample	87 cc
Volume of flue gas sample after contact with oxygen-absorbing chemical	− 83 cc
Amount of oxygen in flue gas sample	.04 cc or 4%

6. The last chamber contains a carbon monoxide-absorbing chemical and identifies the carbon monoxide content in the flue gas sample. For example:

Volume of flue gas sample	83 cc
Volume of flue gas sample after contact with carbon monoxide-absorbing chemical	− 81 cc
Amount of carbon monoxide in flue gas sample	.02 cc or 2%

7. The amount that remains is the nitrogen (N_2) that was in the air used in the combustion process.

The final analysis of the flue gas sample indicates the following contents.

1. carbon dioxide - 13%
2. oxygen - 4%
3. carbon monoxide 2%
4. nitrogen - 81%

S/B
.1
BAD EXAMPLE
WAY TOO HIGH.

The following formula is used to determine the percentage of excess air used in the combustion process.

$$\% \text{ of excess air} = \frac{O_2 - \frac{1}{2}CO}{.263N + \frac{1}{2}CO - O_2} \times 100$$

$$\% \text{ of excess air} = \frac{.04 - (\frac{.02}{2})}{(.263 \times .81) + (\frac{.02}{2}) - .04} \times 100$$

$$\% \text{ of excess air} = \frac{.04 - .01}{.21303 + .01 - .04} \times 100$$

$$\% \text{ of excess air} = \frac{.03}{.18303} \times 100$$

$$\% \text{ of excess air} = 16.39$$

The percentage of excess air will vary depending on the type of fuel used. Current industry practice is to monitor the oxygen level in the gases of combustion. The oxygen level in the flue gas should be kept to a minimum to achieve the highest combustion efficiency. By reducing excess air used in the combustion process without causing smoking, heat loss to the atmosphere through the chimney can also be reduced.

Electronic Flue Gas Analysis

Gases of combustion can be checked quickly and accurately using an electronic flue gas analyzer. Electronic flue gas analyzers use a probe that is inserted in the breeching as close to the boiler as possible. The probe can be inserted temporarily, or permanently mounted. A pump inside the instrument draws in a small sample of gases of combustion. Sensors in the instrument analyze the flue gas for temperature, gases, draft, and smoke. Data from the sensors is sent to the computer to determine combustion efficiency, excess air, and carbon dioxide. The results are displayed and can be printed or plotted as a part of logging shift activities. This information can also be sent to remote locations by direct connection or modem over telephone lines as a management tool to keep records, and control plant operating costs. See Figure 7-5.

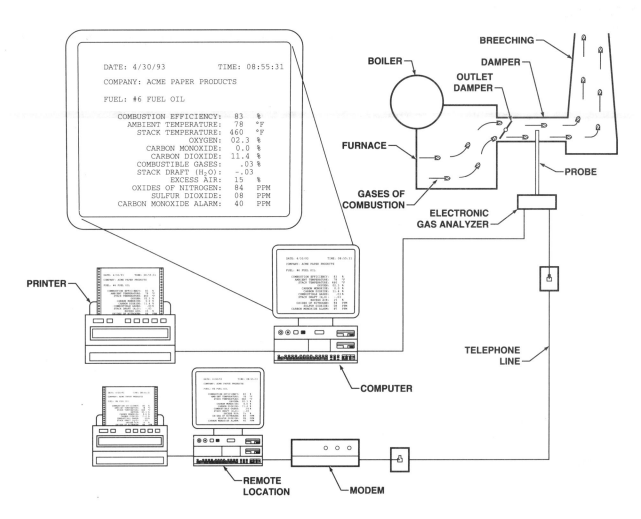

Figure 7-5. Data obtained from an electronic flue gas analyzer can be displayed on screen, print out, or sent to a remote location.

Key Words

British Thermal Unit
combustible
combustion
complete combustion
distillate
electronic flue gas analyzer
excess air
fire point
flash point
furnace volume
Fyrite analyzer
grade
heating value
incomplete combustion
MATT

natural gas
Orsat analyzer
oxygen analyzer
perfect combustion
pour point
primary air
products of combustion
proximate analysis
rank
secondary air
specific gravity
spontaneous combustion
therm
ultimate analysis
viscosity

TECH CHECK ✔ 7

Name _____ Date _____

___D___ 1. Rank refers to the _____ of the coal.
  A. ash content
  B. Btu content
  C. clinker formation
  D. degree of hardness

___A___ 2. Grade refers to the _____ of the coal.
  A. size, heating value, and ash content
  B. size only
  C. clinker formation
  D. degree of hardness

___D___ 3. A proximate analysis of coal provides information regarding its _____.
  A. moisture content
  B. content of volatile matter
  C. fixed carbon and ash content
  D. all of the above

___A___ 4. An ultimate analysis of coal provides information regarding _____.
  A. elements present in the coal
  B. moisture content
  C. volatile matter
  D. fixed carbon and ash content

___B___ 5. In order to determine the heating value of coal in Btu's per pound, the _____.
  A. proximate analysis is used
  B. ultimate analysis is used
  C. percentage of volatile matter is needed
  D. rank of coal is needed

___D___ 6. Bituminous coal has a high _____ content.
  A. lignite
  B. fixed carbon
  C. moisture
  D. volatile

___B___ 7. Anthracite coal has a high _____ content.
  A. lignite
  B. carbon
  C. moisture
  D. volatile

___C___ 8. When the temperature of fuel oil is raised, its viscosity _____.
  A. remains the same
  B. is raised
  C. is lowered
  D. cannot be affected by heat

_____A_____ 9. The temperature at which fuel oil will give off a vapor that will ignite readily when exposed to an open flame is its _____ point.
  A. flash
  B. fire
  C. pour
  D. viscosity

_____C_____ 10. The lowest temperature at which fuel oil will flow is its _____ point.
  A. flash
  B. fire
  C. pour
  D. viscosity

_____B_____ 11. The temperature at which fuel oil will give off a vapor that burns continuously is its _____ point.
  A. flash
  B. fire
  C. pour
  D. viscosity

_____D_____ 12. Fuel oil with a low flash point would be _____.
  A. desirable to use
  B. used only in high pressure plants
  C. used in either high or low pressure plants
  D. dangerous to use

_____B_____ 13. _____ coal is the type of coal most likely to have problems with spontaneous combustion when stockpiling.
  A. Lignite
  B. Anthracite
  C. Bituminous
  D. Anthracite stoker

_____A_____ 14. A _____ fire extinguisher is the correct type to use on fuel oil fires.
  A. foam or dry chemical
  B. soda water
  C. carbon tetrachloride
  D. feedwater

_____D_____ 15. Air that controls the rate of combustion is _____ air.
  A. control
  B. excess
  C. secondary
  D. primary

_____C_____ 16. Air that controls the combustion efficiency is _____ air.
  A. control
  B. excess
  C. secondary
  D. primary

_B_ 17. Air supplied to the burner that is more than the theoretical amount needed to burn fuel is _____ air.
   A. control
   B. excess
   C. secondary
   D. primary

_C_ 18. _____ combustion is when all fuel is burned using only the theoretical amount of air supplied.
   A. Complete
   B. Incomplete
   C. Perfect
   D. Theoretical

_A_ 19. _____ combustion is when all the fuel is burned using the minimal amount of excess air.
   A. Complete
   B. Incomplete
   C. Perfect
   D. Theoretical

_B_ 20. Soot and smoke are the result of _____ combustion.
   A. complete
   B. incomplete
   C. perfect
   D. theoretical

_D_ 21. _____ is a combustible found in fuel.
   A. Carbon
   B. Sulfur
   C. Hydrogen
   D. all of the above

_C_ 22. Gases of combustion that cool on contact with the boiler heating surface before combustion is completed cause a(n) _____.
   A. loss of draft
   B. increase in chimney temperature
   C. formation of soot and smoke
   D. increase in heat transfer

_B_ 23. Air needed for the combustion of fuel is made up of approximately _____% oxygen and _____% nitrogen.
   A. 80, 20
   B. 20, 80
   C. 50, 50
   D. 30, 70

_A_ 24. Carbon dioxide (CO_2) in the flue gas indicates _____.
   A. complete combustion
   B. incomplete combustion
   C. a high chimney temperature
   D. perfect combustion

_____ B

25. Carbon monoxide (CO) in the flue gas indicates _____.
    A. complete combustion
    B. incomplete combustion
    C. a low chimney temperature
    D. complete combustion

_____ D

26. The Orsat gas analyzer measures the percentage of _____ in the flue gas.
    A. carbon dioxide
    B. carbon monoxide
    C. oxygen
    D. all of the above

_____ D

27. _____ is a type of combustion.
    A. Complete
    B. Perfect
    C. Incomplete
    D. all of the above

_____ C

28. No. _____ fuel oil must be heated to reach the required temperature for combustion.
    A. 2
    B. 3
    C. 6
    D. 10

_____ A

29. Higher numbered fuel oils produce _____ lower numbered fuel oils.
    A. more Btu's per gallon than
    B. less Btu's per gallon than
    C. the same amount of Btu's as
    D. one-half the Btu's of

_____ D

30. The heating value of a fuel is expressed in _____.
    A. specific gravity
    B. fire point units
    C. viscosity
    D. British Thermal Units

Chapter 8

COMBUSTION CONTROLS

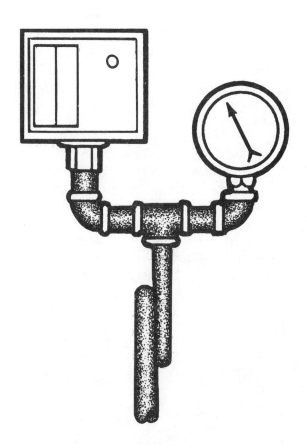

Combustion controls regulate fuel supply, air supply, air to fuel ratio, and removal of gases of combustion to achieve optimum boiler efficiency. The amount of fuel supplied to the burner must be in proportion to the steam pressure and the quality of steam required.

A drop in steam pressure necessitates an increase in the fuel supplied to the burner. Conversely, an increase in steam pressure necessitates a decrease in the fuel supplied. Any change in the amount of fuel supplied requires a corresponding change in the air for combustion supplied to the burner.

To maintain high combustion efficiency, the air to fuel ratio must be balanced from the lowest firing rate to the highest firing rate. If there is an imbalance in the air to fuel ratio, smoking, flame failure (loss of flame in furnace), and/or a furnace explosion could result.

Combustion controls also regulate the removal of gases of combustion by maintaining a consistent furnace pressure throughout different firing rates. By maintaining a consistent firing rate, combustion controls improve regulation of feedwater and superheat temperature. In addition, a consistent firing rate reduces fluctuation of the boiler water level and increases the life of the boiler drum and tubes.

KEY TO ARROWHEAD SYMBOLS

△ - Air	▲ - Water	▲ - Fuel Oil	⌂ - Air to Atmosphere
△ - Gas	△ - Steam	△ - Condensate	⌂ - Gases of Combustion

AUTOMATIC COMBUSTION CONTROLS

Automatic combustion control systems are used to control the amount and frequency of firing in a burner to maintain the required pressure in the boiler. Automatic combustion control systems reduce the risk of human error and aid in overall plant efficiency. The three basic types of automatic combustion control systems are the *ON/OFF control system*, the *positioning control system*, and the *metering control system.*

The ON/OFF control system is used in plants where the steam load allows the burner to be started and stopped. The positioning control system is used in plants that have a steam demand large enough to require the burners to be fired continuously. In the positioning control system, the burner modulates between high and low fire (highest and lowest firing rate) but never shuts down. The metering control system is used in plants that require a constant steam pressure and is much more sensitive to steam pressure variation than the positioning control system.

ON/OFF Control System

The ON/OFF control system consists of the *pressure control, modulating pressure control,* and *programmer* and is found on smaller types of package fire or water tube boilers. The pressure control regulates the operating range of the boiler by starting and stopping the burner on boiler steam pressure demand. The pressure control is connected to the highest part of the steam side of the boiler and is protected from live steam by a siphon. See Figure 8-1.

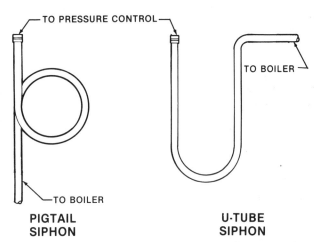

PIGTAIL SIPHON   **U-TUBE SIPHON**

Figure 8-1. A siphon protects the bellows on the pressure control from the high temperature of live steam.

The siphon forms a water seal, protecting the bellows from distortion or rupture caused by the high temperature of the steam. The most commonly used pressure control is the *mercury-tube* type. The mercury-tube pressure control must be installed using a pigtail siphon and maintained in a vertical position for it to function properly. See Figure 8-2.

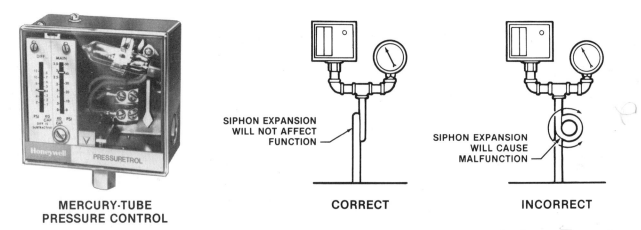

MERCURY-TUBE PRESSURE CONTROL   **CORRECT**   **INCORRECT**

SIPHON EXPANSION WILL NOT AFFECT FUNCTION

SIPHON EXPANSION WILL CAUSE MALFUNCTION

Figure 8-2. The face of the mercury-tube pressure control must be mounted vertically and must also be perpendicular to the pigtail to ensure accuracy in controlling the boiler operating range. (*Honeywell, Inc.*)

The pressure control has two scales. One scale is set at the *cut-in* (starting) *pressure* and the other scale is set at the *differential pressure*, which controls when the burner is cut-out (shut off). When adjusting the scales, cut-in pressure plus differential pressure equals *cut-out pressure*. When the cut-out pressure is reached in the boiler, the burner shuts off. By adjusting cut-in and cut-out pressure settings, the operator can obtain any necessary combination to meet plant needs. *NOTE:* Some pressure controls have a main scale and a differential scale instead of a cut-in scale and a differential scale. The cut-out pressure is determined by setting the main scale set point. The cut-in pressure is determined by the main scale set point minus the differential setting. See Figure 8-3.

The modulating pressure control regulates high and low fire and is connected to the highest part of the steam side of the boiler. A burner must always start in low fire and shut down in low fire. This prevents wasting fuel and reduces the possibility of a flareback (minor furnace explosion) when excess fuel accumulates in the furnace.

The modulating pressure control is installed using a siphon to protect the bellows from the high temperature of steam. The modulating motor, using mechanical linkage, works in conjunction with the modulating pressure control to regulate the primary air, secondary air, and fuel supplied to the burner, which controls the high and low fire of the burner. See Figure 8-4.

The programmer is the mastermind that controls the starting sequence and firing cycle of

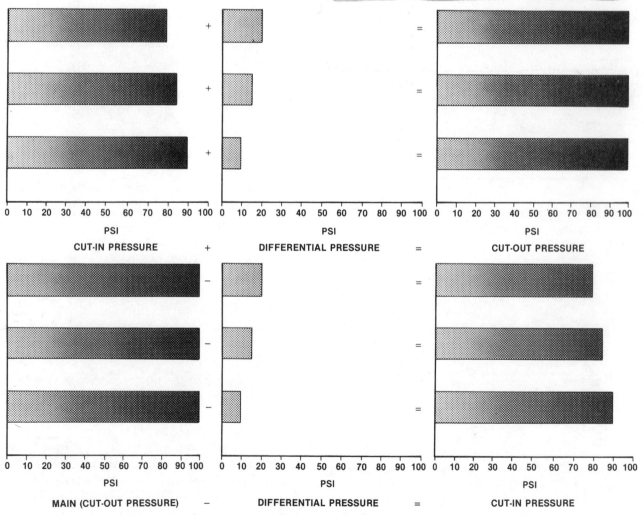

Figure 8-3. Consult the manufacturer's data sheets for proper setting procedures of pressure controls.

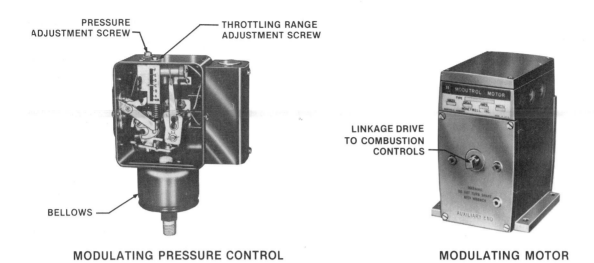

PRESSURE ADJUSTMENT SCREW

THROTTLING RANGE ADJUSTMENT SCREW

BELLOWS

LINKAGE DRIVE TO COMBUSTION CONTROLS

MODULATING PRESSURE CONTROL

MODULATING MOTOR

Figure 8-4. The modulating pressure control sends an electric signal to the modulating motor to regulate the high and low fire of the burner. (*Honeywell, Inc.*)

a burner. The programmer controls the operation sequence of the blower, burner motor, ignition system, fuel valve, and all other components in the ON/OFF control system. Newer programmers operate electronically. However, some electromechanical programmers are still in use. See Figure 8-5.

The programmer also provides a suitable *purge period* before ignition and after burner shutdown when explosive combustibles are

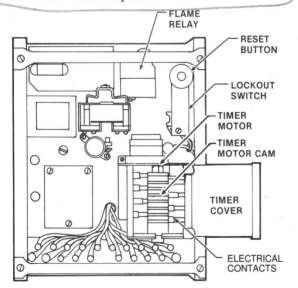

FLAME RELAY

RESET BUTTON

LOCKOUT SWITCH

TIMER MOTOR

TIMER MOTOR CAM

TIMER COVER

ELECTRICAL CONTACTS

Figure 8-5. An electromechanical programmer controls the starting sequence and firing cycle of the burner with a rotating cam that actuates electrical contacts. (*Fireye, Inc.*)

removed. The programmer is designed to de-energize all fuel valves within 4 seconds after loss of the flame signal. In addition, the programmer automatically restarts a new cycle each time the pressure control closes or after a power failure, but locks out and must be reset manually after any flame failure.

ON/OFF Control Firing Sequence. When the steam pressure drops, the pressure control completes an electric circuit, which starts a timer motor cam turning in the programmer. The first contact on the timer motor cam closes and starts the burner motor that rotates the primary air fan. The primary air fan blows air into the furnace to purge any unburned fuel present in a gaseous condition in the furnace.

This process is called *prepurging* the furnace. By prepurging the furnace before pilot ignition, the danger of a furnace explosion is reduced. The purge cycle takes approximately 30 seconds but may take as long as 60 seconds, depending upon the size of the furnace.

The programmer is still operating and when the second contact closes, the circuit to the ignition transformer is completed. This causes a spark in front of the gas pilot tube. At the same time, a solenoid valve is opened in the gas pilot line, allowing gas to flow through the gas pilot tube and be ignited by the spark. The *scanner* is located on the front of the boiler and is used to sight the pilot. See Figure 8-6.

Sighting the pilot through the scanner will verify that the pilot is lit. This process is referred to as *proving pilot*. The programmer is still operating and the next contact closes to complete a circuit to the main fuel valve, which opens only after the scanner has proved pilot. With the main fuel valve open the fuel enters the furnace and is ignited by the pilot. The scanner is then used to prove the main flame.

The programmer continues to operate for a few more seconds, securing circuits to the ignition transformer and the gas pilot. After the circuits are secured, the programmer stops. The burner is now regulated by the pressure control and the modulating pressure control. If the scanner senses a flame failure, the system is purged and secured. The programmer is then manually reset to the start cycle.

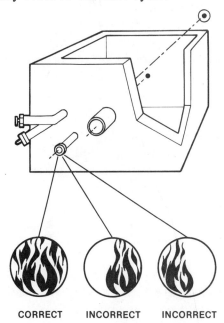

CORRECT   INCORRECT   INCORRECT

Figure 8-6. The scanner monitors the pilot and the main flame of the furnace. (*Fireye, Inc.*)

ON/OFF Control Operation. When the steam load increases, more steam is used and the burner must supply more fuel to the furnace. This means more air for combustion is required to maintain a proper air to fuel ratio to achieve complete combustion, and that more

gases of combustion are released to the chimney. For example, in an operating range from 85 to 100 psi, when the pressure in the boiler drops to 85 psi, the programmer operates, putting the burner through a firing cycle. The burner lights off in low fire and the modulating pressure control will gradually start to bring the burner up to high fire by energizing the modulating motor.

Through mechanical linkage, the modulating motor is connected to the fuel valve, primary air damper, and secondary air damper. As the burner passes from low to high fire, the air and fuel amounts must both change to maintain the proper ratio of air to fuel. When the boiler starts to meet the required plant steam load and the steam pressure starts to increase, the modulating pressure control starts putting the burner back toward the low fire position.

The burner modulates between high and low fire until the boiler reaches its cut-out pressure of 100 psi. The pressure control, activated by the programmer, shuts off the fuel to the burner. The primary air fan attached to the burner motor continues to run, purging the firebox. This is called *postpurge*. Postpurging the furnace requires the same amount of time as prepurging the furnace. The cycle is repeated when the boiler steam pressure drops to the cut-in point.

The burner should always be firing for longer periods than it is not firing. For example, the burner should fire for approximately 30 minutes and be off for 5 minutes, rather than fire for 5 minutes and be off for 30 minutes. This firing schedule improves boiler efficiency by maintaining a constant furnace temperature. Maintaining a constant furnace temperature also helps to reduce refractory maintenance caused by repeated heating and cooling of the brickwork.

Burner Management Controls. Burner management controls have become much more sophisticated since the introduction of solid-state circuitry. Solid-state programmers provide for ignition and main flame failure protection on automatically fired gas or fuel oil fired burners by controlling the burner blower motor, ignition, main fuel valves, and modulating motor. See Figure 8-7. The programmer cycles automatically when the limit operating control (pressure control) closes, but must be reset following a safety shutdown.

Figure 8-7. Solid-state programmers use solid-state components in place of vacuum tubes. *(Fireye, Inc.)*

The solid-state programmer initiates the same firing sequence as a conventional programmer. With the power on and the limit operating control circuit and the main fuel valve interlock closed, the burner blower motor is energized, purging the furnace. The running interlock circuit (air flow switch) closes. The air flow switch proves that air is supplied for purging the furnace before lighting off.

Both the blower and purge indicators light on the programmer. The modulating motor opens the damper to high fire position. The open damper interlock closes, initiating a 30-second prepurge of the furnace. When prepurge is complete, the purge indicator light goes out and the modulating motor returns to the low fire position.

The spark ignition and pilot valve are then energized and the pilot indicator lights. Following a 10-second period after the pilot flame is proven, the main fuel valve opens and the pilot indicator light goes out. After a 10- to 15-second main flame trial for ignition, the pilot ignition is de-energized to shut off the pilot. The modulating motor is switched to automatic control and the "auto" indicator lights. The

burner is now controlled by pressure control and modulating pressure control.

Burner Control Systems. Burner control systems are microprocessor-controlled integrated control systems for gas, fuel oil, and combination gas/fuel oil burners. Burner control systems are programmed for automatic burner sequencing, flame supervision, system status indication, and self-diagnostics. The system saves programmed information in nonvolatile memory that cannot be lost if the power supply is interrupted.

Burner control systems have a flame monitor that provides the operator with operating data and failure-mode information in a simple, easy-to-understand manner. The messages provide clear, concise information concerning system timing, present burner sequence position, lockout causes, and burner historical data. Burner status information is shown on the flame monitor display. See Figure 8-8.

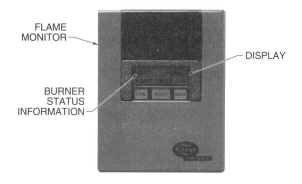

Figure 8-8. The flame monitor provides the boiler operator with burner status information. *(Fireye, Inc.)*

Burner control systems provide for direct connection of limit and operating controls, fuel valve interlock, damper position interlocks, running interlocks (such as air flow, fuel pressure, and temperature), burner motor, ignition, pilot valves, main fuel valves, modulating motor, and alarms.

The flame monitor uses interchangeable microprocessor-based modules for versatility. Inputs from the burner/blower motor, ignition, and fuel valve are connected at the wiring base. See Figure 8-9. A self-diagnostic circuit within the control will identify module failure. For example, if the amplifier module is malfunctioning, the message center will display the message, "Lockout— Replace Amplifier."

Burner control systems also provide the operator or service personnel with an important burner operation history. This takes the guesswork out of troubleshooting a burner problem by identifying the malfunction and the corrective action to be taken.

A safe start component check is performed during each firing sequence. In the firing sequence, a purge period of not less than 30 seconds is performed with a damper actuated to

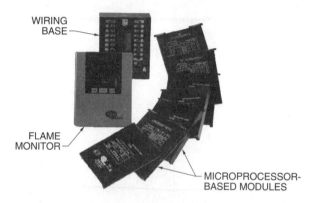

Figure 8-9. Interchangeable microprocessor-based modules permit versatility in the selection of control function timing and flame scanning. (*Fireye, Inc.*)

the open position. An interlock circuit is provided to prove air flow rate during the purge period. A starting interlock circuit is required to ensure that the burner equipment is in the low fire position at the time of ignition.

In addition, an interlock is provided to prove air flow during the purge and firing cycle. Proof of the ignition is restricted to 10 seconds for the pilot flame and 10 to 15 seconds for the main flame for fuel oil or gas. Safety shutdown following flame failure, with fuel and ignition circuits de-energized, is achieved in 4 seconds or less. A postpurge period of 15 seconds follows a burner shutdown.

The burner control system can be upgraded to provide on-site and remote monitoring of the burner. See Figure 8-10. A flame monitor is connected to a communication interface. Data is sent from the communication interface

to an on-site computer. Data from the communication interface can also be sent through telephone transmission lines through a modem to a computer at a remote location. Printers allow burner operating status and history to be recorded on paper.

Burner control systems process data received from sensors located throughout the plant. Outputs which respond to this data are programmed in the boiler controller. See Figure 8-11. The controller/programmer analyzes data from the sensors. If the data received is outside the programmed limits, an annunciator is energized. An *annunciator* is an audible electronic alarm which alerts the operator of an operating condition which needs immediate attention.

Positioning Control System

The positioning control system uses control (compressed) air to control combustion in the furnace. The positioning control system requires an air compressor, special filters, and driers so that only clean, dry air will enter the control air lines. A standby compressor or a cross connection is used to tie in boiler room air in the event of a maintenance problem.

The positioning control system is actuated by changes in the steam header pressure, which operates a master control unit. The master control unit then relays pressure signals to relay units that in turn control the air and fuel supplied to the furnace. See Figure 8-12.

The boiler operator can operate the master control unit or relay units on a manual or automatic basis. When shifting from manual to automatic or from automatic to manual operation, the pressure signals of the manual and automatic controls of the unit must be synchronized before changing over. Failure to synchronize the pressure signals can lead to an improper air to fuel ratio.

The positioning control system must be adjusted so that any change in the steam pressure will produce a corresponding change in the air and fuel fed to the furnace. As the steam pressure increases, both the air and fuel supply decrease. Conversely, if steam pressure drops, the air and fuel supply to the furnace will increase.

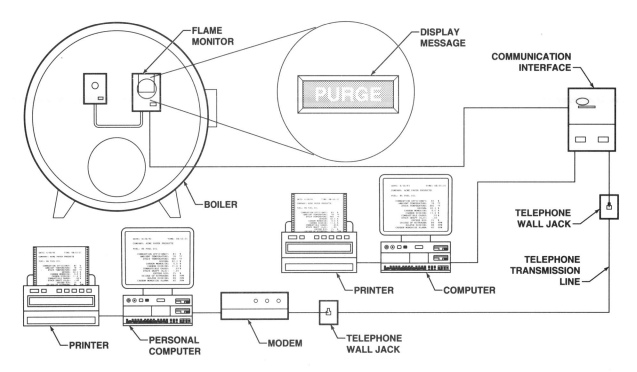

Figure 8-10. Flame monitoring of the burner can be performed at the boiler, within the building, and/or at a remote location with a flame monitor. (*Fireye, Inc.*)

Although it is possible to maintain a fairly constant steam pressure, combustion efficiency can drop off at times. The positioning control must sense the drop or rise in the steam pressure and quickly make the necessary changes in the air and fuel supply. Wear on the mechanical linkage to the fuel valves, and primary and secondary air dampers leads to a slow response, resulting in a fluctuation in the steam pressure that causes the controls to *hunt* (rapidly open and close). The positioning control system is used on medium-sized plants requiring a fairly constant steam demand and can be used when firing with coal, fuel oil, or gas.

Metering Control System

The metering control system generates signals based on the flow of steam (difference of pressure across an orifice) and balances it against signals calling for more or less air and for fuel for combustion. Metering control systems are used in plants that must have a constant steam pressure and a high combustion efficiency, such as generating stations, oil refineries, and large chemical plants. The metering control system is more accurate and sensitive to steam pressure variation than positioning control systems and gives a faster response for air and fuel requirements.

To measure the flow of steam, an orifice is installed in the steam line. The difference in pressure across the orifice varies according to the flow of steam through the orifice. Metering control systems are used on combination gas/fuel oil systems, coal stoker fired systems, and pulverized coal systems.

Metering control systems, like the positioning control system, require clean, dry compressed air for efficient operation. Compressed air tanks must be drained, air filters must be cleaned, and dehumidifiers must be functioning properly in order to operate efficiently.

The metering control system is operated either manually or automatically. In manual operation, when a boiler is taken off-line or is warmed up before cutting it in on the line, the operator must have the combustion controls in the manual position. This enables the operator to have full control of the boiler. As soon as the boiler has been cut in on the line, all

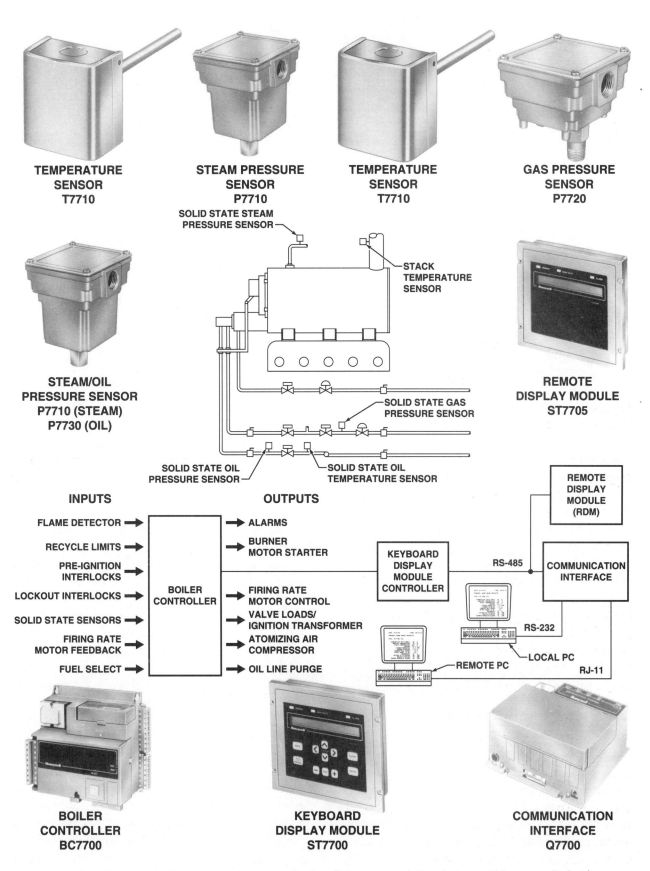

Figure 8-11. Data sent from sensors controls the firing rate of the burner. (*Honeywell, Inc.*)

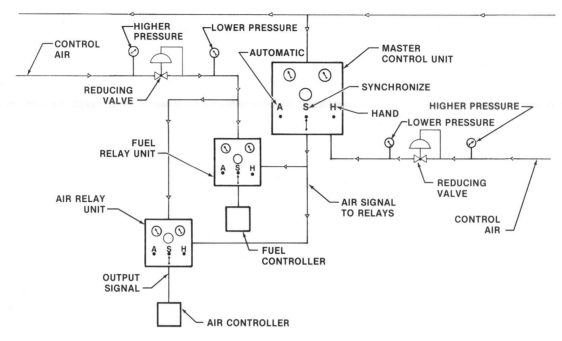

Figure 8-12. The positioning control system regulates the proper air to fuel ratio required for various steam loads.

combustion controls are changed over to the automatic position.

In automatic operation of the combination gas/fuel oil system, the metering control system functions in the following manner. See Figure 8-13. The gas flow control valve (1) on the gas line is controlled by signals from the gas pressure transmitter (2) and the steam pressure transmitter (3).

When using fuel oil, the fuel oil flow control valve (4) is controlled by signals from the steam pressure transmitter, steam flow transmitter (5), and air flow transmitter (6). The forced draft fan damper control (7) is controlled by the steam pressure transmitter, steam flow transmitter, and air flow transmitter. The induced draft fan damper control (8) is controlled by a signal from the furnace draft transmitter (9) to regulate the flow of the gases of combustion.

In automatic operation of the coal stoker fired system, the metering control system functions in the following manner. See Figure 8-14. The stoker feed control drive (1) regulates the amount of coal going to the stoker and is controlled by a signal from the steam pressure transmitter (2). The forced draft damper con-

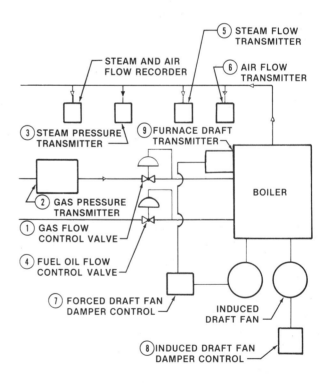

Figure 8-13. Metering control systems in a combination gas/fuel oil system control gas flow or fuel oil flow to the burner based on the flow and pressure of steam generated.

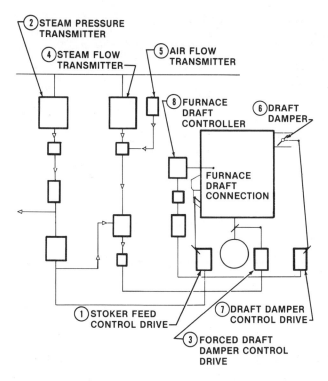

Figure 8-14. Metering control systems in a coal-fired system are used to regulate the amount of coal going to the stoker.

trol drive (3) is controlled by a signal from the steam flow transmitter (4), steam pressure transmitter (2), and air flow transmitter (5). The outlet draft damper (6) is controlled by the outlet draft damper control drive (7), which receives its signal from the furnace draft controller (8) to regulate the flow of the gases of combustion.

When the pulverized coal system is in the automatic position, the metering control system functions in the following manner. See Figure 8-15. The coal feeder (1) and the primary air control drive (2) regulate the amount of coal going through the pulverizer (3) to the burner (4). The signal to control the coal feeder and the primary air control drive comes from the steam pressure transmitter (5).

The signal to the forced draft fan control drive (6) comes from the steam pressure transmitter and the steam flow transmitter (7). The volume of gases of combustion are controlled by an induced draft fan control drive (8) that receives its signal from a furnace draft controller (9) to regulate the flow of the gases of combustion.

Controls for Air for Combustion and Gases of Combustion

Air for combustion and gases of combustion must be controlled to maintain a high combustion efficiency in the boiler. The air for combustion is supplied by forced draft fans. The amount of air for combustion going to the furnace is controlled by one damper or a combination of dampers, adjustable vanes at the fan intake, a variable-speed motor, or a hydraulic coupling between the fan and drive unit. Signals coming from the combustion controls are based on steam demand and can cause the dampers and adjustable vanes to modulate from near closed to fully open.

In conjunction with the dampers, a variable-speed motor drive can be used for changing the fan speed to control the air for combustion. Another method used to control the fan speed is to use a constant speed drive with a hydraulic coupling between the fan and the drive unit.

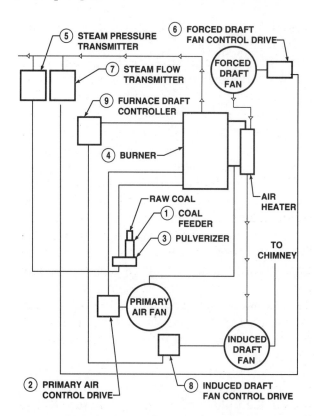

Figure 8-15. Metering control systems are sensitive enough to control the operation of a pulverized coal-fired burner.

The speed of the fan is controlled by the addition or removal of the hydraulic coupling fluid using a small hydraulic pump.

In order to assist in the removal of gases of combustion, induced draft fans are used. The volume of gases removed is controlled by outlet dampers, a variable-speed control that controls fan speed, or a hydraulic coupling that controls fan speed. The outlet dampers are located at the outlet side of the boiler on the breeching before the chimney.

By using a variable-speed motor, the volume of the gases of combustion is controlled so that no back pressure is created in the boiler. The hydraulic coupling on the induced draft fan controls the volume of the gases of combustion, leaving the boiler in the same manner as the hydraulic coupling on the forced draft fan.

The outlet or uptake damper on all fuel systems is controlled by the furnace pressure during automatic operation (balanced draft) or manually from the control panel during manual operation. See Figure 8-16. During automatic operation, the selector relay (1) receives a signal from the furnace pressure (2). The draft positioning controller (3) will position the outlet damper (4) to open or close as the combustion rate increases or decreases.

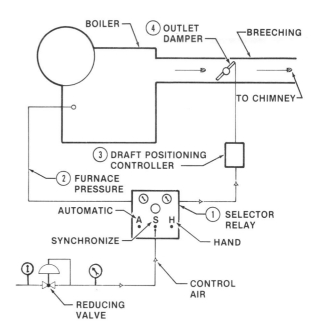

Figure 8-16. Furnace pressure is increased by restricting the flow of gases of combustion through the outlet damper.

Key Words

annunciator
automatic combustion control system
burner control system
burner management control
cut-in pressure
cut-out pressure
differential pressure
flame-monitor
metering control system

nonvolatile memory
ON/OFF control system
positioning control system
postpurge
prepurging
proving pilot
purge period
scanner

_B_ 1. The primary function of a combustion control is to ensure _____.
   A. safe boiler operation
   B. boiler efficiency
   C. safe and efficient boiler operation
   D. temperature regulation of the gases of combustion

_A_ 2. The four elements that must be regulated in a combustion control system
   are _____, _____, _____, and _____.
   A. fuel supply, air supply, ratio of air to fuel, removal of combustion
      gases
   B. fuel supply, water supply, air supply, ratio of water to fuel
   C. temperature of water, temperature of fuel, temperature of steam,
      temperature of exit gases
   D. pressure of water, pressure of steam, pressure of fuel, pressure of air

_B_ 3. The ON/OFF control system is usually found on _____.
   A. boilers with large fluctuating loads
   B. package fire tube boilers
   C. boilers with high steam demand but constant load
   D. low pressure boilers only

_D_ 4. The purpose of the boiler pressure control found in the ON/OFF control
   system is to _____.
   A. regulate steam flow
   B. regulate air flow
   C. regulate fuel flow
   D. start and stop the burner on steam pressure demand

_C_ 5. The ON/OFF pressure control must be connected to the _____.
   A. main steam line
   B. main feedwater line
   C. highest part of the steam side of the boiler
   D. water side of the boiler below the NOWL

_A_ 6. A steam siphon ensures that _____ does not enter the boiler pres-
   sure control.
   A. steam
   B. water
   C. air
   D. gas

_C_ 7. A mercury-tube pressure control will only be accurate when it is installed
   _____.
   A. at the NOWL
   B. below the NOWL
   C. in a vertical position
   D. in a horizontal position

A

8. The two scales found on the boiler pressure control are used to _____.
   A. set the operating steam pressure range of the boiler
   B. eliminate low water
   C. maintain high and low fire
   D. warn the operator of flame failure

C

9. The purpose of the boiler modulating pressure control is to _____.
   A. regulate the water flow
   B. prevent carryover
   C. start and stop the burner on steam pressure demand
   D. regulate the high and low firing rates of the burner

C

10. The modulating pressure control must be connected to the _____.
    A. main steam line
    B. main feedwater line
    C. highest part of the steam side of the boiler
    D. water side of the boiler below the NOWL

B

11. The modulating pressure control is sensitive to _____.
    A. temperature
    B. pressure
    C. water level
    D. all of the above

A

12. The programmer in the ON/OFF control system is used to _____.
    A. control the burner firing cycle
    B. control the boiler operating range
    C. secure the burner in the event of low water
    D. regulate the steam flow

C

13. To eliminate the danger of a furnace explosion during start-up, the firing sequence must first allow for _____.
    A. pilot ignition
    B. proving the pilot
    C. a prepurge period
    D. proving the main flame

C

14. The purpose of the scanner is to prove _____.
    A. only the pilot
    B. only the main flame
    C. both the pilot and the main flame
    D. the proper boiler water level

A

15. The scanner must be installed on the front of the boiler to sight _____.
    A. both the pilot and the main flame
    B. the pilot only
    C. the main flame only
    D. the boiler water level

16. The scanner is sensitive to _____.
    A. heat
    B. temperature
    C. pressure
    D. infrared or ultraviolet rays

(answer: A)

17. In the event of a flame failure, the programmer will _____.
    A. go through a new firing cycle
    B. secure the fuel, purge the firebox, and then shut down
    C. vent the combustion chamber
    D. start the induced draft fan

(answer: C)

18. The positioning combustion control system cannot function without _____ pressure.
    A. steam
    B. water
    C. air
    D. gas

(answer: D)

19. The positioning combustion control system is sensitive to changes in the _____.
    A. boiler water level
    B. firing rate
    C. steam flow
    D. steam header pressure

(answer: C)

20. The metering combustion control system is sensitive to changes in _____.
    A. boiler water level
    B. firing rate
    C. steam flow and pressure
    D. viscosity of the fuel oil

(answer: A)

21. Combustion air is controlled by _____.
    A. inlet dampers, fan intake vanes, and the fan speed
    B. the outlet damper and fan speed
    C. starting and stopping the forced draft fan
    D. variations in control air pressure

(answer: B)

22. Gases of combustion are pulled from the boiler by the _____.
    A. forced draft fan
    B. induced draft fan
    C. variable-speed motor
    D. hydraulic couplings

(answer: A)

23. The most common type of pressure control used is the _____ type.
    A. mercury-tube
    B. microswitch
    C. pigtail
    D. U-tube

Identify the parts of the control for gases of combustion.

_____ 24. Draft positioning controller
_____ 25. Outlet damper
_____ 26. Selector relay
_____ 27. Control air

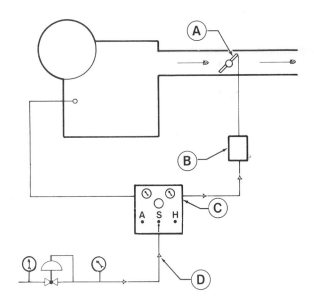

Identify the parts of the pulverized coal metering control system.

_____ 28. Induced draft fan
_____ 29. Forced draft fan
_____ 30. Air heater
_____ 31. Pulverizer

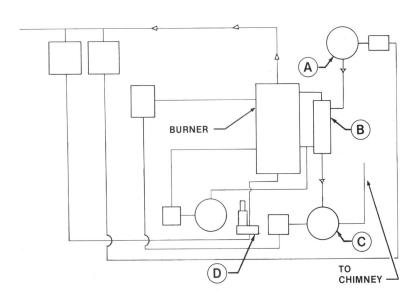

Chapter 9

INSTRUMENTS

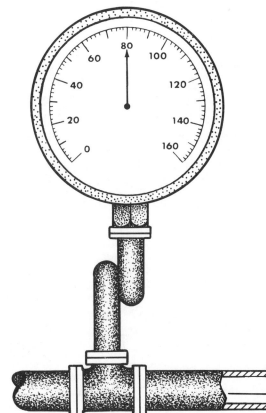

Instruments are required in the boiler room to indicate the status of the boiler system to the operator and are necessary to operate a plant safely and efficiently. Smaller steam plants require fewer instruments than larger, more sophisticated steam plants.

The operator must use instruments such as pressure gauges, thermometers, flow meters, and indicators. Readings from these instruments register on recorders (charts) and are used to document the operation of a steam plant in a given period.

Recorders document the steam pressure, steam flow (in pounds of steam per hour), feedwater temperature and pressure, fuel oil temperature and pressure, flue gas temperature, and other important readings. These readings aid the operator and chief engineer in maintaining overall plant efficiency and complying with Environmental Protection Agency (EPA) standards.

KEY TO ARROWHEAD SYMBOLS			
△ - Air	▲ - Water	▲ - Fuel Oil	⌂ - Air to Atmosphere
⚠ - Gas	△ - Steam	⚠ - Condensate	⚠ - Gases of Combustion

PRESSURE GAUGES

Boiler plants have pressure gauges to indicate the various pressures within the system. Pressure gauges measure air pressure, gas pressure, steam pressure, and suction and discharge pressures on fuel and water lines.

Pressure gauges measure pressure in pounds per square inch (psi). Psi is the pressure above atmospheric pressure (14.7 psi at sea level) and is known as gauge pressure (psig). Absolute pressure (psia) is gauge pressure plus atmospheric pressure. In order to use the steam tables, gauge pressure must be converted to absolute pressure.

A pressure gauge with its pointer at 50 on the face of the gauge is read as 50 pounds per square inch. This reading is written as 50 psi or 50 psig and is simply called 50 pounds.

Different gauge faces are used to indicate standard ranges of pressures. See Figure 9-1. Graduations of pressure on faces will vary, depending on the pressure gauge range required. For example, on a pressure gauge range of 0 to 30 psi, each graduation is in ½ psi increments. On a pressure gauge range of 0 to 300 psi, the graduations are in 5 psi in-

crements. The specific pressure gauge range used is determined by the maximum pressure to be measured and how easy the gauge is to read. The pressure gauge range selected should allow the pointer to be in the 12 o'clock position when the boiler is at its highest operating steam pressure below the MAWP.

Because pressure gauges are precision instruments, care must be taken when handling them to prevent possible damage. It is also recommended that pressure gauges be recalibrated when the pressure gauge reading has an error factor of ±2% of the normal working pressure.

Boiler Steam-Pressure Gauge

A boiler steam-pressure gauge should have a range not less than 1½ times and not more than 2 times the safety valve setting. When ordering a new boiler steam-pressure gauge, the recommended safety valve setting must be known.

The boiler steam-pressure gauge should be connected to the highest part of the steam side of a boiler and must be easily visible from the

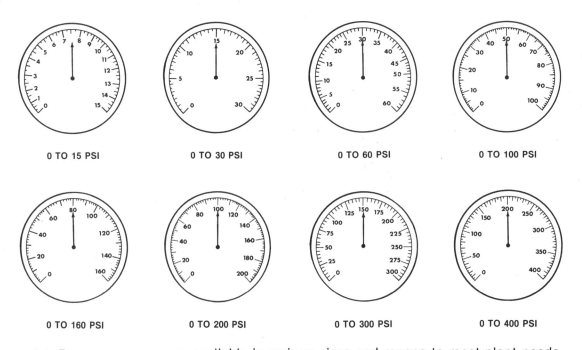

Figure 9-1. Pressure gauges are available in various sizes and ranges to meet plant needs.

operating level. The boiler steam-pressure gauge must be mounted in a location that is free from vibration. The face of the gauge must be clean and well-lit. The gauge must be protected by a siphon. The siphon forms a water-leg, preventing live steam from entering the Bourdon tube.

If the boiler steam-pressure gauge has to be located below the steam and water drum, an allowance must be made for any existing hydrostatic pressure. (See Chapter 2 for more information about hydrostatic pressure.) If steam is allowed to enter the Bourdon tube, the gauge must be tested and/or recalibrated. The boiler steam-pressure gauge is tested by comparing readings with a test gauge or by using a dead-weight tester.

Draft Gauge

A draft gauge measures the difference in draft pressure between the atmosphere and the furnace, uptake, or chimney. It is calibrated in tenths of an inch of water column. Either a manometer draft gauge or a diaphragm draft gauge can be used to measure draft pressures. See Figure 9-2.

The reading on the gauge will vary depending on the location of the reading. The manometer draft gauge is portable and uses a liquid to measure draft pressures. The diaphragm draft gauge measures draft pressures by the difference in pressure across the diaphragm. The diaphragm draft gauge is permanently mounted on the panel board of the boiler and is more popular than the manometer draft gauge.

Vacuum Gauge

A vacuum (suction) gauge is used to measure vacuum. The amount of vacuum is expressed in inches of mercury (Hg) below atmospheric pressure. For example, a vacuum gauge with its pointer at 4 on the face of the gauge is read as 4″ of mercury below atmospheric pressure. This reading is written as 4″ Hg and is simply called 4 inches.

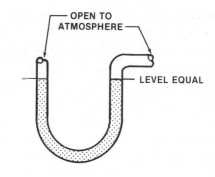

MANOMETER DRAFT GAUGE

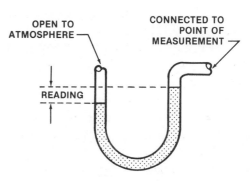

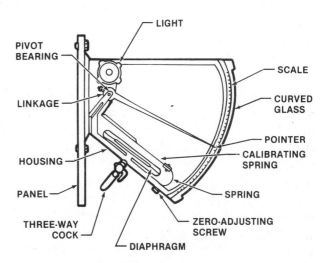

DIAPHRAGM DRAFT GAUGE

Figure 9-2. A manometer draft gauge is a portable device used to indicate the amount of draft pressure by the difference in levels of a liquid. A diaphragm draft gauge is permanently mounted to the panel board and measures draft pressure by the difference in pressure across the diaphragm.

A U-tube manometer, using mercury as the liquid, can be used to measure a vacuum. See Figure 9-3. However, a vacuum gauge with a Bourdon tube is most commonly used in steam plants to measure vacuum and is calibrated in inches of mercury.

Vacuum gauges are used on the suction side of fuel oil pumps and feedwater pumps to indicate proper operation. For example, an unusually high vacuum (suction) reading indicates a clogged suction line, dirty strainer, and/or closed suction valve. Any leakage on the suction side of a pump will allow air into the suction side of the pump. Vacuum gauges are most commonly calibrated to read from 0 to 30 ″ Hg.

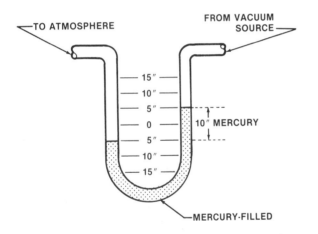

Figure 9-3. A U-tube manometer filled with mercury can be used to measure a vacuum.

TEMPERATURE-MEASURING DEVICES

Temperature-measuring devices are control instruments that give an indication of operating conditions. By logging the various temperature readings hourly, temperature-measuring devices allow the operator to assess plant operation.

An operator must know the proper operating temperatures required in the plant. For example, a sudden rise or fall in the feedwater heater temperature indicates steam traps blowing live steam through. The live steam blowing through may cause the feedwater pump to become steambound, resulting in a low water condition in the boiler.

A drop in feedwater temperature would indicate a loss of condensate return, causing more makeup water to be used. Excessive cold makeup water can result in an increase in fuel consumption and thermal shock to the boiler. If the temperature of the fuel oil is too low, the combustion process will be affected, resulting in the formation of soot and smoke. The two main temperature-measuring devices used in a boiler system are *thermometers* and *thermocouples*.

Thermometers

Thermometers are used to measure the intensity of heat. Thermometers are calibrated in *degrees Fahrenheit* (°F) or *degrees Celsius* (°C) at sea level. In the Fahrenheit system, water freezes at 32°F and boils at 212°F. In the Celsius system, water freezes at 0°C and boils at 100°C.

To convert degrees Fahrenheit to degrees Celsius, the following conversion formula is used.

$$°C = \frac{°F - 32}{1.8}$$

Example 1: Convert 32 °F and 212 °F to °C.

$$°C = \frac{32 - 32}{1.8} = \frac{0}{1.8} \qquad °C = \frac{212 - 32}{1.8} = \frac{180}{1.8}$$

$$°C = 0° \qquad\qquad °C = 100°$$

To convert degrees Celsius to degrees Fahrenheit, the following conversion formula is used.

$$°F = 1.8 °C + 32$$

Example 2: Convert 0° and 100 °C to °F.

$$°F = (1.8 \times 0) + 32 \qquad °F = (1.8 \times 100) + 32$$

$$°F = 32° \qquad\qquad °F = 212°$$

Most thermometers used in steam plants are calibrated in degrees Fahrenheit. Thermometers are classified into two main types: the *liquid-in-glass type* and the *Bourdon tube type*.

Liquid-in-glass Thermometers. Liquid-in-glass thermometers are either mercury-filled or alcohol-filled. See Figure 9-4. The alcohol-filled type is used to measure extremely low temperatures where freezing may occur.

The liquid inside the thermometer expands when heated and contracts when cooled to indicate temperature. This type of thermometer comes in a variety of sizes and ranges from 0 °F to 220 °F; −30 °F to 120 °F; and 20 °F to 220 °F.

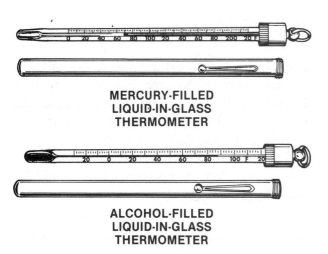

MERCURY-FILLED LIQUID-IN-GLASS THERMOMETER

ALCOHOL-FILLED LIQUID-IN-GLASS THERMOMETER

Figure 9-4. Mercury- or alcohol-filled thermometers can be used for temperature measurement in boiler systems.

Bourdon Tube Thermometer. The Bourdon tube thermometer operates by converting a pressure change to a temperature reading. The three types of Bourdon tube thermometers are the *liquid-filled Bourdon tube, vapor-pressure Bourdon tube*, and *gas-filled Bourdon tube*. See Figure 9-5.

In the liquid-filled Bourdon tube, the bulb (1), the capillary tube (2), and the Bourdon tube (3) are all filled with liquid (4). The expansion

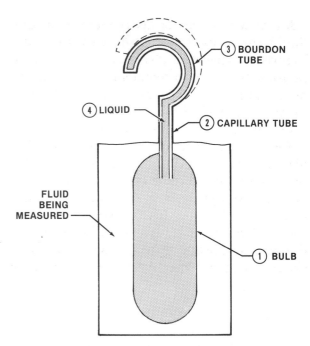

Figure 9-5. Pressure inside the bulb causes expansion or contraction of the Bourdon tube thermometer.

or contraction of the liquid in the bulb applies pressure on the Bourdon tube, causing the Bourdon tube to activate the pointer through mechanical linkage to register the temperature on the face of the gauge. This is not a pressure reading, but a pressure that is converted to a temperature reading.

The vapor-pressure thermometer uses a vapor in the bulb and operates using the same principle as the liquid-filled Bourdon tube. See Figure 9-6. The bulb (1) is only partly filled with liquid (2). The capillary tube (3) and Bourdon tube (4) are filled with vapor (5).

The pressure applied on the Bourdon tube depends on the temperature of the free surface of the liquid in the bulb. The vapor-pressure thermometer can be installed using capillary tubing up to 200' from the source, unlike the liquid-filled thermometer.

The gas-filled Bourdon tube thermometer is similar to the liquid-filled type. See Figure 9-7. It is actuated by the expansion of the gas that fills the bulb (1), capillary tube (2), and Bourdon tube (3). Nitrogen gas is most commonly used for this purpose. Like the vapor-pressure thermometer, the gas-filled thermometer can be installed a great distance from the point of measurement using a capillary tube.

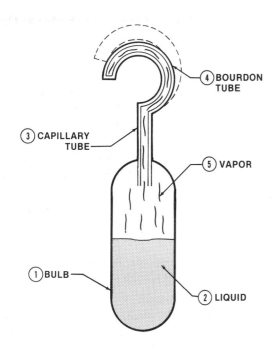

Figure 9-6. The vapor-filled Bourdon tube thermometer can be installed up to 200' from the source.

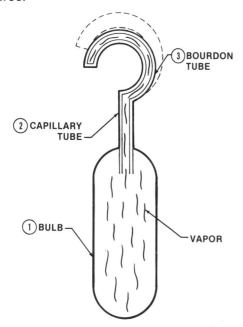

Figure 9-7. Nitrogen is the most commonly used gas in the gas-filled Bourdon tube thermometer.

Thermocouples

Thermocouples used as temperature-measuring devices permit rapid, accurate readings over a wide range of temperatures. Thermocouples can be centrally located, taking readings from several remote locations in the plant. Unlike thermometers, which use liquids and gases, thermocouples use a small electric current and dissimilar metals to measure temperature.

Thermocouples are generally centrally located and can be used for many applications in the operation of a boiler. Thermocouples are used to measure temperatures of superheated steam, desuperheated steam, feedwater entering the boiler, condensate returns, flue gas entering the stack, inlet and outlet condenser water, and combustion air in a steam generating plant.

High-temperature thermocouples are called *pyrometers*. Pyrometers are commonly used to measure furnace temperatures in the range of 100 °F to 2500 °F. The type and size of the steam generating plants will determine how many thermocouples are required.

Thermocouples are usually connected to a strip chart that records and compiles specific readings continuously. Each reading is assigned a number: for example, superheated steam is No. 1, desuperheated steam is No. 2, feedwater temperature is No. 3, and condensate returns are No. 4. The chart then records each specific temperature, such as No. 1 - 600 °, No. 2 - 337 °, No. 3 - 200 °, and No. 4 - 180 °. The operator can then identify the readings at a glance and make any necessary corrections.

Thermocouples are welded together at one end and sealed in a porcelain tube. The wire that is connected to the porcelain tube is either attached to a galvanometer, which is calibrated to measure degrees Fahrenheit, or to an amplifying device in a control circuit. The amount of electric current induced in the thermocouple depends on the difference between the temperature of one end of the thermocouple and the other.

A thermocouple is commonly used to measure the temperatures of the gases of combus-

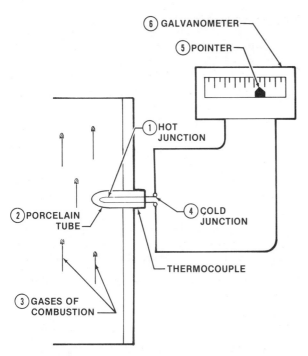

Figure 9-8. Two dissimilar metals possessing different electrical conductivity are used in thermocouples.

tion. See Figure 9-8. The hot junction (1) of the porcelain tube (2) is exposed to the heat of the gases of combustion (3). As this heat is sensed, a very small electric voltage is induced. This voltage is proportional to the difference in temperature between the hot junction and the cold junction (4) (where the porcelain tube connects to the leads).

The current going through the circuit moves the pointer (5) on the galvanometer (6). The scale of the galvanometer has been calibrated to read temperature in degrees Fahrenheit. If a thermocouple is used in a control circuit, the current induced in the thermocouple would be sent to an amplifier to amplify the signal in order to activate another control device.

PNEUMERCATORS

Pneumercators are used to indicate the amount of liquid present in a tank. The pneumercator is specifically designed and calibrated for each tank, according to the size and shape of the tank and the liquid that is held in it. See Figure 9-9.

An air tube (1) is placed vertically in the tank with its open end placed close to the bottom. The top of the tube is connected to an air pressure regulator (2) and a flow control device (3). When the pressure of the air in the air tube supports the column of liquid in the tank, the air pressure remains constant.

The air tube is also connected to an indicator (4) with a gauge glass (5). The air pressure is applied to the gauge glass fluid (6) at the base of the gauge glass. This pressure causes the gauge glass fluid in the gauge glass to rise until the resistance of the gauge glass fluid and the resistance of the fuel oil in the tank is balanced. As the level of the fuel oil in the tank drops, there is less resistance; hence, less air pressure is required to maintain that height within the gauge glass and the gauge glass fluid will fall.

Although pneumercators can be used to measure all types of liquids, in the boiler room they are used primarily to measure fuel oil in the fuel oil tanks. Routine service on pneumercators involves keeping the air tube clean, adding gauge glass fluid when needed, and purging the line to the tank to make sure it is clear.

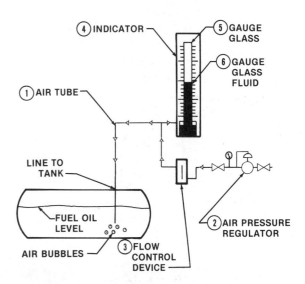

Figure 9-9. The pneumercator can be used to indicate the amount of fuel oil in a fuel oil tank. The pressure on the gauge glass fluid is dependent upon the fuel oil level in the tank.

FLOW METERS

Flow meters are used to determine the rate of flow or the amount of fluid that flows through the meter in a given unit of time. Flow meters are used for air, water, steam, fuel oil, and gases. Flow meters that measure rate of flow include differential-pressure flow meters, variable-area flow meters, and positive-displacement flow meters.

Flow meters must be calibrated for the specific fluid or gas to be measured. For example, the viscosity of fuel oil is not the same as water and will result in a different reading. Flow meter readings can be expressed in gallons, pounds of steam per hour, or cubic feet per minute. Readings can be taken at the flow meter or sent back to an integrator (totalizer) that compiles the flow information.

Differential-Pressure Flow Meters

Differential-pressure flow meters indicate the amount of flow by measuring the pressure differential across a restriction placed in the flow line. See Figure 9-10. The restriction may be an orifice plate, a venturi tube, or a flow nozzle. The pressure difference between the inlet and outlet pressures measured is sent mechanically or electrically to a receiver. The receiver then converts the pressure differential into a rate of flow and transmits it to a recorder.

Some recorders are equipped with integrators that make it possible to determine hourly or daily flow rates. The differential-pressure flow meter is used to measure the flow of air, steam, and gases.

Variable-Area Flow Meters

Variable-area flow meters measure flow by the amount of resistance created by a float or piston that changes the area (size) of the flow path. The movement of the float or piston varies depending on the resistance against the flow rate of the substance measured.

The two types of variable-area flow meters are the *rotometer flow meter* and the *valve flow meter*. See Figure 9-11. The rotometer flow

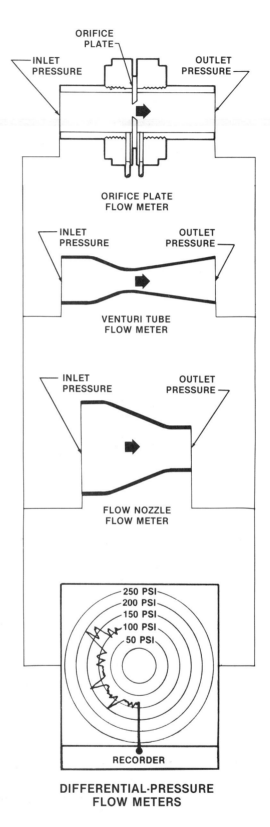

DIFFERENTIAL-PRESSURE FLOW METERS

Figure 9-10. A recorder can be used with differential-pressure flow meters to compile pressures for a given time period.

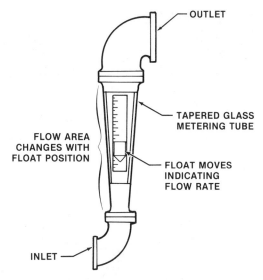

ROTOMETER FLOW METER

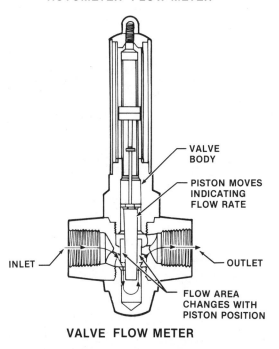

VALVE FLOW METER

Figure 9-11. The variable-area flow meter measures flow by the resistance caused by a float or piston.

meter is primarily used for a remote reading, whereas the rotometer flow meter is used for a direct reading. Both types of variable-area flow meters are commonly used to measure the flow of air, water, and gases.

Positive-Displacement Flow Meters

Positive-displacement flow meters measure and discharge a fixed amount of fluid in a manner similar to a positive-displacement pump. See Figure 9-12. Positive-displacement flow meters use a wobble plate that rotates as fluid enters the feed chamber and is discharged out the discharge chamber while fluid flows through the meter.

The wobble plate rotates with the flow and indicates rate of flow by the revolutions it makes in a given period of time. The reading is taken off the meter on the positive-displacement flow meter. The positive-displacement flow meter is commonly used to measure the flow of fuel oil and water.

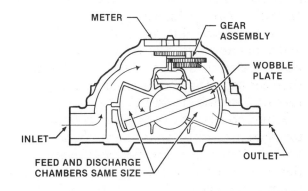

Figure 9-12. The amount of flow can be determined by reading the meter on the positive-displacement flow meter.

RECORDERS

Recorders are used to record rate of flow, pressures, temperatures, humidity, electricity, and liquid levels in the various systems within the steam plant. The recorder may utilize strip charts or circular charts. The

meter consists of a float in a tapered glass metering tube. As fluid flows through the tube, the float rises, changing the area to indicate flow rate.

The valve flow meter consists of a valve body and a piston or plug. The piston or plug moves with various rates of flow. The valve flow charts are available in different sizes, depending on the data recorded. The recorder can be mechanical, electrical, or electromechanical.

Recorders can record data concerning one specific level or several levels present in the boiler system. Recorders document useful data that can later be analyzed to assess plant operation. This allows accurate evaluation of each system to increase plant and production efficiency. See Figure 9-13.

Figure 9-13. Recorders on the panel board are centrally located for quick assessment of boiler functions.

SMOKE INDICATORS

Smoke indicators are used by the boiler operator to determine the condition of the gases of combustion leaving the chimney. In the past, the amount of smoke leaving the chimney was determined by visual inspection. However, visual inspection is not an accurate method because it is affected by the condition of the atmosphere (bright, cloudy, rainy, etc.), the backdrop behind the smoke, and the person making the observation.

A comparative chart known as the Ringelmann chart can be used to determine smoke density. It is made up of six sections and shows readings from 0 to 100% smoke density. The charts are placed 50′ from the observer who then compares the smoke from the chimney to the charts. From this observation, the operator then determines smoke density from the chimney by selecting the chart that matches with the gases of combustion leaving the chimney.

A smoke indicator (smoke gauge) is a more accurate method of evaluating the density of the gases of combustion. See Figure 9-14. Smoke indicators determine smoke density by focusing light through the gases of combustion by using a light source, photoelectric receiver, control, and recorder. The amount of light that is restricted indicates the density of the gases of combustion.

If the gases of combustion passing between the light source and the photoelectric receiver are clear, the reading will be near zero. If the gases are heavy with smoke, the reading will be near 100. The light source and receiver are designed for negative pressure breechings. Sealing flanges must be used to seal off positive pressures up to 1 psi. The light source and receiver are installed on opposite sides of the breeching monitored. The location must receive the true smoke pattern for accurate readings.

The smoke indicator alarm is set by adjusting the alarm point to the desired density percentage. The alarm delay is then set for the desired time. An inadequate alarm delay setting would cause excessive sensitivity of the smoke indicator. This can result in frequent alarms caused when lighting the burner or other temporary periods of high smoke levels. When the smoke indicator senses smoke density exceeding the alarm point and alarm delay, the alarm light is energized and latched. The smoke indicator must then be reset to cancel the alarm.

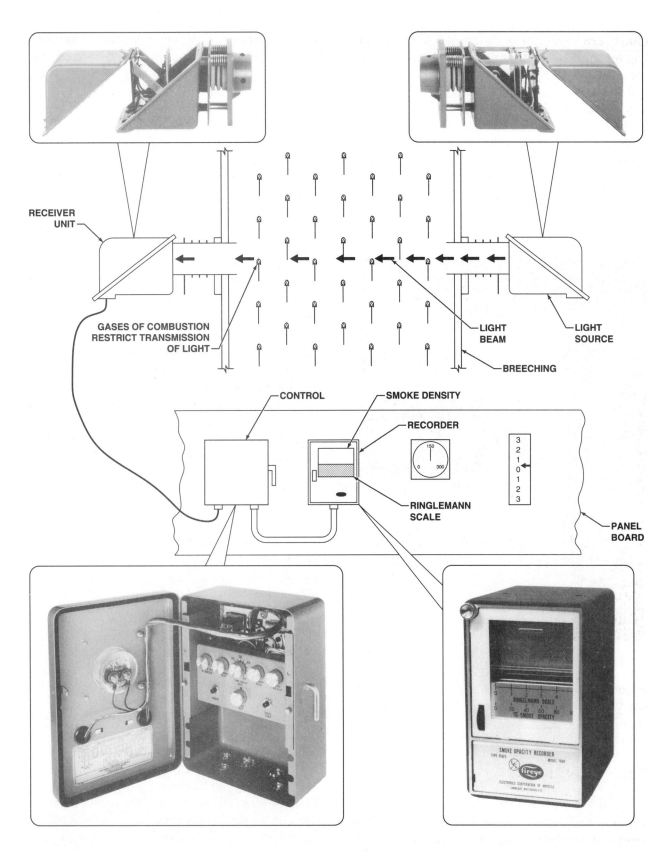

Figure 9-14. Smoke indicators are located in the breeching close to the boiler outlet to reduce possible excess air infiltration. (*Fireye, Inc.*)

Key Words

boiler steam-pressure gauge
Bourdon tube thermometer
differential-pressure flow meter
draft gauge
flow meter
liquid-in-glass thermometer
pneumercator
positive displacement flow meter
pressure gauge
psi

psig
pyrometer
recorder
smoke indicator
temperature-measuring-device
thermocouple
thermometer
vacuum gauge
variable-area flow meter

TECH CHECK ✓ 9

Name _____ Date _____

___D___ 1. Pressure gauges are calibrated in pounds per _____.
A. square foot
B. cubic inch
C. vertical inch
D. square inch

___B___ 2. Absolute pressure is equal to _____.
A. gauge pressure minus atmospheric pressure
B. gauge pressure plus atmospheric pressure
C. atmospheric pressure
D. gauge pressure plus steam pressure

___B___ 3. A boiler steam pressure gauge should have a range of _____.
A. 1–1½ times the safety valve setting
B. 1½–2 times the safety valve setting
C. 2–2½ times the safety valve setting
D. 10% of the MAWP

___C___ 4. The boiler steam-pressure gauge must be connected to the _____ of the boiler.
A. lowest part of the steam side
B. lowest part of the water side
C. highest part of the steam side
D. highest part of the water side

___D___ 5. The boiler steam pressure gauge is protected from high temperatures by _____.
A. a metal frame
B. steam gauge guards
C. a blower
D. a siphon

___A___ 6. Vacuum gauges are calibrated in inches of _____ atmospheric pressure.
A. mercury below
B. water below
C. mercury above
D. water above

___C___ 7. Most thermometers used in a steam plant are calibrated in _____.
A. psig
B. psia
C. degrees Fahrenheit
D. degrees kelvin

___C___ 8. Thermocouples measure _____.
A. gauge pressure
B. absolute pressure
C. temperature
D. heat

B

9. A primary reason for using thermocouples for measuring temperatures is _____.
   A. economy
   B. to centrally take and read the readings for remote plants
   C. to promote boiler efficiency
   D. to promote plant efficiency

D

10. A _____ reading can be read using a thermocouple.
    A. superheated steam
    B. gases of combustion
    C. condensate return
    D. all of the above

A

11. Liquids in a tank may be measured from a remote location using a _____.
    A. pneumercator
    B. thermocouple
    C. pressure control
    D. tank chart

D

12. Flow meters measure the rate of flow of _____.
    A. gases only
    B. liquids only
    C. solids
    D. a variety of fluids

D

13. The differential-pressure flow meter functions by receiving a difference of pressure across a(n) _____.
    A. venturi
    B. orifice plate
    C. flow nozzle
    D. any one of the above

B

14. The rotometer flow meter consists of a _____.
    A. ball in a straight tube
    B. ball in a tapered tube
    C. straight tube
    D. tapered tube

A

15. The types of variable-area flow meters are _____ and _____.
    A. rotometer, valve
    B. pressure, globe valve
    C. temperature, pressure
    D. temperature, gate valve

C

16. Recorders are used to _____.
    A. regulate steam output
    B. regulate the air to fuel ratio
    C. give an overall view of the steam plant operation
    D. they have limited application in steam plants

B

17. A Ringelmann chart is used to determine _____.
   A. atmospheric conditions
   B. smoke density
   C. combustion efficiency
   D. fuel oil density

C

18. Light and a photoelectric cell are sometimes used to indicate _____.
   A. a Ringelmann reading
   B. atmospheric conditions
   C. smoke density
   D. draft conditions

D

19. Smoke indicators are often essential because _____.
   A. they can indicate atmospheric conditions
   B. they can secure the burner to prevent a furnace explosion
   C. they can secure the burner to prevent a boiler explosion
   D. the boiler operator cannot always see the chimney to observe smoking conditions

B

20. Modern steam plants use instrumentation to _____.
   A. decrease productivity
   B. promote safe and efficient operation
   C. reduce plant maintenance
   D. comply with insurance regulations

Identify the parts of Bourdon tube thermometer.

B
C
A
D

21. Capillary tube
22. Bulb
23. Bourdon tube
24. Liquid

Identify the parts of the thermocouple circuit.

_____ 25. Cold junction
_____ 26. Thermocouple
_____ 27. Gases of combustion
_____ 28. Hot junction

Identify the parts of the pneumercator.

_____ 29. Air pressure regulator
_____ 30. Air tube
_____ 31. Indicator
_____ 32. Fuel oil level

Identify the parts of the positive-displacement flow meter.

_____ 33. Meter
_____ 34. Wobble plate
_____ 35. Gear assembly
_____ 36. Feed and discharge chambers

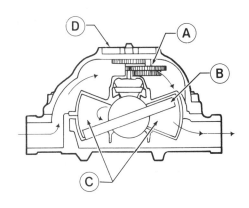

Chapter 10

BOILER WATER TREATMENT

Water used in a boiler must be treated to maintain optimum efficiency and to increase the life of the boiler tubes and drum. Water is seldom pure. Water used in the boiler must be treated regardless of its source.

Rainwater combines with gases and particles as it falls to the ground. Groundwater accumulates dissolved solids such as carbonates of magnesium and calcium as it passes through the ground. Standing water accumulates solid and gaseous industrial pollutants on its surface. Drinking water, although it is chlorinated, still must have dissolved solids removed before use in a boiler.

Water can be treated before use in the boiler (external treatment) or treated within the boiler (internal treatment). Boiler water is best treated with a combination of external and internal treatment.

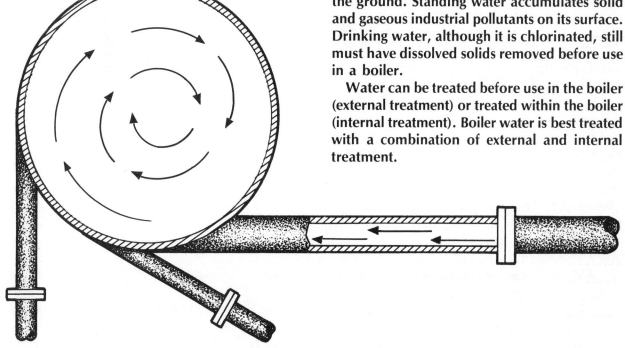

KEY TO ARROWHEAD SYMBOLS			
△ - Air	▲ - Water	▲ - Fuel Oil	⌂ - Air to Atmosphere
△ - Gas	△ - Steam	△ - Condensate	⌂ - Gases of Combustion

BOILER WATER CONDITIONS

The steam boiler must be protected from boiler water conditions that can occur as a direct result of using untreated supply water. Untreated supply water can cause *caustic embrittlement, scale, corrosion,* and *carryover.* Boiler inspectors inspect for caustic embrittlement, scale, and corrosion resulting from improperly treated boiler water during the annual inspection of a steam boiler.

Caustic embrittlement is the collection of high alkaline material which leads to breakdown and weakening of boiler metal. Alkalinity of a solution is affected by the amount of hydroxide, such as caustic soda, present in the solution. Caustic embrittlement can cause metal to crack along the seams and at the ends of tubes in the boiler. If such cracks occur, the boiler must be taken out of service for repairs. If metal cracks are ignored, a boiler explosion may occur, resulting in injury to operating personnel. Caustic embrittlement is prevented by maintaining proper alkalinity of boiler water at all times.

NOTE: All repairs made to the seams and/or tubes in the boiler must be made under the supervision of a boiler inspector (state, local, and/or insurance) and must comply with the ASME code.

Scale is the collection of calcium carbonate and magnesium carbonate deposited on the heating surfaces (tubes and boiler drums) of the boiler. See Figure 10-1. Scale formation on tubes and boiler drums is a direct cause of boiler failure. The boiler metal overheats because scale acts as an insulating material between the combustion side of the boiler and the water. Tubes free of scale absorb more heat from the gases of combustion, thus increasing the boiler efficiency.

In addition, removing scale-forming elements from the water reduces boiler downtime required to remove the accumulated scale from the boiler. Overheating of the boiler metal can cause leaks, cracks, bags (blistering), distortion of tubes and tube sheets, and boiler explosion (complete failure). See Figure 10-2. Scale can be prevented by changing calcium

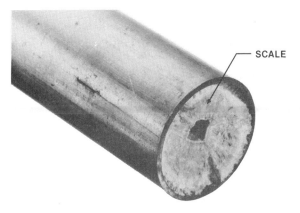

Figure 10-1. Overheating of tubes can result from scale buildup caused by improper treatment of water used in the boiler. (*The Permutit Co., Inc.*)

Figure 10-2. A fire tube boiler explosion can occur from overheating due to heavy scale formation on heating surfaces. (*Factory Mutual System*)

carbonate and magnesium carbonate into non-adhering sludge and by blowing down.

Corrosion is the pitting and channeling of metal caused by gases in water. Corrosion weakens the boiler structurally by thinning the boiler plates and tubes. If left unchecked, corrosion of boiler metal can lead to a boiler explosion. To prevent corrosion, oxygen and carbon dioxide should be removed from the water.

Carryover is the carrying over of water into steam lines caused by high alkalinity, dissolved solids, and sludge. Carryover is a very dangerous condition because of water hammer in the steam lines which can result in steam header or line rupture. Carryover is prevented by maintaining the proper alkalinity of the boiler water.

In addition, dissolved solids and surface impurities such as oil must be minimized to prevent carryover, *priming*, and *foaming*. Priming is the carrying over of small water particles. Foaming is the rapid fluctuation of the water level caused by impurities on the surface of the water, leading to an increase in surface tension of the boiler water.

Boiler Water Analysis

Boiler water analysis is required to determine the condition of the boiler water and the necessary feedwater and boiler water treatment. Boiler water is analyzed for alkalinity, phosphates, sulfite, and total dissolved solids.

Certain minimum levels of chemicals are required in the boiler water to prevent scale formation, pitting, and corrosion of the boiler metal. Chemical concentrations required in the boiler will vary with the temperatures and pressures in the boiler. Follow the manufacturer's recommendations for specific feedwater treatment and residual chemical levels in the boiler water.

INTERNAL BOILER WATER TREATMENT

Internal boiler water treatment is treating the water after it has entered the steam and water drum. The boiler water must be treated to prevent scale formation on tubes and heating surfaces, corrosion of the shell and tubes, caustic embrittlement at seams, and carryover of boiler water into superheater and steam lines.

Internal treatment methods will vary, depending on the condition of the boiler water. Chemicals are added to a steam boiler to correct or prevent boiler water conditions such as scale, corrosion, caustic embrittlement, and foaming and carryover. In most steam boiler plants, chemicals for boiler water treatment

can be regulated and added continuously in a diluted form by using a proportioning chemical pump and a mixing tank. See Figure 10-3.

Figure 10-3. Chemicals are added to the steam boiler by using a proportioning chemical pump and a mixing tank.

A daily boiler water analysis determines whether the chemical amount has to be increased or decreased. Continuous blowdown is used in preference to a bottom blowdown. Bottom blowdown is less efficient than continuous blowdown because lost water and heat must be replaced. Continuous blowdown maintains more consistency in the level of chemicals within the boiler water. See Figure 10-4.

Scale formation can be prevented by adding caustic soda and phosphate to the boiler water to change calcium carbonate and magnesium carbonate into nonadhering sludge. The sludge is then removed from the boiler by using the bottom blowdown or the continuous blowdown

Figure 10-4. Continuous blowdown is preferred over bottom blowdown because it maintains a more consistent level of chemicals in the boiler than bottom blowdown and saves heat.

valves. The level of phosphate in the boiler water is maintained by the addition of phosphates. A color comparison test is used to determine the residual phosphate level in the boiler water.

Scale formation in a boiler is a result of improper boiler water treatment. With properly controlled boiler water treatment, there should not be any scale formation regardless of the condition of the supply water. Preventing scale formation using chemical treatment is much easier than removing the scale after it forms on the boiler heating surface. Scale can only be removed by turbining (mechanical means) the boiler tubes or by acid cleaning. Both methods can lead to thinning of the boiler tubes.

Corrosion is prevented by heating the feedwater before it enters the boiler. This removes carbon dioxide and oxygen from the water. Sodium sulfite is also added to the boiler to remove oxygen. Any oxygen present in the water combines with sodium sulfite to form sulfate. The proper sulfite level must be maintained in the boiler water to prevent oxygen pitting and corrosion of boiler metal. If the residual sulfite level is low, sodium sulfite must be added.

Caustic embrittlement is prevented by maintaining the correct alkalinity level in the boiler and by continuous blowdowns. The proper alkalinity is maintained by the addition of caustic soda or soda ash.

The alkalinity level of boiler water is determined by the pH of the boiler water. *NOTE:* It is usually recommended that the pH of the boiler water is maintained between 7 and 10. A pH of 7 of a given liquid indicates that it is neutral. If the pH is below 7, the liquid is considered to be on the acid side. If the pH is above 7, the liquid is considered to be on the alkaline side. See Figure 10-5.

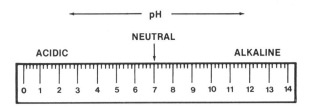

Figure 10-5. In order to protect the boiler from scale formation, the pH value should be kept slightly alkaline as per manufacturer's recommendations.

Caustic embrittlement has become less of a problem as most modern boilers are now welded rather than riveted. Riveted joints in the boiler are more susceptible to caustic embrittlement because of the amount of protruding locations for caustic embrittlement to occur.

Foaming and carryover are prevented by minimizing the total dissolved solids (TDS) and surface impurities in the boiler water. The total dissolved solids in the boiler water must be kept within certain predetermined levels. A conductivity meter is used to determine the total solids present in the boiler water. The total dissolved solids present are regulated by the continuous blowdown valve and/or by using the bottom blowdown valves. Surface impurities are removed with a surface blowdown using the surface blowdown valve.

Many chemical companies specialize in boiler water treatment that can be of great benefit to the steam plant operator. Most companies will send a representative to assess the requirements of a specific boiler and recommend a boiler water treatment program. In addition, many chemical companies will train boiler plant personnel in the proper testing of boiler water, the proper maintenance of chemical residual levels, and the recommended frequency and length of blowdowns.

Boiler water samples are often tested at the company lab to ensure the correct treatment procedures. However, the amount of chemicals added and the frequency of boiler blowdowns can be best determined by daily testing of the boiler water by the boiler operator. See Figure 10-6.

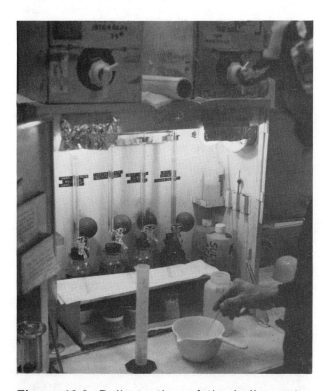

Figure 10-6. Daily testing of the boiler water determines the specific feedwater treatment required.

EXTERNAL BOILER WATER TREATMENT

External treatment is the treatment of water before it enters the boiler. Water treated before it enters the boiler has all or most of the scale-forming salts and gases removed. This allows easier treatment of the boiler water internally. A simple soap solution test can be used to determine the degree of hardness or softness (scale-forming salts present) of water.

When shaken, hard water will not sustain as many soap suds as soft water. The most common external treatment methods used in external water treatment are the *lime-soda process* and the *ion exchange* (zeolite) *process*. Although boiler water is treated externally, a residual amount of chemicals must still be maintained within the boiler for protection.

Lime-soda Process

The two types of lime-soda processes are the *cold lime-soda process* and the *hot lime-soda process*. The cold lime-soda process is performed at ambient temperature. The process softens the water by removing sludge formed by calcium and magnesium compounds. When the sludge is removed, the water is passed through a filter for further treatment. See Figure 10-7.

Water enters through the raw water inlet (1) and immediately blends with the chemicals introduced at the chemical inlets (2). The design causes a swirling action as the mixture passes through the catalyst bed (3). Sludge deposits on the surface of the catalyst as the water moves toward the top. The softened water leaves at the softened water outlet (4).

As the catalytic material becomes heavily coated with sludge, it is removed through the draw-off valve (5) located at the bottom of the softener. Fresh catalyst is added as needed at the top. The test cocks (6) are used to indicate the level of the catalyst material in the softener.

The hot lime-soda process is performed at a temperature above 212 °F. This process uses exhaust or live steam to maintain the high

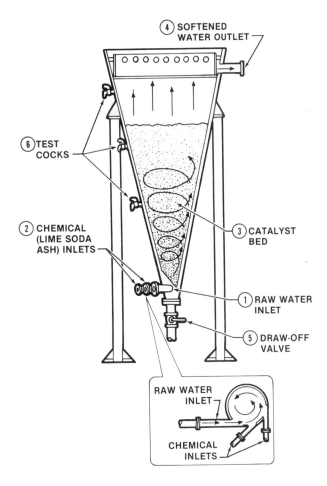

Figure 10-7. The cold lime-soda process produces the quantities of soft water required by large plants. (*The Permutit Co., Inc.*)

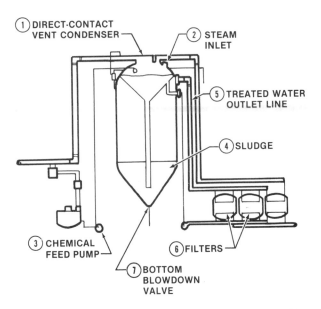

Figure 10-8. The hot lime-soda process uses live or exhaust steam to promote the chemical reaction necessary in the water softening process and is commonly used for boiler water makeup. (*The Permutit Co., Inc.*)

temperatures required. The hot lime-soda process is quicker than the cold lime-soda process and performs the same function. It softens the water and removes sludge. See Figure 10-8.

Water enters through the direct-contact vent condenser (1) at the top of the softener. The steam also enters at the top of the unit through the steam inlet (2). The chemical feed pump (3) delivers the chemicals to the upper section of the softener. The steam, chemicals, and raw water mix together while the noncondensable gases are removed through the vent condenser and discharged to the atmosphere.

Water flows to the bottom before rising through the sludge (4) and discharging through the treated water outlet line (5). The

water then passes through filters (6) on route to the feedwater heater. The sludge is removed at the bottom blowdown valve (7).

Ion Exchange (Zeolite) Process

The ion exchange (zeolite) process is performed at ambient temperature. Zeolite is the name for a group of minerals including silicates of aluminum, sodium, and calcium. The most common use of zeolite is to soften water. Zeolites absorb all of the ions of minerals that cause water to be hard. Zeolite can be manufactured artificially or can be used from the ground.

Zeolite softens the water by changing the calcium and magnesium carbonates into sodium carbonates. When the sodium in the softener is depleted, the unit must be regenerated by passing sodium chloride (common salt) over the zeolite in the resin bed. After rinsing, the unit is ready for service. See Figure 10-9.

During normal operation of the ion exchange softener, water enters at the inlet (1) and pass-

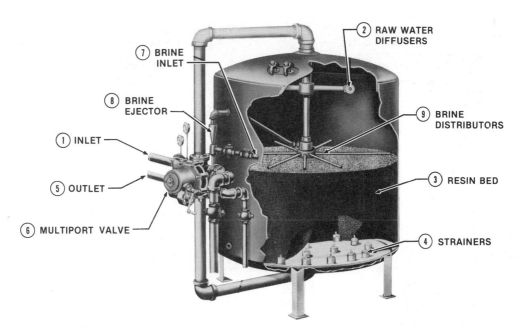

Figure 10-9. The zeolite water softener is used extensively in small- to medium-sized boiler plants to soften water. (*The Permutit Co., Inc.*)

es to the raw water diffusers (2). It is distributed evenly over the resin bed (3) and then moves through the layers until it passes through the strainers (4). The softened water leaves through the outlet line (5).

To regenerate the softener, it must be removed from service and backwashed by moving the multiport valve (6) to flush position. This allows water to pass up through the bottom, flushing the resin bed. After flushing, the multiport valve is moved to the brine position. The brine inlet (7) introduces brine into the softener using the brine ejector (8) through the brine distributors (9). The brine slowly moves through the resin, reacting with the calcium and magnesium to restore the resin to its original sodium condition.

The final step in the regeneration of the softener is to rinse the excess brine and other impurities out. The multiport valve is moved to the rinse-cycle position and a slow flow of water is passed through the softener. When all traces of brine are removed, the softener can be put back in service.

The ion exchange method of external treatment is preferred in many boiler rooms today.

This is due to its compactness and simplicity of operation. Ion exchange (zeolite) softeners are also made so that regeneration can be fully automatic.

AUTOMATIC BLOWDOWN SYSTEM

Automatic blowdown systems are used to maximize control of continuous blowdown operations. The system senses the condition of boiler water during preset timed blowdown intervals. The duration of blowdown is determined by the total dissolved solids present in the boiler water leaving the boiler. The duration of blowdown is increased or decreased as required. The automatic blowdown system includes a *controller*, *sampling assembly*, and *conductivity sensor*. See Figure 10-10.

The controller is a microprocessor device which is programmed to control blowdown interval and duration. The sampling sensor, in conjunction with the conductivity sensor, controls the flow of boiler water, and measures the total dissolved solids present. Total dissolved solids are measured using a conductivity test. Conductivity is the ability of electricity to flow through a substance. The higher the level of total dissolved solids, the greater the flow of electricity or conductivity of the boiler water.

Automatic blowdown systems prolong the life of boilers, pumps, and other system components by reducing the amount of dissolved solids in the steam drum. This reduces carryover and scale build-up. In addition, compliance with environmental laws has increased the need for better control of blowdown operations. Excessive blowdown results in increased usage of fuel, makeup water, and boiler water chemicals. This also results in excessive amounts of treated boiler water discharged into the waste water system.

Automatic blowdown systems are best used on small to medium sized boilers where the main boiler is supplemented by smaller units. This includes commercial heating systems and unit boilers in refineries, chemical plants, and food processing plants. Automatic blowdown

systems are limited to a maximum of 392°F (200°C) and 250 psig.

Automatic Blowdown System Operation

The controller is programmed for the desired blowdown interval and duration. The interval timer controls how often the blowdown valve opens and the duration timer controls how long the blowdown valve is held open. When blowdown occurs at the preset interval, the blowdown valve opens. Conductivity of the boiler water is measured. If the conductivity value exceeds the desired set point, the blowdown valve will remain open until the conductivity value falls to the desired set point. If the conductivity value is less than the desired set point, the blowdown valve is automatically closed to minimize the loss of boiler water.

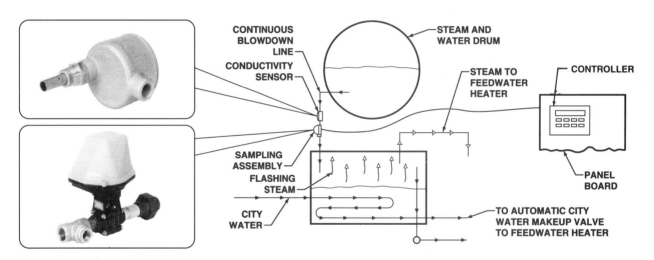

Figure 10-10. Automatic blowdown systems are programmed to minimize the frequency and duration of continuous blowdown to reduce impact to the environment. (*Rosemount Analytical*)

Key Words

automatic blowdown system
boiler water analysis
carryover
caustic embrittlement
cold lime-soda process
corrosion
external boiler water treatment

foaming
hot lime-soda process
ion exchange (zeolite) process
internal boiler water treatment
priming
scale

TECH CHECK ✓ 10   Name _____ Date _____

D
1. Boiler water must be conditioned to prevent _____.
   A. formation of scale
   B. oxygen pitting
   C. carryover   *FORMING*
   D. all of the above

A
2. Natural water may contain _____.
   A. solids, gases, and other pollutants from industrial waste
   B. dissolved solids only
   C. various gases only
   D. no contaminants

C
3. Boiler water having high alkalinity could develop _____.
   A. scale
   B. oxygen pitting
   C. caustic embrittlement   *CAUSTIC*
   D. warping

A
4. Deposits of calcium and magnesium carbonates on the boiler heating surface cause _____.
   A. scale
   B. oxygen pitting
   C. caustic embrittlement
   D. carryover

B
5. Oxygen in the boiler will cause _____.
   A. scale
   B. pitting of boiler metal
   C. caustic embrittlement
   D. carryover

C
6. Water that leaves the boiler with the steam is called _____.
   A. superheated steam
   B. saturated steam
   C. carryover
   D. condensate

C
7. Cracking of the boiler metal along the seams and tube ends can be caused by _____.
   A. scale
   B. oxygen pitting
   C. caustic embrittlement
   D. carryover

D
8. A direct cause of overheating of the boiler tubes is _____.
   A. soot formation
   B. overfiring
   C. insufficient air
   D. scale formation on the tubes

B

9. Carryover is dangerous and could lead to _____ hammer.
   A. steam
   B. water
   C. gas
   D. air

C

10. Chemicals added to the boiler water change the scale-forming salts into _____.
    A. an adhering sludge
    B. oxygen scavengers
    C. a nonadhering sludge
    D. a corrosion inhibitor

C

11. Scale buildup on the water side of a steam boiler is caused by _____.
    A. an impure water supply
    B. scale in the raw water
    C. improper boiler water treatment
    D. scale is found only on the fire side of a boiler

A

12. Oxygen present in the boiler water is removed by _____.
    A. heating the feedwater and using sodium sulfite
    B. heating the feedwater only
    C. using the bottom blowdown valves
    D. using the surface blowdown valves

C

13. The frequency of blowing down a steam boiler is best ascertained by the _____.
    A. chief engineer
    B. boiler inspector
    C. daily testing of boiler water
    D. plant load

D

14. Closer control of boiler water chemical concentrations are maintained by _____.
    A. surface blowdowns
    B. bottom blowdowns
    C. a combination of surface and bottom blowdowns
    D. continuous blowdowns (SURFACE BLOWDOWN AT NOWL)

D

15. External feedwater treatment conditions the feedwater before it enters the boiler and can be a(n) _____ process.
    A. cold lime-soda
    B. hot lime-soda
    C. ion exchange
    D. any one of the above

B

16. The cold lime-soda process softens the boiler water at _____.
    A. temperatures of 212 °F or above
    B. ambient temperature
    C. temperatures below 32 °F
    D. a high, controlled pressure

Chapter 11

STEAM BOILER OPERATION

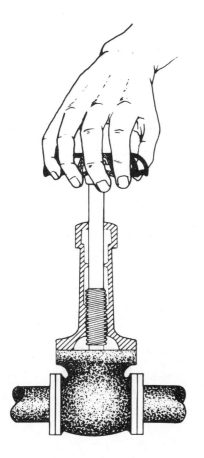

The boiler operator is responsible for the safe and efficient operation of the plant. Each boiler operator is responsible for an 8-hour shift and must be able to make crucial decisions based on plant knowledge.

Boilers can be dangerous; therefore, good judgement is required to operate boilers safely. The use of any substance that may impair the performance of the boiler operator is strictly prohibited. This includes the use of drugs and/or alcohol. If a boiler operator must take prescription drugs, a doctor must be consulted to identify possible adverse effects.

The boiler operator is responsible for relaying the plant conditions accurately to the shift engineer or chief engineer. Inaccurate information could lead to obstacles in troubleshooting, which could result in expensive downtime. In addition, plant data must be recorded accurately in the log. This information may be needed later to determine the cause of a serious accident.

The boiler operator must maintain high standards of safety and efficiency. An operator who is familiar with the equipment and plant will know how to react in an emergency.

KEY TO ARROWHEAD SYMBOLS			
△ - Air	▲ - Water	▲ - Fuel Oil	⌂ - Air to Atmosphere
⚠ - Gas	△ - Steam	⚠ - Condensate	⚠ - Gases of Combustion

Figure 11-1. Testing the low water fuel cutoff control is a routine duty of the boiler operator.

Figure 11-2. Fuel oil burners must be cleaned once a shift to prevent a carbon deposit buildup.

Figure 11-3. Fuel pressures and temperatures are regulated for combustion efficiency.

OPERATOR DUTIES AND RESPONSIBILITIES

Although the duties of the boiler operator may vary from plant to plant, certain duties are always the same. Routine duties and responsibilities of a boiler operator include the following.

1. Maintain the proper water level in the boiler at all times. Failure to do so could result in a high or low water condition. High water could lead to carryover, whereas low water could lead to overheating of boiler heating surfaces. Both of these conditions are considered dangerous.

2. Never leave the boiler room for a period longer than what is considered safe. The operator is responsible for making this judgement, based on how long it takes the water in the gauge glass to go from half a glass to no water showing. The time this process takes varies from 2 to 8 minutes, depending on the boiler.

3. Carry out written and/or verbal instructions from the chief engineer promptly. The chief engineer is responsible for the overall safe and efficient operation of the plant.

4. Maintain the correct operating steam pressure. Variations in steam pressure can have an adverse effect on process plant operation.

5. Test the low water fuel cutoff control to ensure its proper operation. See Figure 11-1.

6. Test the feedwater regulator for proper function to maintain the NOWL.

7. Maintain the burner in good operating condition. This is essential in order to achieve efficient combustion. Burners that are not cleaned regularly (once a shift) will foul with deposits of carbon or noncombustible matter. See Figure 11-2.

8. Maintain the correct fuel pressures and temperatures for proper combustion efficiency. See Figure 11-3.

9. Keep a record of the fuel on hand to determine the current supply of fuel and the daily fuel consumption.

10. Check and maintain the amount of feedwater makeup being used. Any unusual increase in feedwater makeup indicates a loss of condensate returns. Always maintain an adequate supply of feedwater.

11. Maintain correct feedwater temperature. This reduces thermal shock to the boiler metal. Temperatures that are too high can cause the feedwater pump to become steambound. Temperatures that are too low will not remove the free oxygen from the feedwater.

12. Periodically inspect the feedwater pump, fuel oil pump, and draft fans. See Figure 11-4. This aids in reducing maintenance costs and downtime. Minor problems that are corrected immediately can prevent larger problems from developing.

13. Maintain the proper draft in the boiler necessary for complete combustion of the fuel and for the removal of the gases of combustion.

14. Visually inspect the fire in the furnace periodically. This inspection can provide an indication of the quality of combustion. See Figure 11-5. **WARNING: Always wear proper eye protection to prevent possible injury from infrared and ultraviolet rays emitted from the fire in the furnace.**

15. Follow chief engineer's instructions for correct feedwater treatment and boiler blowdown. Use soot blowers when scheduled. Soot acts as an insulator and must be removed from boiler heating surfaces in order to maintain high heat transfer rates, which ensure efficient boiler operation. See Figure 11-6.

16. Identify and document any unusual occurrences, such as steam load changes, steam leaks, low water in the boiler, machinery failures, and any other extraordinary event.

17. Always operate the boiler plant in a safe and efficient manner to avoid emergencies.

Taking Over A Shift

The boiler operator must be prepared to take

Figure 11-4. Feedwater pumps are checked for leakage, unusual noises, and overheating.

Figure 11-5. The boiler operator inspects the fire in a furnace for combustion quality.

Figure 11-6. Soot is removed from boiler tubes using a soot blower.

Figure 11-7. Water columns are blown down to assure an accurate water level reading.

Figure 11-8. Running auxiliaries should be routinely checked for proper lubrication.

Figure 11-9. The chief engineer's log details any extraordinary instructions for the boiler operator.

over a shift and follow the established procedures. These procedures ensure that the boiler plant operates safely and efficiently. Certain steps must be followed when taking over a shift.

1. Report to work early enough to check all operating equipment before relieving the operator of the previous shift.
2. Check the water level in boilers on the line by blowing down the water column and gauge glass. See Figure 11-7. *NOTE:* Boilers that have flat gauge glasses with mica inserts that separate the water and steam from the glass should only have the gauge glasses blown down according to the manufacturer's recommendations.
3. Test the low water fuel cutoff control by blowing down the float chamber.
4. Inspect and check all running auxiliaries and/or accessories for proper temperature, pressure, lubrication, and excessive vibration. See Figure 11-8.
5. Listen for any unusual noises.
6. Check the water level in the open feedwater heater or feedwater tank.
7. Check the burner for the correct flame and the correct fuel oil temperatures and pressures.
8. Determine that the fuel supply is adequate.
9. Review the chief engineer's log for any extraordinary instructions. See Figure 11-9.

Testing Low Water Fuel Cutoff Controls. Low water fuel cutoff controls are tested in two ways: by blowing down the control or by performing an evaporation test. Low water fuel cutoff controls are tested by blowing down the control while the burner is in operation.

The blowdown valve located on the low water fuel cutoff should be opened wide. The fuel valve closes, securing the fire. This procedure should be performed once a shift to test the operation of the control and remove any buildup of sludge and sediment.

The evaporation test should be done at least once a month on a steam boiler equipped with a low water fuel cutoff control. This test consists of securing the feedwater pump and allowing the water level to drop in the boiler to activate the low water fuel cutoff, thus securing fuel to the burner. Some low water controls must be manually reset after the control has tripped.

This procedure does not apply to coal-fired boilers that are not equipped with a low water fuel cutoff control. The boiler operator must exercise caution while the low water condition is created during this test.

Testing Flame Failure Controls. The flame failure control is tested to protect the boiler from a furnace explosion. The scanner will not allow the fuel valve to open if it does not prove pilot. This prevents fuel from entering the furnace of the boiler.

With the burner on, remove the scanner and cover the scanner eye with your hand. This action simulates a flame failure, and the fuel valve should shut off. See Figure 11-10.

Replace the scanner and reset the programmer after it has stopped. The programmer then initiates a normal firing cycle of the burner. The flame failure control should be tested at least once a week.

Maintaining a Boiler Room Log. The boiler operator must maintain a boiler room log. See Figure 11-11. The boiler room log documents an hourly record of all the temperatures, pressures, and other pertinent plant data.

This data includes steam flow, water consumption, fuel consumption, and auxiliaries in operation. In addition, any maintenance done on a shift or any operating problems encountered should be recorded in the log. The readings and data recorded over a 24-hour period allow the chief engineer to determine how efficiently the boiler has been operated. See Figure 11-12.

BOILER START-UP AND SHUTDOWN PROCEDURES

Boiler start-up and shutdown procedures for

Figure 11-10. The flame failure control is tested by covering the scanner eye.

Figure 11-11. The boiler operator is responsible for maintaining a boiler room log.

any boiler vary from plant to plant. The procedures depend on such conditions as the number of boilers, the size of the plant, the type of fuel burned, and whether the plant is operated automatically or manually. Although procedures and methods may vary, they must be performed in a safe and efficient manner.

When starting up a cold plant, the procedures followed differ from procedures followed when starting up a live plant. Cold plant start-ups are less hazardous because no steam pressure is present in the boiler. A cold plant is commonly referred to as a *dead plant*.

During cold plant start-ups, all packing and flange gaskets in the plant and boiler room must be inspected for leaks. Boiler plant shut-

POWER HOUSE LOG

Dates From _____ To _____

TIME	NO. BOILER IN OPERATION	STEAM PRESSURE ON BOILER	FLUE TEMP. °F	FURNACE DRAFT INS. H_2O	NO. BURNERS	BOILER FUEL METER READING	STEAM FLOW INTEGRATOR MAIN PLANT	STEAM FLOW INTEGRATOR BLDG. NO.____	WATER SOFTENER INTEGRATOR	WATER SOFTENER DIAL METER	FEED WATER TEMP. °F	GALLONS OF OIL IN TANK	OIL TEMP. FROM TANK AT PUMP °F	RETURN OIL TEMP. °F	SMOKE ALARM SIGNAL	OUTSIDE TEMP. °F	WEATHER	ENGINEER TO SIGN FOR ACTIVITIES DURING WATCH	ENGINEER'S INITIALS
9 A.M.																			
10																			
11																			
12																			
1 P.M.																			
2																			
3																			
4																			
5																			
6																			
7																			
8																			
9																			
10																			
11																			
12																			
1 A.M.																			
2																			
3																			
4																			
5																			
6																			
7																			
8																			
9																			

BOILER ROOM DAILY RECORD

			SHIFT	NO. OF BOILER	% BOILER EFFICIENCY	% MAKEUP WATER	LBS. OF STEAM/LBS. OF OIL
Actual lbs. steam made	Gallons of fuel burned		NO. 1				
Heat added/lb. steam	Heat value of fuel/gal.		NO. 2				
Equivalent lbs. steam made	Total heat in fuel, million BTU		NO. 3				
Boiler pressure	Efficiency						
Temperature feed water	Average B.H.P. rated						
Quality or superheat steam	Average B.H.P. developed (@ 800,000 BTU/day)						
Total heat added to steam, million BTU	Average per cent rating developed						

Figure 11-12. The boiler room log documents all functions of the boiler over a 24-hour period.

down follows many of the same procedures as boiler plant start-up, but in a reversed sequence. Each step must be followed in the correct sequence to ensure safe plant start-up or shutdown.

Cold Plant Start-Up

Cold plant start-up is performed on boilers that have been out of service for more than two days. Fuel must be properly prepared before lighting off the boilers. How the fuel is prepared is determined by the type of fuel used.

When burning coal, an adequate supply of coal must be available at the stoker or the pulverizing mill. In a stoker-fired boiler, a wood fire must be started in the furnace to ignite the bed of coal. When gas is used, little or no fuel preparation is necessary. The operator must only determine if the correct pressure is at the burner.

Boilers using heavy fuel oils must have fuel oil circulating at the proper temperature before it can be burned. This requires that electric fuel oil heaters be used to heat the fuel oil, or that a lighter grade such as No. 2 or No. 4 fuel oil be used when first lighting off the boiler. All fuel oil strainers and the fuel oil burner assembly should be cleaned prior to lighting off.

The following steps must be taken to start up a cold plant, regardless of the type of fuel burned.

1. Check boiler for any missing inspection opening covers.

2. Remove all chimney coverings and open hand-operated dampers.

3. Make sure the correct water level is present in the gauge glass.

4. Open the automatic nonreturn valve and the main steam stop valve in the main steam line. This allows the whole plant to warm up evenly.

5. Open all drains in the main steam lines and header.

6. Check the feedwater system to see that the system is lined up to the boiler and the proper valves are open.

7. Inspect feedwater pumps and feed-

water regulators. An adequate supply of water is required in the feedwater heater and the feedwater tank.

8. Check all the valves on the boilers for proper position.

9. Close the bottom blowdown valves.

10. Open the water column, gauge glass, steam pressure gauge, and boiler vent valves.

11. Purge the furnace of any combustible gases before the burner is fired. Light off the burner following all the safety procedures necessary for the fuel being burned.

12. Warm up the boiler slowly to allow uniform expansion of the boiler and all steam lines.

13. Maintain the recommended NOWL in the boiler.

14. Close the boiler vent when the steam pressure reaches about 25 psi (ASME code). By this time, all the air is expelled from the steam and water drum.

15. Check the automatic combustion controls, feedwater regulator, and all boiler room auxiliaries to ensure they are operating properly.

16. Gradually switch over all boiler controls to automatic operation as soon as the boiler has reached its normal operating pressure. See Figure 11-13.

At this time, the boiler operator must be aware of any sudden and unusual occurrences.

Figure 11-13. The boiler is switched to automatic after reaching normal operating pressure.

Figure 11-14. The main steam stop valve is opened after the equalizing valve.

Figure 11-15. When the incoming boiler's steam pressure reaches 25 psi, the boiler vent is closed.

Figure 11-16. The automatic nonreturn valve is opened at 75% to 85% of line pressure.

The operation of the boiler plant is at its most critical stage. All boiler room auxiliaries and automatic controls must be monitored very closely.

Live Plant Start-up

When starting up a boiler with other boilers on the line, the operator must make all safety checks before lighting off the burner. Using the same procedure as outlined under cold plant start-up and following the manufacturer's recommendations, warm up the boiler slowly.

1. Make sure both the boiler vent and the drain between the main steam stop valve and the automatic nonreturn valve are open.

2. Open the equalizing valve around the main steam stop valve.

3. Then open the main steam stop valve. See Figure 11-14.

4. Close the boiler vent when steam pressure on the incoming boiler reaches 25 psi. See Figure 11-15.

5. Open the automatic nonreturn valve when the steam pressure reaches approximately 75% to 85% of the line pressure. See Figure 11-16.

6. Test the safety valve by hand at this time. See Figure 11-17.

7. Bring the boiler pressure up slowly and let the automatic nonreturn valve cut the boiler in on the line.

8. Close the drain between the automatic nonreturn valve and the main steam stop valve.

9. Make sure all automatic controls are functioning. See Figure 11-18.

10. Test the flame failure control and low water fuel cutoff control.

A boiler with two hand-operated main steam stop valves is handled the same as previously mentioned, except that the boiler operator must operate both steam stop valves by hand.

1. Open the equalizing line around the main steam stop valve when approximately 85% of the line pressure is on the boiler, warming the main steam line and valve.

2. Open the main steam stop valve.

3. Crack the steam valve closest to the shell of the boiler off its seat and open it slowly when the incoming boiler pressure is slightly below line pressure. This allows steam to flow from the header back to the boiler coming in on the line. Any condensate in the line is forced back into the boiler. This prevents carryover in the event that the operator opens the main steam stop valve too rapidly.

When a boiler is equipped with a superheater, certain precautions must be taken during the warm-up period. The superheater outlet drain valve must be opened and remain open until the boiler is cut in on the line. Steam must flow through the superheater at all times to prevent overheating of superheater tubes.

Different types of superheaters require different handling procedures during warm-up. Refer to the manufacturer's specifications for the recommended start-up and shutdown procedures to prevent damage to superheater tubes.

Boiler Shutdown

Boiler shutdown requires the operator to first secure the fuel to the burner. See Figure 11-19. The superheater outlet drain should be opened as soon as the burner is shut down. After the boiler furnace has cooled and the boiler has stopped steaming, the operator can finish securing the boiler.

1. Close the boiler main steam stop valves and open all steam line drains.

2. Open the boiler vent when the steam pressure is down to 25 psi (ASME code) to prevent a vacuum from forming in the boiler.

3. Maintain the water at the NOWL while the boiler is cooling down.

4. Shut down the feedwater pump and the feedwater system when the boiler has cooled down sufficiently.

BOILER INSPECTION

The operator must prepare the boiler for in-

Figure 11-17. The safety valve is tested by hand before the boiler is brought up to line pressure.

Figure 11-18. Automatic controls on the panel board are checked for proper function.

Figure 11-19. Fuel to the burner must be secured when shutting down the boiler.

spection. The boiler inspector should be notified when the boiler is ready for inspection so an appointment can be arranged.

Prior to inspection, the boiler must be opened up on both the fire and water side and be thoroughly cleaned. Any repairs to the furnace refractory should be made at this time. All pipe plugs on cross connections to the water column, feedwater regulator, gauge glass, and low water fuel cutoff must be removed.

The feedwater regulator and low water fuel cutoff float chambers must also be opened for internal examination. The operator should be on hand to assist the boiler inspector and identify any trouble spots that are present.

The boiler inspector examines the boiler on the steam, fire, and water side, looking for signs of corrosion, overheating, and/or other damage. The chief engineer must make any necessary repairs identified by the boiler inspector.

When the inspection of the boiler is complete, some states require that a written report be filed with the state department of labor and industry. A new boiler certificate may then be issued.

Boiler Inspection Procedures

When preparing a boiler for inspection, specific procedures must be followed in the correct sequence to prevent injury to the operator and damage to the boiler.

1. Always cool a boiler slowly to prevent undue stress to the boiler metal and refractory.

2. Do not allow a vacuum to form on a boiler coming off-line. A vacuum causes stress on the boiler and is dangerous to operating personnel when opening up the steam and water side of the boiler.

3. Secure, lock, and tag out the main steam stop valves and feedwater valves to the boiler. This prevents steam or water from backing into the boiler that has been taken off-line for cleaning and inspection.

4. Never dump a hot boiler because dumping can cause sludge and sediment to

bake onto the heating surfaces. Sludge and sediment are difficult to remove.

5. Never dump a boiler unless it is ready to be opened and flushed out.

6. Always check to make sure that the boiler vent is open before opening the manhole cover to see that there is no vacuum or pressure in the steam and water drum.

7. Secure, lock, and tag out the bottom blowdown valves after dumping, or remove the valves and blank flange the blowdown lines to the blowdown tank.

8. Never enter the steam and water side of the boiler unless you have personally checked to make sure the steam stop valves, feedwater lines, and bottom blowdown lines are properly secured, locked, and tagged out.

9. Never enter the steam and water side of the boiler with a conventional droplight. Use a spotlight or a low voltage droplight to prevent electrocution.

10. Always use approved ladders or scaffolding when cleaning the boiler.

The operator must follow specific procedures if the boiler is to be put back into service after inspection. The steam and water side of the boiler must be inspected for any tools, rags, or other equipment left behind.

A wrench or screwdriver left inside could find its way to a bottom blowdown valve, causing it to jam open. Then the boiler would have to be removed from service, cooled, and dumped so repairs could be made. The steam and water side is then closed up using new gaskets.

All pipe plugs on cross connections that were removed must be replaced. The feedwater regulator and low water fuel cutoff must be completely reassembled, using new gaskets when necessary. Chemically treated water is added to the boiler to bring it close to its NOWL.

Hydrostatic Test

The hydrostatic test is a test of the strength of materials and is applied to all new boilers.

The test is also applied to boilers after any repair work is done on the steam or water side or on boilers that have had a low water condition develop.

When a hydrostatic test is applied on a boiler, the main steam stop valves must be secured. The drains between the two steam stop valves must be left open. This prevents any water buildup if the valve closest to the boiler leaks. The high and low water alarm whistles must be removed and the openings plugged.

The safety valves are blanked or gagged, and the boiler vent is closed after the boiler is full of water at a temperature of 100°F. Gagging of the safety valve is applying a clamp on the valve spindle to keep the valve in full closed position. The water pressure is increased $1\frac{1}{2}$ times the safety valve setting by using a hand pump.

The pressure is then lowered to the safety valve setting. The boiler is inspected for leaks or bulging. When the hydrostatic test and boiler inspection are completed, gags must be removed and safety valves and alarm whistles replaced. **WARNING: Misapplication of gags can result in safety valve seat or spindle damage. Always follow manufacturer's recommendations for applying gags.**

BOILER LAY-UP

Boiler lay-up is done when the boiler will be out of service for an extended period of time. The two ways to lay-up a boiler are the *wet method* and the *dry method*. The chief engineer determines which method must be used.

The method of lay-up used depends on the length of lay-up time and on plant conditions. If the boiler may be needed on short notice, the wet method is recommended. If the boiler will not be needed for a long time or if the boiler may freeze up, the dry method is recommended.

Dry Lay-up

Since the boiler has just been inspected, it should be thoroughly clean on the fire side and the steam and water side. The operator must inspect the fire side and the steam and water side for any material that may have been left during cleaning or inspection.

The boiler must be dried out completely. Steam and water lines must be secured to ensure no moisture enters the boiler. Trays of moisture-absorbing chemicals should be placed in the steam and water side of the boiler.

The steam and water side of the boiler should then be closed up using new gaskets. These chemicals must be inspected periodically and replaced as necessary. The ASME code recommends the use of quick lime or silica gel.

Wet Lay-up

The wet lay-up method is preferred if the boiler may be needed on short notice. The boiler must be thoroughly cleaned on the fire side and the steam and water side to prevent corrosion. After inspecting the steam and water side for materials that may have been left inside during inspection, close it up using new gaskets.

Fill the boiler with warm, chemically treated water at approximately 100°F until it comes out of the boiler vent. This prevents sweating caused by condensation formed because of the difference in temperature of the water in the boiler and the air in the boiler room. Secure the boiler vent and maintain a pressure in the boiler slightly above atmospheric pressure.

EMERGENCY PROCEDURES IN BOILER OPERATION

Emergency procedures specify the exact actions to be taken in the event of an emergency. Emergency procedures vary from plant to plant. The chief engineer is responsible for establishing emergency procedures to handle any situations that may occur in the plant. All operating personnel should be familiar with the emergency procedures.

The chief engineer is responsible for training operators in the established emergency procedures for a specific steam plant. Emergency procedures should be clearly posted and available to all operating personnel.

The boiler operator must act quickly when correcting the two most common conditions that could lead to an emergency: high or low water levels in a boiler and flame failure. If improper action is taken during an emergency, the boiler or furnace could explode.

High or Low Water in a Boiler

Having either high or low water in a boiler is unsafe. Steam boilers are equipped with low water fuel cutoff controls and alarms or high and low water whistles to alert the boiler operator so proper action can be taken.

Many boilers have a high or low water condition. This condition is caused by operator neglect, faulty controls, or boiler failure. The extent of overheating or damage to the boiler is determined by how quickly the operator reacts to remedy the condition. Tube and furnace distortion can result from a low water condition in a boiler. See Figure 11-20.

If the operator cannot see water in the gauge glass or get a water level reading from some secondary means, a low water condition exists and the fuel must be secured. Low water condition procedures vary depending on the type of boiler and the fuel being used. When in doubt about the water level in a boiler, secure the fires immediately.

Air flow must be reduced to allow the boiler to cool slowly. The boiler should be taken out of service and thoroughly examined for any in-

Figure 11-20. Tube and furnace distortion is the result of overheating caused by a low water level. (*Factory Mutual System*)

dication of overheating. If more than one boiler is on the line and only one boiler is having difficulty maintaining its water level, the following steps should be taken.

1. Secure the fuel to the burner of the boiler with the low water condition.
2. Maintain the NOWL on all boilers on the line.
3. Secure the feedwater to the boiler in question if the water level cannot be maintained in all boilers to protect other boilers in the system.

With a low water condition, the steam boiler drum, tubes, and furnace are endangered. With a high water condition, the superheater tubes, headers, and steam equipment such as pumps and turbines are endangered.

Any time the water level in a steam boiler is three-quarters of a gauge glass or higher, water may be carried over with steam. The water level should be corrected immediately. This may require using the bottom blowdown valves. A NOWL in a steam boiler varies from one-third to one-half of a gauge glass. In most plants today, high water alarms and whistles warn the operator of a high water condition in the boiler.

Both steam and water lines to the gauge glass must be kept clean to prevent false water level readings. If the top line to the gauge glass is closed or clogged, the glass would become filled with water. If the bottom line to the gauge glass is closed or clogged, there will be a stationary water level reading (no movement).

This would allow the gauge glass to fill with water caused by steam condensing at the top. If the reading on the gauge glass is questionable, the operator should use a secondary means to determine the boiler water level and then correct the clogged lines.

Flame Failure

Flame failure occurs when the flame in the furnace has been unintentionally lost. A flame failure is one of the most common causes of a furnace explosion.

A furnace explosion is the ignition and instantaneous combustion of explosive or highly flammable gas, vapor, or dust accumulated in a boiler setting. In minor explosions, known as puffs, flarebacks, or blowbacks, flames may blow suddenly for a distance of many feet from all firing and access doors. Furnace explosions can cause personal injuries and costly damage to boiler plants.

Flame failures in a plant fired by fuel oil are caused by cold fuel oil, water in the fuel oil, air in the fuel oil lines, clogged strainers, a clogged burner tip, and/or loss of fuel oil pressure.

Flame failures in a gas-fired plant are caused by insufficient pressure in gas lines and/or water in the gas. Flame failures in a plant fired by pulverized coal are caused by wet coal, loss of primary air, and/or loss of coal to the pulverizing mill caused by feeder failure or blockage.

In a plant protected by automatic controls, the operator checks the firebox for signs of excess fuel. The controls are reset and the burner is put through a purge cycle and a firing cycle.

Not all boilers are equipped with automatic flame failure controls. Small package boilers are equipped with a scanner or similar device that prevents the main fuel valve from opening if the pilot fails. The scanner also shuts the main fuel valve if the main flame is lost.

Most large plants rely on the boiler operator to handle flame failures safely. When a flame failure occurs, the operator must quickly secure the fuel and purge the furnace.

The cause of the flame failure must be determined before the furnace is lit again. If flame failure occurs in large plants that have no automatic shutdown, the boiler operator must secure the fuel and manually purge the boiler to prevent a furnace explosion.

The operator must be thoroughly familiar with the equipment and follow the manufacturer's specifications on length of purge and number of air changes required before trying a new lightoff. Under no circumstances should a burner be lit off the hot brickwork or another burner because this can result in a serious explosion.

ROUTINE BOILER PLANT MAINTENANCE

Routine boiler plant maintenance can extend the life of the equipment and reduce downtime. The type of preventive maintenance program varies with each plant, depending on the type of equipment in use. Each plant should establish specific daily, weekly, monthly, semi-annual, and/or annual maintenance schedules.

A preventive maintenance program includes an annual internal and external boiler inspection, as recommended by the ASME code. During this inspection, the boiler and all fittings and controls are inspected to determine if they are in proper working order.

One of the components used most in the steam boiler system is valves. Valves are automatically or hand-operated. Because of the important role of hand-operated valves in the boiler system, proper functioning is imperative. To ensure the proper operation of valves, never use undue force when opening or closing a valve. If the valve is difficult to move, service may be required.

Never use a gate valve for throttling service because it may leak around the gate afterward. Apply only recommended lubricants to packing, per manufacturer's specifications.

Never tighten the packing gland on the valve too tight because it may damage the valve permanently. Routine maintenance procedures performed on valves include replacing packing, glands, gaskets, and/or valve stems. In addition, seats, gates, and discs must be reground or replaced as necessary.

Automatic valves have diaphragms and pilot valves, which also receive preventive maintenance on a regular basis. New gaskets should always be installed before assembling a reconditioned valve. Gaskets for line flanges on a flange-connected valve should be replaced when reinstalling.

The boiler operator is also responsible for several other preventive maintenance duties, including the following tasks.

1. Clean and grease pump and motor bearings once or twice a year. Clean and flush oil pumps on turbine auxiliaries,

following manufacturer's operating procedures.

2. Drain air compressor tanks of condensate every shift. Change compressor oil according to manufacturer's recommended procedure.

3. Repack auxiliary pumps when excessive leakage is evident.

4. Monitor and clean blades on draft fans whenever there is a sign of buildup on the blades or excessive vibration occurs.

5. Clean dirty gauge glass. Replace a gauge glass if it is broken or leaking. The type of gauge glass to be replaced determines the removal and installation procedures required. (See Chapter 2 for information about gauge glasses.)

The boiler operator is also in charge of feedwater pumps, vacuum pumps, oil pumps, and sump pumps. In some plants, boiler operators are expected to perform minor repairs and service on boiler room equipment.

Packing glands and mechanical seals require lubrication or flushing with water to assure good operation. When shaft pump seals start leaking, the seal must be completely replaced. Shaft packing can be adjusted with the packing gland nuts to ensure minimum leakage from the pump. When there is excessive leakage due to packing or shaft wear, the packing and/or shaft must be replaced.

Bearings, unless sealed, require lubrication. See Figure 11-21. Follow the manufacturer's

Figure 11-21. Bearings are lubricated as part of routine boiler plant maintenance.

specifications for the type of lubricant to use.

When bearings are worn, they should be replaced. If worn bearings are not replaced, damage to the shaft or bearing housing can result. The operator should observe the general operating condition of each pump. If a pump starts to drop in efficiency because of mechanical wear, the pump must be removed from service for a general overhaul.

Many plants have a preventive maintenance schedule set up for all pump overhauls. Proper maintenance and service to pumps can extend their life for many years.

Cleaning New or Retubed Boilers

During the boiler manufacturing process, boiler steam and water sides are contaminated by oil, grease, and other organic matter. These contaminants must be removed to allow optimum heat transfer on the heating surfaces of the boiler tubes. In addition, these contaminants can cause surface impurities in the boiler water, resulting in increased surface tension that may lead to carryover.

A good cleaning agent, such as an alkaline detergent solution, will remove oil, grease, and other foreign matter from drums, tubes, and headers within the boiler. Follow the manufacturer's recommendations when cleaning a new or retubed boiler.

BOILER ROOM SAFETY

Boiler room safety must be constantly exercised by all boiler room personnel. Most large industrial plants have safety engineers who identify hazards in the boiler room. Safety engineers design safe operating procedures to prevent plant accidents.

Industrial accidents can cause injuries and death. In addition, plant downtime caused by accidents is very costly. Key factors in maintaining boiler room safety include boiler operator safety, the reporting of accidents, and fire prevention.

Boiler Operator Safety

The boiler operator is the person responsible for the safe and efficient operation of the boiler.

STUDY SAFTEY FOR TEST

The boiler operator must develop safety habits to prevent personal injury, injury to others, and damage to equipment. Safety rules vary depending on the type and size of the plant. However, the basic safety rules listed are common to all boiler rooms.

1. Wear approved clothing and shoes in the plant at all times.

2. Wear appropriate eye protection in all designated areas. Use hand shields when visually inspecting the furnace fire.

3. Do not use hands to stop moving equipment.

4. Wear gloves when handling hot lines or cleaning fuel oil burner tips.

5. Always use low voltage droplights when working inside boiler steam and water drums.

6. Always secure and tag steam stop valves, bottom blowdown valves, and feedwater valves when a boiler in battery is removed from service for cleaning and inspection.

7. Open the boiler vent to prevent a vacuum from forming before opening manhole and handhole covers.

8. Do not use unsafe ladders or substitutes for ladders.

9. Do not leave loose tools on ladders, catwalks, tops of boilers, or scaffolds.

10. Do not carry tools in back pockets.

11. Do not throw a tool to anyone at any time.

12. Use the proper tool for the job.

13. Do not use defective tools.

14. Never start any equipment that has been tagged out for safety reasons.

15. Precheck all equipment for starting hazards.

16. Wear goggles and respirators when cleaning the fire side of the boiler, breeching, or chimney.

17. Make sure the equipment has been secured and tagged out before attempting to clean or repair.

18. Clean up liquid spills at once.

19. Store all oily rags or waste in approved containers to prevent fires caused by spontaneous combustion.

20. Only use approved safety cans to store cleaning solvents.

21. Check all fire safety equipment on a regular basis to be sure it is in proper working condition.

22. Check fire extinguishers periodically for proper charge and correct location.

23. Move quickly and with purpose in emergencies, but do not run.

24. Make repairs on live equipment only in extreme emergencies.

25. Personally double check the plant and equipment before starting up or making repairs. Do not take any boiler function for granted.

26. Always report any unsafe condition in the plant to the immediate superior.

Reporting Accidents

Most plants have a specific procedure for reporting accidents. The boiler operator must become familiar with how to report an accident. Even if safety rules are followed conscientiously, the possibility of an accident always exists.

All accidents should be reported regardless of their nature. If complications arise as the result of an accident that was not reported or put on file, serious problems can occur regarding insurance claims.

Accident reports commonly include the following information: date, time and place of accident, immediate superior, name of injured person, nature of injury, what injured person was doing at time of accident, and cause of accident. See Figure 11-22. Accident reports are also used to document plant safety records.

Boiler Room Fire Prevention

Boiler room fire prevention procedures are necessary because of the combustible nature of the materials used in the boiler room. Combustible materials burn readily and require special handling by the boiler operator.

Insurance statistics reveal that there are approximately 400 industrial fires in the United States every day. The boiler operator must know what is necessary to start and sustain

Company Name	Plant Protection Department	AMBULANCE, INJURY AND SICK REPORT

Date	Time _____ ☐AM ☐PM

Type of Call:

☐ Ambulance   ☐ Injury

☐ Doctor   ☐ Sickness

Requested By	Phone Extension

Name of Sick or Injured

Dept. No.	Index No.	Division

Street Address

City, State and Zipcode

Plant Location of Sick or Injured Person

Taken to *(Name of Hospital or Doctor)*	Location *(City of Hospital or Doctor)*

Taken By:

☐ Ambulance   ☐ Taxi   ☐ Private Auto

Describe Injury or Illness

WITNESSES

Full Name	Dept. No.	Index No.	Division
Full Name	Dept. No.	Index No.	Division
Full Name	Dept. No.	Index No.	Division

GUARDS RESPONDING

Name	Name	Name

BRIEF SUMMARY

Name of Guard Submitting Report	Date Report Submitted

Figure 11-22. All accidents should be reported and recorded using an accident report form.

a fire in order to know how to put the fire out.

Fuel (combustible material), heat, and oxygen are required to start and sustain a fire. The fire will go out when any one of these is removed. See Figure 11-23. Fuel may be fuel oil, wood, paper, textiles, or any other material that burns readily. The fuel must be heated to its ignition temperature. Oxygen is required to support the combustion process.

Since the main ingredient is the combustible material, waste or oily rags must be stored in safety containers and volatile liquids in safety cans. By maintaining careful control of the combustible materials in a boiler room, the danger of a fire hazard is reduced.

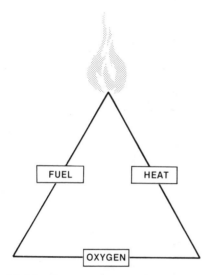

Figure 11-23. Fuel, oxygen, and heat are required to support combustion. The fire will go out when any one is removed.

Classes of Fires. The class of fire is determined by the combustible material burned. The three most common classes of fire are Class A, Class B, and Class C. Class A includes fires that burn wood, paper, textiles, and other ordinary combustible material containing carbon. Class B includes fires that burn oil, gas, grease, paint, or other liquids that convert into gas when heated. Class C includes electrical, motor, and transformer fires.

Class D is a rare, specialized class of fires including fires caused by combustible metals such as zirconium, titanium, magnesium, sodium, or potassium. A special powder is used to put out this class of fire and may be applied with a scoop or shovel.

The boiler operator must know where every fire extinguisher is located in the boiler room and plant. The boiler operator must also know what type of fire extinguisher is used for each class of fire and how to use different types of fire extinguishers. See Figure 11-24.

Fire extinguishers are not meant to take the place of the plant fire brigade or the local fire department. Fire extinguishers are only meant to put out small fires or help to contain larger ones until additional help arrives.

The number and type of fire extinguishers needed are determined by the authority having jurisdiction and are based on how fast a fire may spread, potential heat intensity, and accessibility to the fire. Additional fire extinguishers must be installed in hazardous areas. The National Fire Protection Association lists these areas as *light hazard* (low), *ordinary hazard* (moderate), and *extra hazard* (high).

Light hazard areas include buildings or rooms that are used as churches, offices, classrooms, and assembly halls. The contents in buildings and rooms of this nature are either noncombustible or not anticipated to be arranged in a manner that would be conducive to the rapid spread of a fire. Class B flammables (for example, fluid for duplicating machines) stored in a light hazard area must be stored in closed containers.

Ordinary hazard areas include shops and related storage facilities, light manufacturing plants, automobile showrooms, and parking garages. Additionally, ordinary hazard areas include any location where Class A combustibles and Class B flammables exceed those expected for light hazard areas.

Extra hazard areas are those locations where Class A combustibles and Class B flammables exceed those expected in ordinary hazard areas. Extra hazard areas include woodworking shops, manufacturing plants using painting or dipping, and automotive repair shops.

196 *HIGH PRESSURE BOILERS*

Each class of fire calls for the right kind of extinguisher. Using the wrong extinguisher is dangerous and may do more harm than good. For your own protection, you should know the classes of fire, the different types of extinguishers, how to use them and why.

Type of Agent	Tri-Class Dry Chemical Monoammonium Phosphate	Regular Dry Chemical Sodium Bicarbonate	Carbon Dioxide	Water
 **A** Fires in ordinary combustible materials—paper, wood, fabrics, rubber, and may plastics. Quenching by water or insulating by Multi-Purpose (ABC) dry chemical is effective.	**Yes—excellent** Adheres to burning materials and forms a coating which smothers the fire and minimizes reflash.	**No**	**No**	**Yes** Water saturates material and prevents rekindling.
 **B** Fires in flammable liquids—gasoline, oils, greases, tars, paints, laquers, and flammable gases. Multi-Purpose (ABC), Regular Dry Chemical, Halon 1211, and Carbon Dioxide agents smother these fires.	**Yes—excellent** Dry chemical agent smothers fire. Screen of agent shields user(s) from heat.	**Yes—excellent** Dry chemical agent smothers fire. Screen of agent shields user(s) from heat.	**Yes—excellent** Carbon dioxide leaves no residue, and may not normally affect or damage equipment.	**No** Water spreads flammable liquids and does not put it out.
 **C** Fires in live electrical equipment—motors, generators, switches, and appliances—where a non-conducting extinguishing agent Multi-Purpose (ABC), Regular Dry Chemical, Halon 1211, or Carbon Dioxide is required.	**Yes—excellent** Dry chemical agent is non-conductive. Screen of agent shields user(s) from heat.	**Yes—excellent** Dry chemical agent is non-conductive. Screen of agent shields user(s) from heat.	**Yes—excellent** Carbon dioxide is non-conductive, leaves no residue, and may not affect or damage electrical equipment.	**No** Water, a conductor, should never be used on live electrical fires.

Figure 11-24. Fire extinguishers are used to put out small fires and are classified by the combustible material burned. *(Walter Kidde)*

_C_

1. When taking over a shift, the boiler operator must first check _____.
   A. the boiler room log
   B. the fuel oil supply
   C. the water level on all boilers that are on the line by blowing down the water column and gauge glass
   D. the bottom blowdown valves

_D_

2. The duties of a boiler operator taking over a shift are to _____ _____.
   A. test the low water fuel cutoff control
   B. inspect and check the feedwater pumps, bearings, and all lubrication oil levels
   C. check the burner and the fire for correct flame, including the fuel temperature and pressure
   D. all of the above

_A_

3. The low water fuel cutoff control can be tested _____.
   A. by blowing down the low water fuel cutoff or allowing the water level in the boiler to drop
   B. with the burner in operation or when the blowdown valve is used
   C. when the fuel valve is opened or when sludge and sediment has to be removed
   D. by an evaporation test or with the feedwater pump

_B_

4. The purpose of a flame failure control is to protect the boiler from _____ _____.
   A. a possible boiler explosion
   B. a possible furnace explosion
   C. exceeding its MAWP
   D. starting in low fire

_D_

5. The operator in charge of a shift must maintain a boiler room log that indicates _____.
   A. system pressures
   B. steam flow and water consumption
   C. fuel consumption and the operation of auxiliary equipment
   D. hourly readings of all pertinent steam plant data

_C_

6. Regardless of the type of fuel being used, before lighting off a boiler during a cold start-up, the operator must first _____.
   A. close all hand-operated outlet dampers
   B. close all boiler main steam stop valves
   C. check for the correct boiler water level
   D. close all drains on the main steam lines and headers

_____C_____ 7. After establishing the proper boiler water level, the burner may be lit off after _____.
  A. purging the steam and water drum
  B. venting the drum condenser
  C. purging the furnace
  D. purging the superheater

_____D_____ 8. In order to prevent uneven expansion of the boiler on a cold start-up, the boiler must be _____.
  A. brought up to full steam pressure as quickly as possible
  B. thoroughly vented
  C. heated using steam from outside sources
  D. warmed up slowly

_____D_____ 9. According to the ASME code, the boiler vent should remain open until a pressure of approximately _____ psi is on the boiler.
  A. 5
  B. 10
  C. 15
  D. 25

_____B_____ 10. The automatic nonreturn valve on a boiler being cut in on the line should be opened when the steam pressure on the boiler reaches _____.
  A. the line pressure
  B. 75% to 85% of the line pressure
  C. 5 to 10 pounds above line pressure
  D. 5 to 10 pounds below line pressure

_____C_____ 11. It is good operating procedure to test the safety valve on the incoming boiler by hand _____.
  A. after the boiler is cut in on the line
  B. when the boiler reaches 50 psi
  C. before the boiler is cut in on the line
  D. before the boiler burner is lit off

_____A_____ 12. The free-blowing drain between the boiler's automatic nonreturn valve and the main steam stop valve should be _____ the boiler is cut in on the line.
  A. closed as soon as
  B. closed before
  C. opened as soon as
  D. closed just before

_____C_____ 13. When cutting a boiler in on a line equipped with two hand-operated steam stop valves, the steam pressure on the boiler should be _____ line pressure.
  A. slightly higher than
  B. equal to
  C. slightly lower than
  D. at any pressure above 75% of

_____B_____ 14. Boilers equipped with a superheater must be protected during warm-up by _____.

    A. keeping the superheater drain valve closed until the boiler is cut in on the line
    B. keeping the superheater drain valve open until the boiler is cut in on the line
    C. passing the feedwater through the superheater tubes
    D. bypassing the superheater tubes

_____B_____ 15. Superheaters are prevented from overheating by the circulation of _____.

    A. air
    B. steam
    C. water
    D. gases of combustion

_____D_____ 16. Before and after the boiler has been cut in on the line, the boiler operator should _____.

    A. check the steam, feedwater, and fuel lines for signs of leakage
    B. test the low water fuel cutoff and the flame failure control
    C. test the boiler safety valves with at least 75% of line pressure
    D. all of the above

_____C_____ 17. When the steam pressure in the boiler has dropped to 25 psi, the _____ should be opened.

    A. safety valve
    B. free-blowing drain
    C. boiler vent
    D. bottom blowdown valve

_____A_____ 18. As the boiler is cooling down, the boiler operator must maintain a _____.

    A. NOWL
    B. normal draft condition
    C. normal feedwater temperature
    D. 10% CO_2 reading

_____C_____ 19. To prepare a boiler for inspection, the boiler must be _____.

    A. cleaned only on the fire side
    B. cleaned only on the water side
    C. cleaned on both the fire and water sides
    D. inspected before being cleaned

_____B_____ 20. After a boiler has had major repair work made on its steam or water side or has developed a low water condition, it should be subjected to _____.

    A. an accumulation test
    B. a hydrostatic test   *STRUTURAL INTERGRETY TEST*
    C. an evaporation test
    D. both an accumulation and a hydrostatic test

_____ A   21. When performing a hydrostatic test, the pressure on the boiler should not exceed _____.
   A. 1½ times the safety valve setting
   B. 2½ times the safety valve setting
   C. 6% above the MAWP   *SAFTEY VALVE SETTING*
   D. 2 times the working pressure

_____ D   22. Boilers that are out of service for an extended period of time can be _____ _____.
   A. stored with a NOWL
   B. filled with oxygen
   C. filled with CO_2
   D. layed up either wet or dry

_____ C   23. If there is a danger of the boiler freezing, the boiler should be layed up _____.
   A. with a light fire
   B. by using steam from the header to keep the boiler warm
   C. completely dry
   D. by using an antifreeze

_____ D   24. Plant emergency procedures should be established by the _____.
   A. operator on duty
   B. insurance inspector
   C. ASME code
   D. chief engineer

_____ C   25. The whistle valve, which is located in the boiler water column, _____ _____.
   A. secures the burner in the event of high water
   B. secures the burner in the event of low water
   C. warns the operator of high or low water
   D. is not found on steam boilers

_____ B   26. A low water fuel cutoff _____.
   A. shuts the boiler down
   B. shuts off the fuel supply
   C. adds water to the boiler
   D. purges the boiler firebox

_____ A   27. A boiler that has experienced a low water condition should be _____ _____.
   A. thoroughly examined for signs of overheating
   B. thoroughly examined for scale buildup
   C. brought up to full steam pressure to test for leaks
   D. brought up to the NOWL

_____ C   28. A high water level condition in the boiler can be corrected by using _____ _____ blowdown.
   A. continuous
   B. surface
   C. bottom
   D. waterwall

_B_

29. If a boiler that was on-line is down because of low steam pressure, the cause is _____.
  A. a stuck automatic nonreturn valve
  B. either a flame failure or a low water condition
  C. a low water condition only
  D. a flame failure only

_B_

30. Flame failure controls are _____.
  A. found on all boilers
  B. equipped with a scanner or similar device
  C. found only on high pressure boilers
  D. found only on low pressure boilers

_D_

31. A furnace explosion can be caused by _____.
  A. excess draft
  B. a low water condition
  C. an overheated furnace
  D. an accumulation of combustible gases

_B_

32. The ASME code recommends that boilers be inspected internally and externally every _____.
  A. 6 months
  B. year
  C. 2 years
  D. 3 years

_D_

33. Preventive maintenance of boiler room equipment _____.
  A. extends the life of the equipment
  B. increases overall efficiency
  C. promotes plant safety and reduces downtime
  D. all of the above

_C_

34. If a gauge glass breaks when the boiler is under pressure, _____
_____.
  A. the boiler must be removed from service
  B. the boiler inspector must be notified
  C. the operator should change the gauge glass following safe operating procedures
  D. the boiler may be operated using a secondary means of checking the water level until the boiler can be taken off-line

_A_

35. New or retubed boilers should be cleaned with _____.
  A. an alkaline detergent solution
  B. a degreasing agent
  C. a high pressure water hose
  D. a steam lance

_B_

36. The primary purpose of establishing a set of plant safety rules is to _____
_____.
  A. increase plant efficiency
  B. protect workers and equipment
  C. comply with government regulations
  D. increase employment opportunities for safety engineers

_____C_____ 37. Reporting accidents is the responsibility of the _____.
A. plant engineer
B. safety engineer
C. person involved
D. insurance inspector

_____B_____ 38. When someone finds an unsafe condition in the plant, that person should report it to _____.
A. the shop steward
B. the immediate superior
C. the insurance inspector
D. the plant personnel department

_____D_____ 39. The three ingredients needed to start a fire are _____, _____, and _____.
A. fuel, heat, CO_2
B. fuel, combustible material, CO_2
C. fuel, heat, nitrogen
D. fuel, heat, oxygen

_____B_____ 40. A fire caused by oil, gas, grease, or paint would be classified as a Class _____ fire.
A. A
B. B
C. C
D. D

_____D_____ 41. Locations where painting or dipping is performed are examples of a(n) _____ hazard area.
A. light
B. moderate
C. ordinary
D. extra

_____A_____ 42. The low water fuel cutoff control should be blown down _____.
A. once a shift
B. weekly
C. monthly
D. during manual inspection

Chapter 12

TESTING

Licensing examinations are given for the purpose of licensing boiler operators and stationary engineers. These licensing examinations ensure that boiler operators are qualified to operate and maintain steam boilers and their related equipment.

Not every state has licensing requirements. However, states that do not issue a state license may require operators to obtain a license through a local municipal certifying agency. Any person preparing to take a licensing examination should be aware of all requirements set by the certifying agency.

Licensing agencies may have specific requirements governing age, experience, and knowledge of equipment operation expected of the operator. In addition, registration fees, identification, and specific writing utensils may be required.

The number of questions on a licensing examination varies from agency to agency. The questions in this chapter give an indication of the scope of a licensing examination.

LICENSING EXAMINATION

QUESTIONS

1. A low pressure steam boiler has a maximum allowable working pressure (MAWP) of up to _____
   A. 15 psi
   B. 35 psi
   C. 100 psi
   D. no MAWP

2. The evaporation of 34.5 pounds of water per hour from and at a feedwater temperature of 212°F is defined as _____
   A. a factor of evaporation
   B. one boiler horsepower
   C. latent heat of fusion
   D. an evaporation test

3. In a fire tube boiler, the heat and gases of combustion pass _____
   A. through the tubes
   B. around the tubes
   C. only through the combustion chamber
   D. both A and B

4. A fire tube boiler may be used _____
   A. only in low pressure plants
   B. only in high pressure plants
   C. in high or low pressure plants
   D. only for process steam

5. Because of the large volume of water, the boiler most likely to cause a boiler explosion is _____
   A. a water tube boiler
   B. a fire tube boiler
   C. either a water tube or fire tube boiler
   D. boilers cannot explode

6. As steam pressure in a boiler increases, there is a corresponding increase in the _____
   A. temperature
   B. superheat
   C. volume of steam
   D. boiler horsepower

7. A sudden drop in boiler steam pressure without a corresponding drop in boiler water temperature could result in _____
   A. a loss of efficiency
   B. a boiler explosion
   C. an increase in surface tension
   D. no effect on the boiler

KEY TO ARROWHEAD SYMBOLS			
△ - Air	▲ - Water	▲ - Fuel Oil	⌂ - Air to Atmosphere
◭ - Gas	△ - Steam	◬ - Condensate	◩ - Gases of Combustion

The following agencies, municipalities, and states have provided sample test questions that are included in this chapter.

1. Block and Associates
   5700 S.W. 34th Street, #1303
   Gainesville, FL 32608

2. Alaska Department of Labor
   Mechanical Inspection Division
   3301 Eagle Street, Suite 301
   Pouch 7-020
   Anchorage, AK 99510

3. Arkansas Department of Labor
   Boiler Inspection Division
   1022 High Street
   P.O. Box 1797-72203
   Little Rock, AR 72202

4. The Commonwealth of Massachusetts
   Department of Public Safety
   Engineering Section,
      Division of Inspection
   John W. McCormack Building
   One Ashburton Place
   Boston, MA 02108

5. State of Ohio
   Department of Industrial Relations
   2323 West Fifth Avenue
   P.O. Box 825
   Columbus, OH 43216

6. City of Dearborn
   Department of Public Works
   Building & Safety Division
   Town Hall Annex West
   4500 Maple Street
   Dearborn, MI 48126

7. City of Elgin
   150 Dexter Court
   Elgin, IL 60120

8. City of Milwaukee
   Building Inspection and
      Safety Engineering
   Room 1008
   841 North Broadway
   Milwaukee, WI 53202

9. City of Philadelphia
   Department of Licenses and
      Inspections
   Municipal Services Building
   Philadelphia, PA 19102

10. Salt Lake City Corporation
    Department of Building
       and Housing Services
    412 City and County Building
    Salt Lake City, UT 84111

11. City of Sioux City
    Board of Examiners of
       Mechanical Stationary Engineers
    Inspection Services Division
    City Hall, 6th & Douglas
    P.O. Box 447
    Sioux City, IA 51102

12. City of Terre Haute
    Office of the Board
       of Examining Engineers
    City Hall
    Terre Haute, IN 47802

13. Province of Alberta
    Labour
    General Safety Services Division
    Boilers Branch
    6th Floor, 10808
    99 Avenue
    Edmonton
    Alberta, Canada, T5K OG2

_____ 1. The bottom blowdown on a boiler _____.
   A. removes sludge and sediment from the mud drum
   B. reduces boiler steam pressure
   C. adds makeup to the boiler
   D. increases boiler priming

_____ 2. Boiler tubes are sized using the _____.
   A. tube thickness
   B. circumference
   C. outside diameter
   D. inside diameter

_____ 3. A boiler fusible plug is brass or bronze with a core of _____.
   A. zinc
   B. tin
   C. titanium
   D. iron oxide

_____ 4. Spalling in a boiler refers to _____.
   A. hairline cracks in the steam drum
   B. hairline cracks in the refractory
   C. slugs of water in the steam
   D. water in the fuel oil

_____ 5. Boiler horsepower is the evaporation of _____ pounds of water per hour from and at a feedwater temperature of 212°F.
   A. 34.5
   B. 180
   C. 345
   D. 970.3

_____ 6. The pH of the boiler water should be _____.
   A. 1.5 to 2
   B. 3.5 to 6
   C. 9 to 10
   D. 14 to 18

_____ 7. The boiler superheater raises the temperature of the _____.
   A. feedwater
   B. gases of combustion
   C. air for combustion
   D. steam leaving the boiler

_____ 8. An economizer is used to preheat _____.
   A. air for combustion
   B. fuel oil
   C. feedwater
   D. condensate

9. Fires caused by spontaneous combustion would probably start in the _____.
   A. fuel oil tank
   B. oily waste rags
   C. boiler firebox
   D. boiler ash pit

10. A high suction reading on the fuel oil pressure gauge indicates _____.
   A. dirty strainers
   B. a high tank temperature
   C. dirty burners
   D. leaky pump packing

11. The _____ is a secondary means of determining boiler water level.
   A. water column
   B. gauge glass blowdown valve
   C. high and low water alarm
   D. try cock

12. A(n) _____ is used to measure furnace temperature.
   A. Fyrite analyzer
   B. pyrometer
   C. Orsat analyzer
   D. Ringelmann chart

13. A siphon installed between the boiler and the pressure gauge protects the Bourdon tube from _____.
   A. water
   B. the gases of combustion
   C. steam temperature
   D. steam pressure

14. The range of a boiler pressure gauge must not be less than _____ times the safety valve setting.
   A. 1½
   B. 2
   C. 2½
   D. 3

15. Boiler feedwater is chemically treated to _____.
   A. increase circulation
   B. increase oxygen concentration
   C. prevent formation of scale
   D. decrease boiler makeup

16. Pressure gauges are calibrated with a(n) _____.
   A. pressure gauge pump
   B. Orsat analyzer
   C. lightweight tester
   D. deadweight tester

17. In a fire tube boiler, soot settles on the _____.
    A. inside tube surface
    B. outside tube surface
    C. waterwall surface
    D. lowest part of the water side

18. Carbon dioxide in the flue gas is a sign of _____ combustion.
    A. perfect
    B. complete
    C. incomplete
    D. half-complete

19. Carbon monoxide in the flue gas is a sign of _____ combustion.
    A. perfect
    B. complete
    C. incomplete
    D. half-complete

20. _____ valves should be used for throttling services.
    A. Check
    B. Globe
    C. Gate
    D. Swing

21. A gradual increase in chimney temperature indicates _____.
    A. a broken baffle
    B. good combustion
    C. a high Btu content in the fuel
    D. a dirty heating surface

22. The pressure applied on the boiler during a hydrostatic test is _____ times the MAWP.
    A. 1½
    B. 2
    C. 2½
    D. 3

23. Boiler safety valve capacity must be such that the steam pressure can never go higher than _____ % above the MAWP.
    A. 4
    B. 5
    C. 6
    D. 10

24. As fuel oil is heated, its viscosity is _____.
    A. the same
    B. increased
    C. decreased
    D. ignited

_____ 25. No. _____ fuel oil has the highest Btu content per gallon.
   A. 1
   B. 2
   C. 4
   D. 6

T   F   **26.** All steam boilers must have one or more safety valves.

T   F   **27.** An open feedwater heater vents gases to the atmosphere.

T   F   **28.** A hydrostatic test will determine whether a steam boiler has sufficient relieving capacity.

T   F   **29.** When boilers are set in battery, the main steam stop valves, bottom blowdown valves, and feedwater valves should be locked closed before anyone enters the boiler drums.

T   F   **30.** Open and closed feedwater heaters are never used at the same time.

T   F   **31.** In an open feedwater heater, the water and steam come into direct contact; in a closed feedwater heater, the water and steam are separated.

T   F   **32.** An economizer is a fuel-saving device that reclaims heat from the gases of combustion.

T   F   **33.** Soot accumulation on the tubes of a water tube boiler does not affect the efficiency of the boiler.

T   F   **34.** Scale protects the boiler heating surfaces.

T   F   **35.** Boiler corrosion cannot be prevented as long as water is in contact with metal.

T   F   **36.** To prevent water hammer, water should be drained out of all high pressure steam lines.

T   F   **37.** Dry saturated steam is in a semigaseous state.

T   F   **38.** Pressure on water does not change the boiling point of the water.

T   F   **39.** The stop valve in a boiler feedwater line should have the pump discharge pressure on the top of the valve disc when the valve is closed.

T   F   **40.** According to the ASME code, weighted lever safety valves cannot be used on boilers.

T   F   **41.** The interior of the Bourdon tube in a steam pressure gauge is always filled with live steam when it is operating.

T   F   **42.** Safety valves on superheaters should be set to open before main safety valves on boilers.

T   F   **43.** When air preheaters or economizers are used in a boiler, induced draft is usually employed.

T   F   **44.** Waterwalls permit a greater heat release per cubic foot of furnace volume than refractory walls.

T   F   **45.** A steam trap is a device that removes air and condensate without loss of steam.

T	F	**46.** Steam traps are only used on high-temperature hot water systems.
T	F	**47.** Steam traps are used wherever air or condensate collects.
T	F	**48.** A boiler feedwater pump cannot become steambound.
T	F	**49.** In both fire tube and water tube boilers, the fire is inside the tubes.
T	F	**50.** Foaming can lead to carryover.

Identify the parts of the pop-type safety valve shown.

_____ **51.** Valve disc
_____ **52.** Huddling chamber
_____ **53.** Steam pressure
_____ **54.** Spring pressure

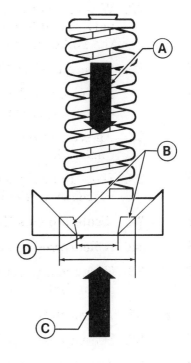

Identify the parts of the water column shown.

_____ **55.** Gauge glass
_____ **56.** Try cock
_____ **57.** Cross "T"
_____ **58.** Alarm whistle

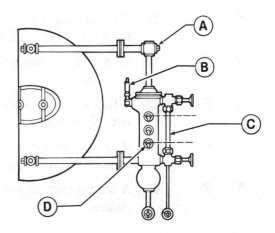

Identify the parts of the dry-top vertical fire tube boiler shown.

	59. Safety valve
_____	**60.** Siphon
_____	**61.** Staybolt
_____	**62.** Blowdown valve

Identify the parts of the wet-top vertical fire tube boiler shown.

	63. Handhole
_____	**64.** Try cocks
_____	**65.** Main steam valve
_____	**66.** Steam pressure gauge

Identify the parts of the low pressure gas burner system shown.

	67. Zero pressure gas chamber
_____	**68.** Gas and air to burner
_____	**69.** Air
_____	**70.** Gas

TEST 2

1. The rotary cup fuel oil burner must be adjusted so that the flame _____.
   A. hits all sides of the combustion chamber
   B. is bright yellow
   C. does not strike the rear wall of the combustion chamber
   D. is white hot

2. In a coal-fired boiler with a balanced draft system, the pressure over the fire should be approximately _____ ".
   A. −.02
   B. −.05
   C. +.2
   D. +.5

3. _____ is necessary to burn the volatile matter in coal more efficiently.
   A. Underfire air
   B. Overfire air
   C. An increased amount of moisture in coal
   D. Some anthracite coal

4. The induced draft fan is located between the _____ and _____.
   A. feedwater pump, heater
   B. first pass, heater
   C. boiler, economizer
   D. boiler, chimney

5. The flash point of fuel oil is the minimum temperature at which the fuel oil will _____.
   A. support combustion
   B. no longer flow
   C. flash when exposed to an open flame
   D. have its highest Btu content

6. The fire point of fuel oil is the minimum temperature at which the fuel oil will _____.
   A. burn continually
   B. no longer flow
   C. flash when exposed to an open flame
   D. have its highest Btu content

7. The pour point of fuel oil is the _____ temperature at which fuel oil will _____.
   A. lowest, burn
   B. lowest, flow
   C. highest, burn
   D. highest, flow

8. Fuel oil with a low flash point is _____.
   A. used with high pressure boilers
   B. dangerous to handle
   C. only used in low pressure plants
   D. heated to increase its viscosity

9. _____ dioxide is a major cause of air pollution, and is caused by burning fuel oil.
   A. Nitrous
   B. Vanadium
   C. Hydrogen
   D. Sulfur

10. In a closed feedwater heater, the steam and water _____.
    A. come into intimate contact
    B. only mix on the discharge side
    C. do not mix
    D. steam is never used in a closed feedwater heater

11. The operating range of a steam boiler is controlled by a(n) _____.
    A. pressure control
    B. air flow interlock
    C. scanner
    D. program clock

12. Water hammer in steam lines is caused by _____.
    A. low steam pressure
    B. high steam pressure
    C. condensation in the line
    D. a sudden drop in plant load

13. A manometer measures _____.
    A. flue gas temperature
    B. volume of air flow
    C. atmospheric pressure
    D. difference in pressure between two points

14. A barometer measures _____.
    A. flue gas temperature
    B. volume of air flow
    C. atmospheric pressure
    D. difference in air pressure

15. In boiler room work, HRT means _____.
    A. highly regulated therm
    B. high return tubular
    C. hot return tubular
    D. horizontal return tubular

16. Staybolts are used in box header water tube boilers to prevent _____ under internal pressure.
    A. bagging
    B. bulging
    C. sagging
    D. blistering

17. To ensure good heat transfer in a water tube boiler, the outside of the tubes are kept clean by _____.
    A. soot blowers
    B. cold lime water softeners
    C. ion exchange water softeners
    D. bottom and continuous blowdown

18. To ensure good heat transfer in a fire tube boiler, the outside of the tubes are kept clean by _____.
    A. soot blowers
    B. recommended feedwater treatment
    C. daily surface blowdowns
    D. overfire air

19. When economizers are used to heat boiler feedwater, every 10% rise in feedwater temperature is accompanied by a _____ % savings in fuel.
    A. ¼ of 1
    B. 1
    C. 5
    D. 10

20. Proper safety procedure requires that _____ before anyone is allowed to enter the steam and water drum.
    A. safety valves must be tagged
    B. the inspector must be notified
    C. he or she must have a safety light
    D. the boiler's main steam stop valves, feedwater lines, and bottom blow-down lines must be closed, locked, and tagged out

21. The safety valves on the boiler drum and superheater safety valves of a steam boiler are set so that _____.
    A. both drum safety valves open together
    B. only one drum safety valve opens
    C. the superheater safety valve opens first
    D. one drum safety valve opens and then the superheater safety valve opens

22. Boilers taken off-line for cleaning and inspection may be dumped (emptied) when the _____.
    A. boiler pressure is about 50 psi
    B. boiler setting is cool enough to enter the firebox
    C. boiler water temperature is 175 °F
    D. automatic nonreturn valve cuts the boiler off the line

23. The best time to blow down a boiler is when it is _____.
  A. at its peak load
  B. at 75% of its peak load
  C. at its lowest load
  D. being taken out of service

24. The frequency of blowing down the boiler can best be determined by _____.
  A. the boiler operator
  B. the boiler inspector
  C. the blowdown meter
  D. testing the boiler water

25. In most plants, the suggested operating procedure is to blow down the water column and gauge glass _____.
  A. at least once a week
  B. at least once a shift
  C. only when taking the boiler off-line
  D. they should never be blown down under pressure

T   F   **26.** Softened water is used in a boiler to prevent pitting of the boiler metal.

T   F   **27.** All fire tube boilers are horizontal boilers.

T   F   **28.** If the top line to a boiler gauge glass was closed, the water in the glass would rise to the top.

T   F   **29.** The boiling point of water is not affected by boiler pressure.

T   F   **30.** Priming can be a direct result of maintaining too high a water level in the boiler.

T   F   **31.** In the closed feedwater heater, steam and water come into direct contact with each other.

T   F   **32.** The automatic nonreturn valve is on the main steam line.

T   F   **33.** If a plant has only one boiler, an automatic nonreturn valve is not necessary.

T   F   **34.** It is unnecessary to blow down a boiler if proper feedwater treatment is used.

T   F   **35.** A high pressure cutoff control can take the place of a safety valve.

T   F   **36.** Both stop and check valves must be installed on the boiler feedwater line.

T   F   **37.** Try cocks on a water column can be used to determine the water level if the gauge glass is broken.

T   F   **38.** Boiler explosions would not occur if all boilers had a MAWP of 15 psi.

T   F   **39.** The purpose of safety valves is to protect the boiler from exceeding its MAWP.

T   F   **40.** The discharge outlet size of a safety valve must not be restricted or reduced.

T   F   **41.** A safety valve discharge line cannot be discharged outside of the boiler room.

T   F   **42.** Corrosion of the seat and disc of a safety valve can cause the valve to stick in a closed position.

T   F   **43.** In a pop-type safety valve, the huddling chamber is constructed to assist in opening the valve.

T   F   44. If a safety valve leaks after testing, the valve should be fully opened using the test lever. If the valve continues to leak, the boiler should be removed from the line as soon as possible and the safety valve should be repaired or replaced.

T   F   45. The low water fuel cutoff control shuts off the fuel to a burner when a low water condition occurs.

T   F   46. A low water fuel cutoff control should be tested by blowing down the float chamber at least once a shift.

T   F   47. The water column reduces the turbulence of the water to give a more accurate reading in the gauge glass.

T   F   48. Boiler blowdown tanks do not require vents because the water is discharged to the sewer.

T   F   49. Blowing down the water column and gauge glass too frequently can cause a false water level.

T   F   50. A false water level reading can occur if the water column or gauge glass blowdown valves are not fully closed.

Identify the parts of the feedwater system shown.

_____   51. Check valve
_____   52. Bypass valve
_____   53. Stop valve
_____   54. Regulating valve

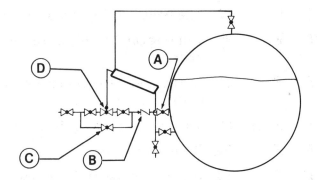

Identify the parts of the feedwater system shown.

_____   55. Open feedwater heater
_____   56. Internal overflow line
_____   57. Closed feedwater heater
_____   58. Feedwater pump

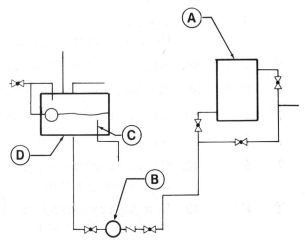

Identify the parts of the dry pipe separator shown.

_____ 59. Steam and water drum
_____ 60. Main steam outlet
_____ 61. Steam
_____ 62. Dry pipe

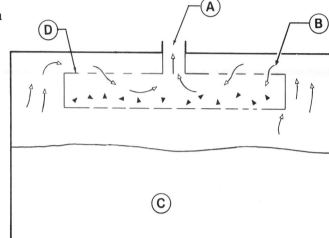

Identify the parts of the cyclone separator shown.

_____ 63. Baffle
_____ 64. Cyclone
_____ 65. Scrubber
_____ 66. Primary scrubber

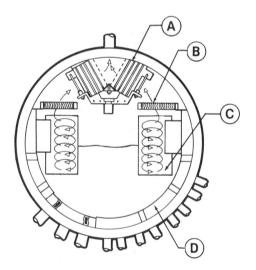

Identify the parts of the reciprocating feedwater pump shown.

_____ 67. D-type slide valve
_____ 68. Steam connection
_____ 69. Rocker arm
_____ 70. Main exhaust

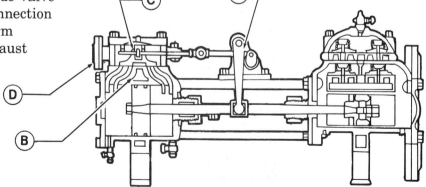

TEST 3

Name _____ Date _____

_____ 1. Boilers that are laid up dry have trays of _____ put in the steam and water drums to absorb moisture.
  A. calcium chloride
  B. hot soda lime
  C. silica gel
  D. potash

_____ 2. To obtain complete combustion of a fuel, _____, _____, _____, and _____ are required.
  A. mixture, atomization, temperature, and time
  B. CO_2, O_2, CO, CO_3
  C. turbulence, feedwater, air, flue gas
  D. hot refractory, air, draft, gases of combustion

_____ 3. Oxygen in the boiler causes _____.
  A. scale
  B. pitting
  C. foaming
  D. carryover

_____ 4. A Ringelmann test is used to _____.
  A. analyze feedwater
  B. measure CO_2 in flue gas
  C. measure CO in flue gas
  D. determine smoke density

_____ 5. Scale buildup in the tubes of a water tube boiler can be removed by _____.
  A. washing down the boiler with high pressure water
  B. an air- or water-driven turbine
  C. wire brushes
  D. boiling out the boiler with caustic soda

_____ 6. When the boiler low water alarm is ringing, the operator should _____.
  A. call the chief engineer
  B. increase the firing rate
  C. decrease the feedwater
  D. secure the fires

_____ 7. According to the ASME code, when no boiler water analysis is made the boiler should be blown down at least once _____.
  A. every 8 hours
  B. every 24 hours
  C. a month
  D. a week

8. A ¾ " blowdown line may be used if the boiler has _____ square feet of heating surface.
   A. more than 100
   B. less than 199
   C. more than 500
   D. none of the above

9. The superheater drain _____ the superheater.
   A. removes gases from
   B. removes condensate from
   C. relieves pressure from
   D. establishes a steam flow through

10. An infrared scanner _____.
    A. acts as a flame failure control
    B. detects smoke
    C. measures temperature
    D. prevents low water

11. A furnace explosion can be prevented by _____.
    A. checking the water level once a shift
    B. testing the safety valves once a month
    C. purging after ignition failure
    D. testing the safety valve regularly

12. A sudden raise in chimney temperature without a corresponding increase in steam demand indicates _____.
    A. a dirty boiler
    B. a broken baffle
    C. too much air
    D. a closed damper

13. A lead sulfide cell, which is used for flame detection, is sensitive to _____.
    A. infrared light
    B. light
    C. heat
    D. temperature increases

14. An economizer heats _____.
    A. steam
    B. air for combustion
    C. fuel oil
    D. feedwater

15. The air switch, which is located on the forced draft fan housing of a rotary cup burner, ensures _____.
    A. gas pressure at the pilot
    B. positive draft pressure
    C. emergency shutoff
    D. fuel oil pressure

16. The Btu content of natural gas is _____ Btu's per _____.
    A. 100,000; therm
    B. 100,000; cubic foot
    C. 152,000; therm
    D. 152,000; cubic foot

17. Chemicals are added to the boiler water by _____.
    A. the feedwater pump
    B. the vacuum pump
    C. the proportional chemical pump
    D. mixing in the reservoir

18. The boiler feedwater stop valve is between the _____ and _____.
    A. boiler, check valve
    B. check valve, feedwater pump
    C. boiler, feedwater pump
    D. boiler, main header

19. A pop-type safety valve is a _____ type.
    A. hand and lever
    B. pin and disc
    C. deadweight
    D. spring-loaded

20. Steam left on a soot blower element continuously without rotating the soot blower causes _____.
    A. clean fire
    B. tube damage
    C. fires to go out
    D. a chemical reaction with soot

21. Tubes in a fire tube boiler are _____.
    A. rolled and beaded
    B. welded
    C. collared and peened
    D. bolted and nutted

22. The purge cycle of a combination gas/fuel oil boiler is _____ when burning fuel oil as when burning gas.
    A. the same
    B. shorter
    C. twice as long
    D. three times as long

23. To test a low water fuel cutoff using an evaporation test, the boiler operator must _____.
    A. close the feedwater stop valve
    B. secure all of the feedwater going to the boiler
    C. completely drain the regulator chamber
    D. have an inspector on hand

_____ 24. The bypass damper on an air heater _____.
        A. reduces the fan load
        B. secures the preheater
        C. prevents corrosion at low rating
        D. none of the above

_____ 25. A flash tank _____.
        A. acts as a separator
        B. recovers steam and condensate
        C. controls blowdowns
        D. recovers low pressure steam

T   F   **26.** A closed boiler room that does not permit the proper flow of outside air to the furnace will have combustion problems.

T   F   **27.** An airtight boiler room will prohibit complete combustion.

T   F   **28.** Weighted lever-type safety valves can be used on steam boilers that operate at pressures not exceeding 50 psi.

T   F   **29.** Steam boilers that are out of service can be laid up wet or dry.

T   F   **30.** The dry method of boiler lay-up requires the boiler to be opened and air circulated to keep the boiler drums and tubes dry.

T   F   **31.** Chemical treatment of the boiler water is not necessary when laying a boiler up wet if the water has been deaerated.

T   F   **32.** The flash point of fuel oil is lower than the fire point.

T   F   **33.** The fire point of fuel oil is the minimum temperature at which fuel oil burns continuously.

T   F   **34.** No. 6 fuel oil burns with a clean flame when it is not heated.

T   F   **35.** Poor grades of No. 6 fuel oil can be used quite well with a steam atomizing burner.

T   F   **36.** The most common causes of boiler accidents or explosions are low water and insufficient purging of the combustion space.

T   F   **37.** A steam pressure gauge is calibrated in pounds per square foot.

T   F   **38.** The Bourdon tube of a steam pressure gauge does not have to be protected.

T   F   **39.** An increase in chimney temperature indicates soot on the heating surfaces of a boiler.

T   F   **40.** Absolute pressure is pressure below the atmospheric pressure.

T   F   **41.** The dry pipe separator is in the steam and water drum.

T   F   **42.** A dry pipe separator increases the quality of steam leaving a steam boiler.

T   F   **43.** Excess air for combustion is indicated by testing for CO_2 in the gases of combustion.

T   F   **44.** A change in water pressure will change the boiling point of water.

T   F   **45.** Boiler tube dimensions are based on the inside diameter of the tube.

T   F   **46.** The safety valve on the superheater header should be set to blow before the safety valves on the steam and water drum.

T   F   **47.** A globe valve offers less resistance to flow than a gate valve does.

T   F   **48.** To control the flow of steam, the gate valve is opened halfway.

T   F   **49.** The largest heat loss in a boiler is caused by heat being carried with the gases of combustion to the atmosphere.

T   F   **50.** The bottom blowdown valves can be used to lower the boiler steam pressure.

Identify the parts of the blowdown tank shown.

_____   **51.** Vent to atmosphere
_____   **52.** Blowdown tank
_____   **53.** Waste to sewer
_____   **54.** Blowdown line from boiler

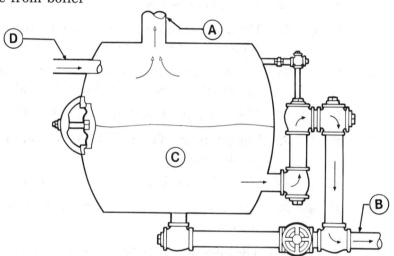

Identify the parts of the soot blower shown.

_____   **55.** Endless chain
_____   **56.** Packing
_____   **57.** Element
_____   **58.** Gooseneck

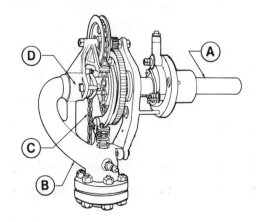

Identify the parts of the float-type alarm whistle shown.

_____ **59.** High water float
_____ **60.** Gauge glass
_____ **61.** Whistle valve
_____ **62.** Low water float

Identify the parts of the pigtail siphon shown.

_____ **63.** Gate valve
_____ **64.** To pressure gauge
_____ **65.** To inspector's test gauge
_____ **66.** To boiler

Identify the parts of the deadweight tester shown.

_____ **67.** Weight platform
_____ **68.** Piston
_____ **69.** Gauge being tested
_____ **70.** Screw plunger

TEST 4

_____ **1.** In a rotary cup burner, atomization is achieved by _____.
    A. fuel oil pressure
    B. air pressure
    C. the rotary cup
    D. the rotary cup and primary air

_____ **2.** To prevent a vacuum from forming on a boiler that is coming off-line, _____.
    A. open the air cock
    B. blow down the boiler
    C. dump the boiler
    D. pop the safety valve

_____ **3.** Staybolts are most commonly found on _____.
    A. feedwater heaters
    B. fire tube boilers
    C. superheater headers
    D. all modern water tube boilers

_____ **4.** According to the ASME code, when warming up a boiler the air cock should remain open until _____ psi of pressure are on the boiler.
    A. 10
    B. 15
    C. 20
    D. 25

_____ **5.** High pressure boilers equipped with quick-opening and screw-type valves are blown down by opening the _____ valve first and closing it _____.
    A. quick-opening, first
    B. screw-type, last
    C. quick-opening, last
    D. quick-opening valves are never used on high pressure boilers

_____ **6.** A slow-opening valve requires _____ complete turns to be fully opened or closed.
    A. three
    B. five
    C. seven
    D. nine

_____ **7.** Overheating of tubes in a water tube boiler is caused by _____ on the _____ of the tubes.
    A. scale, inside
    B. scale, outside
    C. soot, inside
    D. soot, outside

8. The viscosity of fuel oil is the measurement of the _____ in the fuel oil.
   A. Btu content
   B. fire point
   C. flash point
   D. internal resistance to flow

9. According to the ASME code, the maximum size of the boiler bottom blowdown line is _____ ".
   A. 1½
   B. 2
   C. 2½
   D. 3

10. According to the ASME code, the setting or adjusting of a boiler safety valve must be done by the _____.
   A. boiler inspector
   B. plant manager
   C. watch engineer
   D. person familiar with the construction, operation, and maintenance of a safety valve

11. According to the ASME code, any repairs done on a boiler safety valve must be done by the _____.
   A. boiler inspector
   B. person familiar with the construction, operation, and maintenance of a safety valve
   C. watch engineer
   D. manufacturer or an authorized representative of the manufacturer.

12. Feedwater is treated chemically before it enters the boiler to _____.
   A. prevent foaming
   B. eliminate blowing down the boiler
   C. change the scale-forming salts to a sludge that will stick to the heating surface, making cleaning easier
   D. change scale-forming salts to a nonadhering sludge

13. Soot blowers are most commonly found _____.
   A. on an HRT boiler
   B. on a water tube boiler
   C. in main breeching
   D. on vertical fire tube boilers over 150 horsepower

14. A duplex reciprocating feedwater pump operates on the principle that _____.
   A. the steam side must be 2 to 2½ times larger in area than the water side
   B. the water piston must be 2 to 2½ times larger in area than the steam piston
   C. the steam piston must be 2 to 2½ times larger in area than the water piston
   D. the piston speed squared will equal gallons per minute

15. Complete combustion is defined as burning all fuel using _____.
A. the theoretical amount of air
B. a minimal amount of excess air
C. no excess air
D. CO_2 and CO

16. When testing the safety valve by hand, _____.
A. there should be no pressure in the boiler
B. notify the boiler inspector
C. the boiler should be at least 75% of popping pressure before testing
D. first secure the fires

17. The absolute pressure of a steam boiler carrying 160 psig would be _____ psia.
A. 145.3
B. 174.7
C. 200
D. none of the above

18. The _____ test is used to test the density of smoke leaving a boiler.
A. Ringelmann
B. smoke intensity
C. Orsat analysis
D. Fyrite analysis

19. An automatic nonreturn valve is found on the _____.
A. discharge side of the feedwater pump
B. inlet line to the open feedwater heater
C. boiler main steam line between the main stop valve and the header
D. boiler main steam line between the boiler and the main stop valve

20. A boiler steam pressure of 100 psi with a temperature of 500 °F indicates _____.
A. dry steam
B. supersaturated steam
C. superheated steam
D. steam at its corresponding pressure and temperature

21. If three boilers are connected to a common header and each boiler is at 100 psi, the master gauge on the header would read _____ psi.
A. 100
B. 275
C. 298
D. 300

22. To aid in the delivery of moisture-free steam, the steam leaves the steam and water drum through the _____.
A. dry pipe
B. superheater
C. desuperheater
D. internal feedwater pipe

_____ **23.** A broken baffle in a water tube boiler causes _____.
A. smoke coming from the chimney
B. a rise in chimney temperature
C. a drop in chimney temperature
D. steam coming from the chimney

_____ **24.** The water column on a high pressure steam boiler _____.
A. reduces fluctuation in water level to prevent carryover
B. reduces the turbulence of water in the gauge glass
C. provides a place to install the gauge glass and try cocks
D. a water column is never used on a high pressure boiler

_____ **25.** Safety valves on high pressure boilers can be tested _____.
A. only by hand
B. only by pressure
C. by hand or pressure
D. safety valves should never be tested

T F **26.** One of the purposes of a bottom blowdown line is to remove impurities from the boiler.

T F **27.** The main function of a steam trap is to remove air and condensate without the loss of steam.

T F **28.** A therm of natural gas has 10,000 Btu's.

T F **29.** In a natural draft system, the lowest draft reading is obtained at the furnace.

T F **30.** Burning fuel is a chemical reaction that releases heat.

T F **31.** The main function of a continuous blowdown system is to lower the total concentration of solids in the boiler.

T F **32.** The high and low water level alarm floats are components of the boiler feedwater system.

T F **33.** A calorimeter measures excess air being used for combustion.

T F **34.** When conducting a hydrostatic test, all safety valves are either gagged or removed and blank flanged, and the pressure is increased to 1½ times the MAWP.

T F **35.** Boiler drum safety valves must open before the superheater safety valve to ensure a back flow.

T F **36.** The atmospheric pressure at sea level will support a column of mercury approximately 30″ high.

T F **37.** A flow meter integrator totalizes the temperature and pressure of steam.

T F **38.** Purging a furnace before firing can prevent a furnace explosion.

T F **39.** Try cocks are not effective above a steam pressure of 250 psi.

T F **40.** A pyrometer measures the amount of moisture in steam leaving a boiler.

T F **41.** The forced and induced draft fans on a boiler are the same size and operate at the same speed.

T	F	**42.** Three methods of heat transfer are radiation, convection, and conduction.
T	F	**43.** The size of a boiler tube is determined by the inside diameter of the tube.
T	F	**44.** Superheating steam is impossible at low steam pressures.
T	F	**45.** Preheaters heat air for combustion.
T	F	**46.** An economizer is a heat exchanger that absorbs heat from the gases of combustion leaving the boiler.
T	F	**47.** A desuperheater is only used in low pressure steam plants.
T	F	**48.** Safety valves are located on the uppermost part of the steam and water drum and the outlet of the superheater header.
T	F	**49.** All boilers are equipped with a water column.
T	F	**50.** An adequate supply of air is the only thing needed for good combustion.

Identify the parts of the overfeed coal stoker shown.

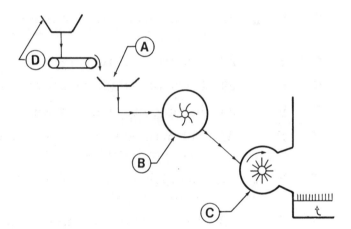

_____ **51.** Coal feeder
_____ **52.** Spreader
_____ **53.** Coal scale
_____ **54.** Coal bunker

Identify the parts of the natural draft system shown.

_____ **55.** Inlet damper
_____ **56.** Outlet damper
_____ **57.** Column of cold air
_____ **58.** Column of hot air

Identify the parts of the rotary cup burner shown.

_____ **59.** Solenoid valve
_____ **60.** Primary air fan
_____ **61.** Spinning cup
_____ **62.** Secondary air damper

Identify the parts of the sprayer plate pressure atomizing burner shown.

_____ **63.** Atomized fuel oil
_____ **64.** Burner tip
_____ **65.** Sprayer plate
_____ **66.** Burner tube

FRONT VIEW   END VIEW

Identify the parts of the fuel oil storage tank shown.

_____ **67.** Vent line
_____ **68.** Return line
_____ **69.** Fill line
_____ **70.** High suction line

TEST 5

_____ 1. Before laying up a boiler, the boiler operator must _____.
  A. notify the boiler inspector
  B. remove the boiler certificate
  C. thoroughly clean the fire and water sides
  D. only clean the water side because soot acts as an insulator

_____ 2. If water comes out of the top try cock, the boiler operator must _____.
  A. notify the chief engineer
  B. blow down the boiler
  C. bypass the try cocks and feed by hand
  D. leave the boiler alone; this is normal

_____ 3. If steam comes out of the bottom try cock, the boiler operator must _____.
  A. secure the fires to the boiler, allow the boiler to cool slowly, and notify the chief engineer
  B. bypass the try cocks and feed by hand
  C. leave the boiler alone; this is normal
  D. start up a new feedwater pump

_____ 4. A stationary water level in the gauge glass indicates that _____.
  A. the top line is closed or clogged
  B. the bottom line is closed or clogged
  C. both lines are closed or clogged
  D. a good fireman is on duty

_____ 5. While replacing a broken gauge with the boiler under pressure, the water level is checked by _____.
  A. blowing down the water column
  B. giving the boiler a bottom blow
  C. using try cocks
  D. using air cocks

_____ 6. If the steam valve to the gauge glass is closed or the top line is clogged, the gauge glass will be _____.
  A. full
  B. half full
  C. three-quarters full
  D. empty

_____ 7. A scotch marine boiler is a _____ boiler.
  A. water tube
  B. cast iron
  C. cast iron fire tube
  D. fire tube

8. According to the ASME code, a boiler that has more than _____ square feet of heating surface must have two or more safety valves.
   A. 100
   B. 300
   C. 500
   D. 700

9. A(n) _____ test is used to test the relieving capacity of a safety valve.
   A. hydrostatic
   B. accumulation
   C. Orsat analysis
   D. Ringelmann

10. An open feedwater heater is located _____.
   A. above the feedwater pump on the discharge side
   B. above the feedwater pump on the suction side
   C. in the boiler room
   D. between the feedwater pump and the boiler

11. A closed feedwater heater is located _____.
   A. above the feedwater pump on the discharge side
   B. above the feedwater pump on the suction side
   C. in the boiler room
   D. between the feedwater pump and the boiler

12. To start a centrifugal pump, the discharge valve must be _____.
   A. closed
   B. opened
   C. primed
   D. there is no discharge valve

13. At a water temperature of 212 °F, one boiler horsepower is equivalent to the evaporation of _____ pounds of water per hour.
   A. 34.5
   B. 62.5
   C. 180
   D. 970.3

14. The valves located between the boiler and the water column are _____ valves and must be locked and sealed open.
   A. check
   B. os&y or lever
   C. gate
   D. globe

15. To cut a boiler in on a line equipped with hand-operated main steam stop valves the steam pressure on the incoming boiler should be _____.
   A. slightly lower than line pressure
   B. slightly higher than line pressure
   C. equal to line pressure
   D. no different; pressure will equalize

16. According to the ASME code, the suggested range of a boiler pressure gauge is _____.
    A. 1½ to 2 times the safety valve setting
    B. 2 times the MAWP
    C. not more than 6% above the MAWP
    D. gauge pressure plus atmospheric pressure

17. When making a hydrostatic test on a boiler, the pressure is _____.
    A. 2 times the safety valve setting
    B. 1½ times the MAWP
    C. 1¼ times the MAWP
    D. operating pressure plus atmospheric pressure

18. The bottom blowdown line of a high pressure water tube boiler is connected to the _____.
    A. waterleg
    B. main steam drum
    C. mud drum
    D. surface blow

19. The feedwater regulator element is located _____.
    A. at the NOWL
    B. on the right side of the steam drum
    C. on the left side of the steam drum
    D. on the feedwater heater

20. With all of the safety valves popping, the boiler pressure should not go higher than _____.
    A. 1½ times the MAWP
    B. 6% above the MAWP
    C. 8% above the set pressure
    D. 10% above the set pressure

21. Water polluted with foreign matter causes an increase in _____.
    A. makeup
    B. blowdown
    C. fuel consumption
    D. surface tension

22. Boiler waterwalls should be blown down _____.
    A. daily
    B. weekly
    C. when the firebox is cool but the boiler still has pressure
    D. every six months

23. Before draining a boiler, the operator should _____.
    A. allow the setting to cool
    B. call the boiler inspector
    C. open the blowdown valves with 10 to 12 psi on the boiler
    D. use the surface blow

24. A safe maximum water concentration in steam generators serving low makeup plants is maintained by _____.
  A. daily blowdowns
  B. continuous blowdown
  C. surface blowdowns
  D. increased makeup

25. According to the ASME code, if a boiler has a MAWP that exceeds 100 psi the boiler must have _____ blowdown valve(s).
  A. zero
  B. one
  C. two
  D. three

26. According to the ASME code, the minimum size pipe connecting the water column to the boiler is _____".
  A. ½
  B. 1
  C. 1½
  D. 2

27. Pyrometers measure _____.
  A. air duct velocity
  B. draft
  C. superheater flow
  D. temperature

28. An automatic nonreturn valve is used with a(n) _____.
  A. engine
  B. pump
  C. boiler
  D. condenser

29. _____ is the difference in pressure between two points of measurement.
  A. Draft
  B. Feedwater
  C. Condensate
  D. Carryover

30. Viscosity is the internal resistance of a fluid to flow. No. 6 fuel oil has _____ viscosity.
  A. no
  B. a high
  C. a medium
  D. a low

31. The air switch attached to the housing of a fully automatic rotary cup burner becomes operative when there is _____.
  A. low oil pressure
  B. fan failure
  C. excess primary air
  D. excess secondary air

32. An evaporation test should be performed _____ to check the low water fuel cutoff control.
   A. daily
   B. weekly
   C. monthly
   D. yearly

33. The size of bottom blowdown lines can be reduced when _____.
   A. the boiler is under 100 psi
   B. using a vertical fire tube boiler
   C. the boiler has under 100 square feet of heating surface
   D. none of the above

34. A pressure control is sensitive to _____.
   A. pressure
   B. temperature
   C. electricity
   D. all of the above

35. A vaporstat control is sensitive to _____.
   A. pressure
   B. temperature
   C. electricity
   D. infrared rays

36. A lead sulfite cell is sensitive to _____.
   A. pressure
   B. temperature
   C. electricity
   D. infrared rays

37. Saturated steam at 200 psi that passes through a reducing valve and is reduced to 20 psi becomes low pressure steam that is _____.
   A. superheated
   B. dry steam
   C. supersaturated
   D. steam at its corresponding temperature and pressure

38. Anthracite coal has a _____ content.
   A. high volatile
   B. low hydrogen
   C. high fixed carbon
   D. high ash

39. Bituminous coal has a _____ content.
   A. high volatile
   B. high hydrogen
   C. high fixed carbon
   D. high ash

40. For the efficient combustion of pulverized coal, it is necessary to maintain _____.
   A. 50% excess air
   B. a high furnace temperature
   C. a low furnace temperature
   D. positive furnace pressure

41. The surface blowdown on a steam boiler is located _____.
   A. at the lowest visible part of the gauge glass
   B. on the mud drum
   C. at the highest part of the steam and water drum
   D. at the NOWL

42. When using No. 6 fuel oil, the boiler operator must _____.
   A. blend it with No. 2 fuel oil
   B. bring it up to its flash point in the tank
   C. heat the fuel oil as it comes from the fuel oil tank
   D. No. 6 fuel oil should never be heated

43. The function of the fuel oil burner is to _____.
   A. preheat the fuel oil
   B. pump fuel oil into the firebox
   C. atomize the fuel oil completely
   D. pump fuel oil back to the fuel oil tank

44. When burning coal, if there is no water showing in the gauge glass the boiler operator must _____.
   A. add makeup water at once
   B. cover the fire with green coal, leave the firing doors open, and then find the water level
   C. start the feedwater injector
   D. start the second feedwater pump

45. The check valve on the boiler feedwater line _____.
   A. controls the flow of feedwater in one direction only
   B. allows the stop valve to be repaired without dumping the boiler
   C. allows the water level in the boiler to equalize
   D. prevents the bottom blowdown from backing into the feedwater lines

46. When making a hydrostatic test on a boiler, the safety valves must be _____.
   A. kept free to pop at set pressure
   B. set at 1½ times the MAWP
   C. plugged at the discharge end
   D. gagged or removed, and the openings must be blank flanged

47. On boilers that have both quick-closing and screw-type blowdown valves, the quick-closing valve must be located _____.
   A. after the screw-type valve
   B. at the NOWL
   C. closest to the boiler and followed by the screw-type valve
   D. on the bottom blowdown tank

48. An automatic feedwater regulator _____.
    A. warns of high or low water
    B. maintains a constant water level
    C. shuts the burner off in the event of low water
    D. adds city water makeup automatically

49. Boiler CO_2 readings of 12.5% over the fire, 11.5% in the second pass, and 8% at the damper indicate _____.
    A. leaks through the boiler side wall
    B. too much primary air
    C. too much secondary air
    D. excess air at the burner

50. On a rotary cup burner, the air switch is electrically interlocked with the _____.
    A. warp switch
    B. magnetic oil valve
    C. low water fuel cutoff
    D. pressure control

Identify the parts of the shell-and-coil steam fuel oil heater shown.

51. Fuel oil inlet
52. Steam inlet
53. Condensate outlet
54. Fuel oil outlet

Identify the parts of the automatic temperature regular shown.

55. Piston
56. Diaphragm
57. Thermostatic expansion bellows
58. Thermostatic bulb

PRESSURE SETTING

Identify the parts of the vaporstat shown.

_____ **59.** Pressure-adjusting screw
_____ **60.** Leveling screw indicator
_____ **61.** Mercury switch
_____ **62.** Differential adjusting screw

Identify the parts of the underfeed stoker shown.

_____ **63.** Retort chamber
_____ **64.** Dump grates
_____ **65.** Fuel bed
_____ **66.** Air chamber

_____ **67.** Pusher blocks
_____ **68.** Fuel bed
_____ **69.** Hopper
_____ **70.** Coal ram

_____ 1. Boiler water with a pH of 11 is _____.
A. alkaline
B. neutral
C. acid
D. hard

_____ 2. Neutral on the pH scale is _____.
A. 0
B. 4
C. 7
D. 14

_____ 3. Foaming may be caused by _____.
A. a high water level
B. a low water level
C. a leaking surface blowdown
D. impurities on the boiler water surface

_____ 4. The blowdown line must be protected from _____.
A. excessive heat
B. corrosion
C. freezing
D. all of the above

_____ 5. The Bourdon tube in a steam pressure gauge is protected by a _____.
A. steam trap
B. siphon
C. steam strainer
D. stopcock

_____ 6. Heat is transferred from the fire to the boiler heating surface surrounding the fire by _____.
A. radiation
B. conduction
C. convection
D. inversion

_____ 7. A dry pipe on a boiler _____.
A. removes moisture from steam
B. supplies adequate makeup water
C. maintains a NOWL
D. is used in the event of a fire

_____ 8. Draft is measured with a _____.
A. pyrometer
B. hydrometer
C. manometer
D. pressure gauge

9. Scale deposit in an HRT boiler can cause _____.
    A. a higher rate of heat transfer
    B. overheating of the boiler metal
    C. carryover
    D. purging

10. A deaerating feedwater heater removes noncondensable gases such as air, free oxygen, and CO_2 from the feedwater that can cause _____.
    A. corrosion
    B. foaming
    C. carryover
    D. pumps to become vaporbound

11. A steam boiler is blown down to _____.
    A. lower the oxygen
    B. test the safety valve
    C. remove sludge and sediment
    D. clean the lines

12. When checking the NOWL in a steam boiler with try cocks, _____.
    A. steam and water flow out of the middle try cock
    B. water flow out of the top try cock
    C. steam flows out of the bottom try cock
    D. steam and water flow out of the top try cock

13. The furnace of an HRT boiler is _____.
    A. within the boiler shell
    B. constructed without refractory
    C. protected from excessive heat
    D. outside of the boiler shell

14. The superheater header safety valve is set to pop at _____ the steam and water drum safety valves.
    A. the same pressure as
    B. the MAWP of
    C. a lower pressure than
    D. a higher pressure than

15. The tubes in a straight-tube water tube boiler are _____ into drums, headers, or sheets to remain stationary.
    A. screwed
    B. beaded
    C. expanded and flared
    D. welded and bolted

16. A scotch marine boiler has _____.
    A. an internal furnace
    B. an external furnace
    C. a brick setting
    D. water tubes

17. A compound pressure gauge indicates _____.
    A. differential pressure
    B. pressure or vacuum
    C. absolute pressure
    D. the sum of the steam pressures on two boilers

18. Scale on a water tube boiler is removed by _____.
    A. a steam lance
    B. a fire hose
    C. wire brushing
    D. hydraulic turbine cutters

19. _____ coal has the highest amount of fixed carbon.
    A. Bituminous
    B. Anthracite
    C. Sub-bituminous
    D. Semianthracite

20. Beginning with the largest size, _____, _____, _____, and _____ are the grades of anthracite coal.
    A. pea, barley, buckwheat, rice
    B. pea, buckwheat, rice, barley
    C. pea, rice, barley, buckwheat
    D. buckwheat, pea, barley, rice

21. Beginning with the largest size, _____, _____, _____, and _____ are the grades of bituminous coal.
    A. run of mine, lump, nut, slack
    B. run of mine, slack, lump, nut
    C. nut, lump, slack, run of mine
    D. slack, nut, lump, run of mine

22. Soot on the inside of boiler tubes is removed by a _____.
    A. steam turbine
    B. water turbine
    C. steam lance
    D. wire brush and vacuum cleaner

23. Soot on the outside of boiler tubes is removed by a _____.
    A. steam turbine
    B. water turbine
    C. soot blower
    D. wire brush and vacuum cleaner

24. Overheating of tubes on a water tube boiler can be caused by _____.
    A. excessive soot on the tubes
    B. the water level being too high
    C. the water circulation being too rapid
    D. scale buildup inside the tubes

25. Steam atomizing burners can be used to burn _____ fuel oil at lower temperatures.
    A. distilled
    B. No. 6
    C. No. 7
    D. condensed

26. _____% of the steam generated in the boiler is used for the steam atomizing burner.
    A. Four
    B. Eight
    C. Twelve
    D. Sixteen

27. Atomization of fuel oil in a rotary cup burner is caused by the _____.
    A. rotating cup
    B. rotating cup and primary air
    C. pressure of the fuel oil
    D. secondary and primary air

28. The underfeed stoker in steam plants uses _____.
    A. natural draft
    B. ash to keep the grates cool
    C. an ignition arch
    D. forced draft

29. A proximate analysis of coal is used to determine the _____.
    A. volume of volatile matter, fixed carbon, moisture, and ash
    B. volume of carbon, hydrogen, oxygen, and sulfur
    C. weight of moisture, fixed carbon, volatile matter, and ash
    D. weight of moisture, oxygen, sulfur, and ash

30. If the discharge valve of a centrifugal pump is closed when the pump is running, the _____.
    A. pressure will increase indefinitely
    B. relief valve will open
    C. pressure will increase a fixed amount
    D. drive will overload

31. In a closed feedwater heater, the _____.
    A. steam and water come into direct contact
    B. feedwater pressure is higher than the boiler pressure
    C. feedwater pressure is lower than the boiler pressure
    D. noncondensable gases are removed from the top

32. Condensate is returned to the boiler with the makeup water in the _____.
    A. condenser
    B. open feedwater heater
    C. hot well
    D. makeup tank

33. Economizers are used in large plants so that _____.
  A. the dew point can be lowered
  B. impure feedwater can be used
  C. higher flue gas temperatures can be maintained
  D. heat from the gases of combustion can be reclaimed

34. In a balanced draft system, the pressure in the furnace is approximately _____.
  A. +0.1 inches of water
  B. −1.0 inches of water
  C. atmospheric
  D. atmosphere plus gauge

35. A Ringelmann chart in a steam generating plant is helpful in determining the _____.
  A. condition of the boiler water
  B. rate of feed of the feedwater
  C. CO_2 present in the gases of combustion
  D. density of the smoke leaving the boiler

36. A pyrometer measures _____.
  A. temperature
  B. steam pressure
  C. draft
  D. the quality of steam leaving the boiler

37. A steam pressure gauge is calibrated in _____ per _____.
  A. cubic feet, minute
  B. pounds, square foot
  C. cubic inches, second
  D. pounds, square inch

38. The Orsat analyzer is used to determine the _____.
  A. required chimney temperatures
  B. combustion efficiency
  C. steam quality in the boiler
  D. heating value of the fuel

39. Staybolts are most commonly used in _____ boilers.
  A. fire tube
  B. water tube
  C. bent-tube
  D. cast iron sectional

40. Sludge and sediment from the mud drum of a boiler are discharged into _____.
  A. the sewer
  B. a settling tank
  C. a blowdown tank
  D. a river or pond

41. A stop-and-check valve is installed in the _____.
   A. main steam header
   B. outlet superheater
   C. blowdown line
   D. feedwater line

42. A dry pipe _____.
   A. removes moisture from the steam
   B. connects the dry drum to the steam and water drum
   C. increases water circulation
   D. acts as a receiver

43. Smoke is the result of _____.
   A. complete combustion
   B. incomplete combustion
   C. too much excess air
   D. too much primary air

44. In a plant that used forced draft, the pressure at the base of the chimney is _____ pressure.
   A. at atmospheric
   B. above atmospheric
   C. below atmospheric
   D. none of the above

45. The throttling calorimeter determines _____.
   A. heat in the condensate
   B. saturated steam temperature
   C. superheated steam temperature
   D. the amount of moisture in the steam

46. The try cocks on a water column are used _____.
   A. as a secondary means of determining the water level
   B. to blow down the water column
   C. as sampling cocks for water testing
   D. to remove impurities from the surface of the water

47. _____ and _____ are used to soften feedwater.
   A. Calcium chloride, soda ash
   B. Lime, soda ash
   C. Lime, hydrochloric acid
   D. Calcium, magnesium carbonate

48. An ignition arch is used with a(n) _____ stoker.
   A. sidefeed
   B. spreader
   C. underfeed
   D. chain grate

_____ **49.** A difficulty found when burning pulverized coal is _____.
A. the formation of slag
B. improper pulverization
C. furnace design
D. inability to meet steam load changes

_____ **50.** In a reciprocating feedwater pump, the _____.
A. water piston is larger than the steam piston
B. water and steam piston are the same size
C. steam piston is larger than the water piston
D. steam valve has to be as large as the water valve

Identify the parts of the chain grate stoker shown.

_____ **51.** Coal hopper
_____ **52.** Regulating coal gate
_____ **53.** Ignition arch
_____ **54.** Ash to ash hopper

Identify the parts of the pulverizer shown.

_____ **55.** Exhauster
_____ **56.** Pulverizing mill
_____ **57.** To burners
_____ **58.** Raw coal inlet

Glossary

A

absolute pressure. The sum of gauge pressure and atmospheric pressure.

accessory. Piece of equipment not directly attached to the boiler but necessary for its operation.

accumulation test. Test used to establish the relieving capacity of boiler safety valves.

air cock. See *boiler vent.*

air ejector. Steam-driven device that removes air and other noncondensable gases from the condenser, thus maintaining a higher vacuum.

air flow switch. Proves that primary air is supplied to the burner.

air to fuel ratio. Amount of air and fuel supplied to the burner over high and low fire.

air heater. Supplies heated air for combustion. Located in the breeching between the boiler and chimney.

ambient temperature. Temperature of the surrounding air.

alkalinity. Determined by boiler water analysis. Boiler water with a pH over 7 is considered alkaline.

annunciator. Audible alarm that is produced electronically.

anthracite coal. Hard coal that has a high fixed carbon content.

ash hopper. Large receptacle used to store ashes until they can be disposed of.

ASME code. Code written by the American Society of Mechanical Engineers that controls the construction, repairs, and operation of steam boilers and their related equipment.

atmospheric pressure. Pressure at sea level (14.7 psi).

atomize. To break up liquid into a fine mist.

automatic blowdown system. System programmed to control frequency and duration of continuous blowdown operations.

automatic nonreturn valve. Valve located on the steam line closest to the shell of the boiler that cuts the boiler in on the line and off-line automatically. This valve also protects the system in the event of a large steam leak on any boiler.

automatic nonreturn valve

auxiliaries. Equipment necessary for the operation of a boiler.

B

baffles. Direct the path of the gases of combustion so that the maximum heat will be absorbed by the water before the gases of combustion enter the breeching and chimney.

balanced draft. When the intake damper is automatically controlled by the pressure in the furnace. Furnace pressure is maintained slightly below atmospheric pressure.

bent-tube boiler. A water tube boiler with more than one drum in which the tubes connect the drums.

bituminous coal. Soft coal that has a high volatile content.

blowdown tank. Coded tank vented

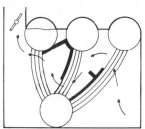
bent-tube boiler

to the atmosphere that protects sewer lines from boiler pressure and high temperature when blowing down.

blowdown valves. Found on the boiler blowdown line at the lowest part of the water side of the boiler.

boiler capacity. Pounds of steam per hour that a steam boiler is capable of producing.

boiler explosion. Caused by a sudden drop in pressure (failure on the steam side) without a corresponding drop in temperature.

boiler horsepower. The evaporation of 34.5 pounds of water per hour from and at a feedwater temperature of 212 °F.

boilers in battery. Two or more boilers connected to a common steam header.

boiler lay-up. Removing a boiler from service for an extended period of time. A boiler can be layed up wet or dry.

boiler room log. A data sheet used to record pressures, temperatures, and other operating conditions of a boiler on a continuous basis.

boiler shutdown. A sequence of operations completed when taking a boiler off-line.

boiler start-up. A sequence of operations completed when preparing a steam boiler for service.

boiler tubes. Used to carry water or heat and gases of combustion. May be straight or bent tubes.

boiler vent. Line coming off the highest part of the steam side of the boiler that is used to vent air from the boiler when filling with water and when warming the boiler. Also used to prevent a vacuum from forming when taking the boiler off-line. Also known as *air cock*.

Bourdon tube. Connected by linkage to a pointer that registers pressure inside pressure gauges.

box header. Requires staybolts to prevent the headers from bulging. Found on older water tube boilers.

breeching. Duct connecting boiler to chimney.

Bourdon tube

British thermal unit (Btu). A measurement of the quantity of heat. The quantity of heat necessary to heat one pound of water to 1 °F.

burning in suspension. Combustion of a fuel when burned in air without support.

butterfly valve. A balanced valve used to control gas flow to gas-fired boilers.

bypass damper. Controls the air temperature in air heaters to prevent corrosion.

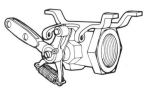
butterfly valve

bypass line. A pipeline that passes around a control, heater, or steam trap. Used so that a plant can operate while equipment is serviced or repaired.

C

calibrate. Adjusting a pressure gauge to conform to a test gauge.

carryover. Particles of water that flow with the steam into the main steam line.

caustic embrittlement. The collection of high alkaline material that leads to breakdown and weakening of boiler metal.

centrifugal force. Force caused by a rotating impeller that builds up in a centrifugal pump.

centrifugal pump. Works on the principle of centrifugal force that is converted into pressure.

chain (traveling) grate stoker. A cross-feed stoker that is used with larger capacity boilers because of its ability to feed coal at a faster rate than other stokers.

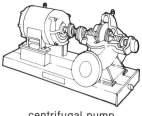
centrifugal pump

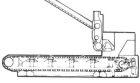
chain (traveling) grate stoker

check valve. Automatic valve that controls the flow of a liquid in one direction.

chemical compound. Formed when two or more chemical elements combine into a new substance.

chemical concentration. The amount of a specific chemical in the boiler water.

chemical energy. Energy in the fuel that converts to heat energy during the combustion process.

chimney. Used to create draft. Also an outlet to the atmosphere for the gases of combustion.

classes of fires. The three classes of fires are: Class A, started from wood, paper, or rags; Class B, started from oil, grease, or flammable liquids; and Class C, which is an electrical fire.

coal bunker. An overhead bin where large quantities of coal are stored.

coal conveyor. Mechanism to move coal in a system.

coal feeder. Controls the flow of coal entering the pulverizer.

coal gate. Used to control the depth of coal entering the boiler furnace on chain grate stokers.

coal ram. Distributes coal evenly into the center retort on underfeed stokers and forces the coal up to the top where it is burned.

coal scale. Measures and records the amount of coal fed to stoker-fired or pulverized coal fired boilers.

combustible material. Any material that burns when it is exposed to oxygen and heat.

combustion. The rapid union of oxygen with an element or compound that results in the release of heat.

combustion control. Regulates the air to fuel ratio supplied to the burner.

complete combustion. The burning of all supplied fuel using the minimum amount of excess air.

compressive stress. Occurs when two forces of equal intensity act from opposite directions, pushing toward the center of an object. Fire tubes in a fire tube boiler are subjected to compressive stress.

condensate. Steam that has lost its heat and has returned to water.

condensate pump. Used to return condensed steam to the open feedwater heater.

condensate tank. Where condensed steam (water) is stored before it is delivered back to the open feedwater heater by the condensate pump.

condense. Process whereby steam turns back to water after the removal of heat.

conduction. A method of heat transfer in which heat moves from molecule to molecule.

conductivity. A measure of the ability of electrons to flow through a solution.

continuous blowdown. Used to control chemical concentrations and total dissolved solids in the boiler water.

convection. A method of heat transfer that occurs as heat moves through a fluid.

convection superheater. Located in a boiler and receives heat from convection currents.

counterflow. Principle used in heat exchangers where the medium being heated flows in one direction and the medium supplying the heat flows in the opposite direction.

cracking open. Slowly opening a steam valve to allow pressure to equalize.

cross "T". Used on connections on a water column for inspection of steam and water lines to ensure they are clean and clear.

cyclone separator. Separates water droplets from steam using centrifugal force and by changing direction.

D

damper. Used to control the flow of air or gases.

data plate. A plate that must be attached to a safety valve containing data required by the ASME code.

deadweight tester. Used to test a pressure gauge so that it can be recalibrated.

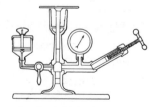

deadweight tester

deaerating feedwater heater. Type of open feedwater heater equipped with a vent condenser.

desuperheating. Removing heat from superheated steam to make it suitable for process.

deaerating feedwater heater

discharge piping. Piping attached to the outlet side of a safety valve that conveys steam to the atmosphere.

draft. The difference in pressure between two points that causes air or gases to flow.

dry pipe separator. A closed pipe perforated at the top with drain holes on the bottom that remove moisture from the steam.

duplex strainers. Remove solid particles from the fuel oil in fuel oil systems.

E

economizer. Uses the gases of combustion to heat the feedwater.

electric boiler. Boiler that has heat produced by electric resistance coils or electrodes.

electronic flue gas analyzer. Device used to analyze flue gas for temperature, gases, draft, and smoke.

element. A basic substance consisting of atoms.

enthalpy. Total heat in the steam.

erosion. Wearing away of metal caused by wet steam.

equalizing line. Line used to warm up the main steam line and equalize the pressure around the main steam stop valve.

evaporation test. Test that checks the operation of the low water fuel cutoff.

excess air. Air more than the theoretical amount of air needed for combustion.

exhauster. Discharges a mixture of coal and warm air to the burner.

expansion bends. Installed on boiler main steam lines to allow for expansion and contraction of the lines.

external treatment. Boiler water treated before it enters the boiler to remove scale-forming salts, oxygen, and noncondensable gases.

extraction steam. Steam that is extracted from a steam turbine at a controlled pressure for process.

F

factor of evaporation. A correction factor used to determine boiler horsepower.

feathering. That point when a safety valve is about to lift.

feedwater. Water that is supplied to the steam boiler.

feedwater heater. Used to heat feedwater before it enters the steam and water drum.

feedwater lines. Lines leaving the open feedwater heater and going to the boiler.

feedwater pump. Takes water from the open feedwater heater and delivers it to the boiler at the proper pressure.

feedwater regulator. Control used to maintain a NOWL that cuts down the danger of high or low water.

feedwater treatment. Can be internal, using chemicals, or external, using water softeners. Protects boiler from scale and corrosion.

field-erected boiler. Boiler that must be erected in the field because of its size and complexity.

fire extinguisher. Portable unit used to put out small fires or contain larger fires until the company fire brigade or the fire department arrives.

fire point. The temperature at which fuel oil burns continuously when exposed to an open flame.

firebox. The part of the boiler where combustion of fuel takes place.

fire tube boiler. Has heat and gases of combustion passing through tubes surrounded by water.

firing rate. Amount of fuel the burner is capable of burning in a given unit of time.

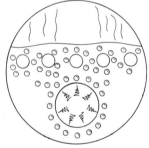

fire tube boiler

fittings. Trim found on the boiler that is used for safety, and/or efficiency.

flame failure. When the flame in a furnace goes out.

flame scanner. Device found on a boiler that proves pilot and main flame.

flareback. Flames discharging from the boiler through access doors or ports caused by delayed ignition or furnace pressure buildup.

flash economizer. A heat recovery system

used to reclaim the heat from the boiler blowdown water and used in conjunction with the continuous blowdown system.

flash point. Temperature at which fuel oil, when heated, produces a vapor that flashes when exposed to an open flame.

flash steam. Created when water at a high temperature has a sudden drop in pressure.

flash tank. Used with a continuous blowdown system to recover the flash steam from the water being removed from the steam and water drum.

flat gauge glass. Type of gauge glass used for pressures over 250 psi.

flexible joint. Used to allow for expansion and contraction of steam or water lines.

flat gauge glass

flow meter. Meter used to measure the flow of steam or water in the system.

fly ash. Small particles of noncombustible material found in gases of combustion.

fly ash precipitator. An electric device that traps and holds fly ash until it is properly disposed of.

rotometer flow meter

foaming. Rapid fluctuations of the boiler water level that can lead to priming or carryover. Caused by impurities on the surface of the boiler water.

forced draft. Mechanical draft produced by a fan supplying air to the furnace.

free-blowing drain Used to remove condensate from the main steam line.

front header. Device (line) connecting the steam and water drums by downcomer nipples.

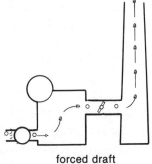

forced draft

fuel oil heater. Used to heat fuel so it can be pumped and is at the correct temperature for burning. Can be electric or steam.

fuel oil pump. Pump that takes fuel oil from the fuel oil tank and delivers it to the burner at the proper pressure.

furnace explosion. Occurs when fuel oil or combustible gas build up in the fire side of the boiler.

furnace volume. Amount of space available in a furnace to complete combustion.

Fyrite analyzer®. Instrument used to measure the percentage of carbon dioxide in the gases of combustion.

G

gagging. Application of a clamp on a safety valve spindle to keep the valve in full closed position during a hydrostatic test.

galvanometer. Used to measure small electric currents.

gas analyzer. Used to analyze the gases of combustion to determine combustion efficiency.

gas calorimeter. Used to determine the Btu content of natural gas.

gas cock. A manual quick-closing shutoff valve.

gas leak detector. Device used to locate gas leaks in a boiler room.

gas mixing chamber. Where air and gas mix before they enter the furnace in low pressure gas burners.

gas pressure regulator. Used to supply gas to the burner at the required pressure needed for combustion of the gas.

gases of combustion. Gases produced by the combustion process.

gate valve. Valve used on boilers as the main steam stop valve that when open offers no restriction to flow. Must be wide open or fully closed.

gauge glass blowdown valve. Valve used to remove any sludge and sediment from gauge glass lines.

gauge pressure. Pressure above atmospheric pressure that is read on a pressure gauge and is recorded as psi or psig.

globe valve. Used to take a piece of equipment out of service for maintenance. Used in conjunction with a bypass line and bypass valve.

grade. Refers to the size, heating value, and ash content of coal.

grates. Where the combustion process starts in a coal-fired furnace.

H

handhole. A part found on both fire tube and water tube boilers that is removed when cleaning the water side of the boiler.

heat energy. Kinetic energy caused by molecular motion within a substance.

heat exchanger. Any piece of equipment where heat is transferred from one substance to another.

heat recovery system. Equipment that is installed to reclaim heat that is normally lost during the blowdown process.

heat transfer. Movement of heat from one substance to another that can be accomplished by radiation conduction or convection.

heating surface. That part of the boiler that has heat and gases of combustion on one side and water on the other.

heating value. Expressed in Btu's per gallon or per pound. Heating value varies with the type of fuel used.

high and low water alarm. Warns the operator of high or low water. Found inside the water column.

high fire. Point of firing cycle when burner is burning the maximum amount of fuel per unit of time.

high pressure steam boiler. Boiler that operates at a steam pressure over 15 psi and over 6 boiler horsepower.

horizontal return tubular boiler. Type of fire tube boiler that consists of a drum suspended over the firebox.

hot well. A reservoir located at the bottom of a condenser where condensate collects.

huddling chamber. Part on a safety valve that increases the area of the safety valve

disc, thus increasing the total upward force, causing the valve to pop open.

hydraulic coupling. Coupling between the drive element and fan or pump.

hydrogen. A basic element present in gas, coal, and fuel oil.

hydrostatic pressure. Water pressure per vertical foot (.433) exerted at the base of a column of water.

hydrostatic test. Water test made on a boiler after repair work on the steam or water side or overheating of boiler metal.

I

ignition. The lightoff point of a combustible material.

ignition arch. Made of refractory material that absorbs the heat from the fire and radiates it back to the green coal.

impeller. The rotating element found in a centrifugal pump that converts centrifugal force into pressure.

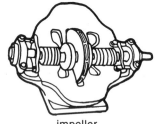
impeller

impingment (fuel oil). Fuel oil striking brickwork or the boiler heating surface that results in formation of carbon deposits and smoke.

impingment (steam). Steam that strikes the boiler heating surface, causing erosion of boiler metal.

incomplete combustion. Occurs when all the fuel is not burned, resulting in the formation of smoke and soot.

induced draft. Draft that is produced mechanically using a fan located between the boiler and the chimney.

infrared. Invisible light rays produced by the combustion process and detected by a flame scanner.

induced draft

insulation. Material used to cover steam, water, and fuel oil lines to cut down on radiant heat losses.

integrator. A calculating device used on differential-pressure flow meters to determine hourly or daily flow rates.

interlock. Used with burner controls to ensure proper operating sequence.

internal feedwater line. Perforated line located at the NOWL in the boiler that distributes the relatively cool feedwater over a large area to prevent thermal shock to the boiler metal.

internal furnace. Furnace that is located within the boiler and is surrounded by water in the scotch marine boiler.

internal overflow. A pipeline located in an open feedwater heater that prevents the water level from exceeding a fixed level and flooding the system.

internal treatment. The addition of chemicals directly into the boiler water to control pitting, scale, and caustic embrittlement.

instrument (boiler). Device that measures, indicates, records, and controls boiler room systems.

ion (zeolite) exchanger. Water softener that uses zeolite to soften water for use in the boiler.

instruments

L

lighting off. The initial ignition of the fuel.

lignite. Coal with a low heating value (Btu content) and a high moisture content.

lime-soda process. A process that uses lime and soda ash to soften water.

live steam. Steam that leaves the boiler directly without having its pressure reduced in process operations.

low fire. Point of firing cycle where burner is burning the minimum amount of fuel per unit of time.

low pressure steam boiler. Boilers that operate at a steam pressure of no more than 15 psi.

low water. Whenever the water level in the gauge glass is below the NOWL.

low water fuel cutoff. A device located a little below the NOWL that shuts off the boiler burner in the event of low water, preventing burning out of tubes and possible boiler explosion.

M

main header. That part of the system which connects boilers in battery and then distributes the steam to wherever it is needed.

main steam stop valve. Valve or valves found on the main steam line leaving the boiler.

makeup water. Water that must be added to the boiler to make up for leaks in the system, water that is lost through boiler blowdowns, or condensate that is dumped because of contamination.

malleable iron. Used for construction of water columns in boilers carrying a pressure between 250 psi and 350 psi.

manhole. Opening found on the steam and water side of a boiler that is used for cleaning and inspection of the boiler.

manometer. Instrument used to measure boiler draft.

manual reset valve. Used to secure the gas in the event of a low water condition or a pilot flame failure on a low pressure gas system.

manometer

master control. Unit that receives the primary signal and relays signals to individual control units.

MATT. For efficient combustion, it is necessary to have the proper mixture, atomization, temperature, and time to complete combustion.

MAWP (maximum allowable working pressure. Determined by the design and construction of the boiler in conformance with the ASME code.

mercury switch. Switch in which the movement of mercury in a capsule controls the flow of electricity in a circuit.

mica. Used to protect the flat gauge glass from the etching action of steam and water.

microprocessor. A computer acting as a flame-monitoring device that programs the burner, blower motor, ignition, and fuel valves to provide for safe burner operation.

modulating motor. Receives signals from the modulating pressure control and repositions the air to fuel ratio linkage.

modulating pressure control. Located at the highest part of the steam side of the boiler and sends a signal to the modulating motor that controls firing rate.

mud drum. Lowest part of the water side of a water tube boiler.

multiple-pass boiler. Boilers that are equipped with baffles to direct the flow of the gases of combustion so that the gases make more than one pass over the heating surfaces.

N

natural draft. Caused by the difference in weight between a column of hot gases of combustion inside the chimney and a column of cold air of the same height outside the chimney.

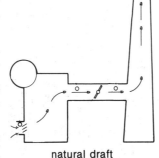

natural draft

natural gas. A combustible gas found in pockets trapped underground that consists mainly of methane.

nonadhering sludge. Residue formed when feedwater chemicals are added to boiler water containing scale-forming salts.

noncondensable gases. Gases found in boiler makeup water (oxygen) and in condensate returns.

nonvolatile. Any substance not easily vaporized under average temperature.

NOWL (normal operating water level). Water level carried in the boiler gauge glass during normal operation (approximately one-third to one-half glass).

O

oil separator. A device that removes oil from the exhaust steam before it enters the open feedwater heater.

operating range. Range that must be set when using an ON/OFF combustion control in order to prevent extremes in firing rate.

orifice plate. Plate with a fixed opening that is installed in a pipeline to give a certain pressure drop across the opening where liquid or steam is flowing.

Orsat analyzer. A flue gas analyzer that measures the percentage of carbon dioxide, oxygen, and carbon monoxide in the gases of combustion.

Orsat analyzer

outside stem and yoke valve (os&y). Shows by the position of the stem whether it is open or closed. Used as boiler main steam stop valves.

overfeed stoker. A coal-firing system that burns coal in suspension and on grates. Also known as a *spreader stoker.*

overfire air. Air introduced over the fire to aid in complete combustion. Used mostly when burning soft coal that has a high volatile content.

outside stem and yoke valve

P

package boiler. Comes completely assembled with its own feedwater pumps, fuel system, and draft fans.

packing gland. Holds packing or seals in place on valves and pumps to minimize leakage.

package boiler

perfect combustion. Burning of all the fuel with the theoretical amount of air. Can only be achieved in a laboratory.

pilot. Used to ignite fuel at the proper time in a firing cycle.

pipeline heater. Electric heater attached to the fuel oil line in order to maintain proper fuel oil temperature (viscosity) for moving fuel oil.

pneumatic system. A system of control that uses air as the operating medium.

pneumercator. A fuel oil level indicating device that gives a direct reading in gallons.

popping pressure. Predetermined pressure at which a safety valve opens and remains open until the pressure drops.

pop-type safety valve. Valve with a predetermined popping pressure. Commonly found on steam boilers.

positioning controller. A control that regulates air and fuel going to a boiler furnace.

postpurge. The passing of air through a furnace after normal burner shutdown.

pour point. Lowest temperature at which fuel oil flows as a liquid.

prepurge. The passing of air through a furnace prior to lightoff.

pressure control. Attached to the highest part of the steam side of a boiler to control its operating range.

pressure gauge. Used to indicate various pressures in the system.

pressure-reducing governor. Used on low pressure gas burner systems to reduce the gas pressure to 0 psi.

pressure gauge

pressure-reducing station. Where higher pressure steam is reduced in pressure for plant process.

pressurized furnace. Furnace that operates at slightly above atmospheric pressure.

primary air. Air supplied to the burner that regulates the rate of combustion.

process steam. Steam used in the plant for manufacturing purposes.

products of combustion. Gases that are formed as a fuel is burned in the furnace.

programmer. Control that puts the burner through a firing cycle.

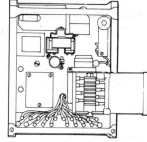
programmer

proportioning chemical feed pump. Pump that can be adjusted to feed chemicals to a boiler over a 24-hour period.

proving pilot. Sighting the pilot through the scanner to verify that the pilot is lit.

proximate analysis. Provides information regarding moisture content, volatile matter, fixed carbon, and ash content of coal.

psi (pounds per square inch). Unit of measurement used to express the amount of pressure present in a given structure or system.

pulverized coal. Coal that has been pulverized to the consistency of talcum powder and that is highly explosive.

pulverizing mill. Grinds coal to the consistency of talcum powder before it is delivered to the furnace, where it burns in suspension.

pump controller. Starts and stops a feedwater pump, depending on the water level in the boiler.

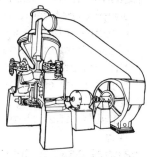
pulverizing mill

purge period. Before ignition and after burner shutdown when explosive combustibles are removed.

pyrometer. Thermocouple used to measure high furnace temperatures.

Q

quality of steam. Term used to express the moisture content present in saturated steam. Quality of steam effects the Btu content of the steam.

quick-closing valve. Valve that requires a one-quarter turn to be fully open or closed.

R

radiant superheater. A nest of tubes that the saturated steam passes through to acquire heat.

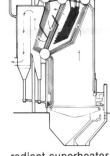
radiant superheater

rank. Refers to how hard the coal is.

rate of combustion. The amount of fuel that is being burned in the furnace per unit of time.

raw water. Untreated water from wells or city water lines.

rear header. Found on straight-tube water tube boilers. Connected to front header by water tubes.

reciprocating pump. Positive-displacement pump used to pump liquids.

recorder. An instrument that records data such as pressures and temperatures over a period of time.

refractory. Brickwork used in boiler furnaces and for boiler baffles.

relief valve. Used to protect liquid systems from excessive pressure.

reset. Switch that must be reset manually after tripping.

retort. Space below the grates of an underfeed stoker.

Ringelmann. Chart used as a means of determining smoke density.

rivets. Fasteners used to connect steel plates.

rotometer. Variable-area flow meter that measures the flow of a fluid.

S

safety valve blowdown. Drop in pressure between popping pressure and reseating pressure (usually 2 to 8 psi below popping pressure).

safety valve capacity. Measured in pounds of steam per hour safety valves can discharge.

saturated steam. Steam at a temperature that corresponds with its pressure.

scale. Deposits caused by improper boiler water treatment.

scale-forming salts. Salts such as calcium carbonate and magnesium carbonate that when in solution tend to form a hard, brittle scale on hot surfaces.

scanner. Device that monitors the pilot and main flame of the furnace. The scanner is used to prove the pilot and main flame.

scotch marine boiler. A fire tube boiler with an internal furnace.

scrubber. Device that removes undesirable gaseous elements from flue gas.

secondary air. Air needed to complete the combustion process.

sediment. Particles of foreign matter present in boiler water.

shear stress. Two forces of equal intensity act parallel to each other but in opposite directions.

sinuous header. Found on water tube boilers. Tubes are expanded, rolled, and beaded into front and rear headers.

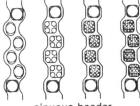
sinuous header

siphon. Protective device used between the steam and Bourdon tube in a steam pressure gauge.

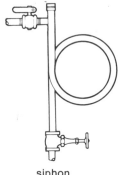
siphon

slow-opening valve. Valve that requires five full turns of its handwheel to be fully open or closed.

sludge. Accumulated residue produced from impurities in water.

smoke density. Varies from clear to dark. Determined by the amount of light that passes through the smoke as it leaves the boiler.

smoke indicator. An indicating or recording device that shows the density of the smoke leaving the chimney.

solenoid valve. An electromagnetic valve positioned open or closed.

solid state. An electronic system using transistors in place of electronic tubes.

soot. Carbon deposits resulting from incomplete combustion.

soot blowers. Used to remove soot from around tubes to increase boiler efficiency. Mostly found on water tube boilers.

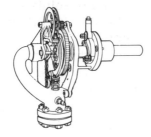

soot blowers

spalling. Hairline cracks in boiler brickwork (refractory) due to changes in furnace temperature.

spontaneous combustion. Occurs when combustible materials self-ignite.

stay. Brace used to reinforce flat surfaces.

staybolts. Bolts used in boilers to reinforce flat surfaces to prevent bulging.

steam. Water in a semi-gaseous condition. Steam is a vapor not a gas.

steam and water drum. The pressure vessel in a steam boiler that contains both steam and water.

steam boiler. A closed pressure vessel in which water is converted to steam by the application of heat.

steambound. Condition that occurs when the temperature in the open feedwater heater gets too high and the feedwater pump cannot deliver water to the boiler.

steam separator. Device used to increase the quality of steam. Found in the steam and water drum.

steam space. The space above the water line in the steam and water drum.

steam strainer. Used before steam traps and turbine throttle valves to remove solid impurities.

steam trap. An automatic device that removes gases and condensate from steam lines and heat exchangers without the loss of steam.

steam turbine. Used to drive boiler auxiliaries or generators in large plants.

stopcock. A quick-opening or closing valve usually found on gas lines.

strip chart. Recording chart that records temperatures and pressures in the system.

suction pressure. Pressure on the liquid at the suction side of a pump.

sulfur. A combustible element found in coal and fuel oil.

superheated steam. Steam at a temperature above its corresponding pressure.

superheater. Used to increase the amount of heat in the steam.

superheater drain. Valve found on the superheater header outlet. Used to maintain flow throughout the superheater during start-up and shutdown.

superheater header. Main inlet and outlet line to and from the superheater tubes in the superheater.

super-jet safety valve. Valve set to open at a predetermined pressure.

surface blowdown valve. Used to remove impurities from the surface of the water in a steam and water drum.

surface condenser. A shell-and-tube vessel used to reduce the exhaust pressure on the outlet end of turbines or engines.

surface tension. Caused by impurities on the top of the water in the steam and water drum.

suspension sling. Used to support the drum of an HRT boiler.

synchronize. To balance out combustion controls before switching to automatic.

T

tensile stress. Occurs when two forces of equal intensity act on an object, pulling in opposite directions. Affects boiler plates and staybolts.

tensile stress

therm. Unit used to measure Btu content of natural gas. A therm has 100,000 Btu.

thermal efficiency. The ratio of the heat absorbed by the boiler to the heat available in the fuel per unit of time.

thermocouple. Used to measure temperatures in the system and send them back to a recording chart.

thermometer. Instrument used to measure temperature (degree of heat). Calibrated in degrees Celcius or degrees Fahrenheit.

thermometer

through stays. Found on fire tube boilers (HRT and scotch marine) to keep front and rear tube sheets from bulging.

through stays

total force. Total pressure that is acting on an area, determined by diameter and pressure.

totalizer. Dial that determines hourly or daily flow rates.

try cocks. Secondary way of determining the water level.

tube brushes. Used in fire tube boilers to remove soot from inside of tubes.

tube sheet. Tubes are rolled, expanded, and beaded into front and rear tube sheets of HRT and scotch marine boilers and upper and lower tube sheets of vertical fire tube boilers.

tubular gauge glass. Round gauge glass used for pressures up to and including 250 psi.

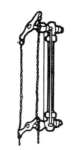

tubular gauge glass

turbine stages. That part of the turbine where steam gives up its energy to the turbine blades. As the steam pressure drops, the stages (blades) become larger.

turbulence. Movement of water in the steam and water drum.

U

ultimate analysis. Used to determine the elements present in a coal sample.

ultraviolet. A form of light that is produced during combustion.

underfeed stoker. A coal-firing system that introduces the coal under the fire.

U-tube manometer. When filled with mercury, used to measure vacuum. U-tube manometers are calibrated in inches.

V

vacuum. A pressure below atmospheric pressure.

vacuum gauge. Pressure gauge used to measure pressure below the atmosphere that is calibrated in inches of mercury.

valve flow meter. Measures flow of a substance by the movement of a piston in a valve caused by resistance to flow of the substance.

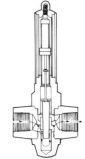

valve flow meter

vaporstat. Control with a large diaphragm that makes it highly sensitive to low pressure.

variable-area flow meter. Measures the flow of a substance by how much resistance is created by a float or piston which changes the area (size) of the flow path.

vaporstat

vent condenser. Removes oxygen and other noncondensable gases in a deaerating feed-water heater.

venturi. A constricting device used in pipelines to measure flow.

vertical fire tube boiler. One-pass boiler that has fire tubes in a vertical position. Vertical fire tube boilers are classified as wet-top or dry-top.

viscosity. Measurement of a fluid's internal resistance to flow.

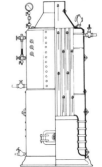

vertical fire tube boiler

W

warping. Bending or distortion of boiler or

superheater tubes, usually caused by over-heating.

water column. Reduces fluctuations of boiler water to obtain a better reading of the water level in the boiler gauge glass. Located at the NOWL.

water column blowdown valve. Valve on the bottom of the water column used to remove sludge and sediment that might collect at the bottom of the water column.

water hammer. A banging condition that is caused by steam and water mixing in a steam line.

water softening. The removal of scale-forming salts from water.

water tube boiler. Boiler that has water in the tubes with heat and gases of combustion around the tubes.

waterwall. Vertical or horizontal tubes found in the furnace area of water tube boilers that lengthen the life of the refractory.

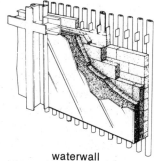

waterwall

waterwall blowdown valve. Approved valve used to remove sludge and sediment from waterwalls and waterwall headers.

weight-type alarm whistle. Alarm whistle which signals high or low water by the gain or loss of buoyancy of weights in water within the water column.

windbox (plenum chamber). Pressurized air chamber that supplies air to a furnace.

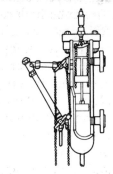

weight-type alarm whistle

Z

zeolite. A resin material that is used in the process of softening water.

Index

Illustrations are listed in italic.

Furnace grate surface, 57
Furnace pressure, *147*
Furnace volume, 128–129
Fusible plugs, 20
Fyrite analyzers, 129, *129*
  and slide rule calculator, *130*

G

Gagging, 189
Gas and fuel oil draft system, 116, *116*
Gas burners, 95–100
Gas control valve, 96–97
Gas-filled Bourdon tube thermometer, 157–158, *158*
Gas/fuel oil burners, combination, 100, *100*
Gas/fuel oil systems, 55–57, *56*
Gas fuel systems, 52–59
Gas lines and controls, for high pressure gas burners, 96–98
Gas pressure reducing valve, 99, *99*
Gas pressure regulator, *97*
Gate valve, 35
Gauge faces, 154, *154*
Gauge glass, 26–27, *27*
  on water column, 25
Gauge pressure (psi), 3, 28
Gear-type fuel oil pumps, 95, *95*
Globe valve, *77*, 78
Grade
  of coal, 124
  of fuel oil, 124–125. *125*
Grate stokers, chain (traveling), 102–103
Green (fresh) coal, 101
Groundwater, 169

H

Hard coal, 100
Hardness of water, 173
Headers, *9*
Heaters, fuel oil, 93–94
  electric, 94, *94*
  steam, 94
Heating value, of fuel, 124
Heat recovery system, 39–41, *41*
High pressure gas burners, 96–98, *96*
  blowers for, 98
  gas lines and controls, 96–98
High pressure gas system, 53–54, *54*
High pressure steam boilers, 2
Horizontal deaerating feedwater heater, *70*
Horizontal return tubular (HRT) boiler, 5, *6*
  fusible plug and, 20
Hot lime-soda process, 173, *174*

Huddling chamber, *22*
Hunt, 144
Hydrostatic pressure, 30, *30*
Hydrostatic test, 188–189

I

Ignition arch, and chain grate stoker, 103
Impingement, 32
Impulse steam trap, 83
Inclined-tube type draft gauge, 110, *110*
Incomplete combustion, 127
Induced draft, 112–113, *113*
Induced draft fan, 116
Inside mixing steam atomizing burner, 91, *91*, 92
Instruments, 153–165
  flow meters, 160–161
  pneumercators, 159
  pressure gauges, 154–156
  recorders, 161–162
  smoke indicators, 162–163
  temperature-measuring devices 156–159
Internal boiler water treatment, 169, 171–173
  chemicals and, 171, *171*
Internal furnace, *5*
Inverted bucket steam trap, 83, *83*
Ion exchange (zeolite) process, 174–175, *175*

L

Leak detector, 53
Licensing examinations, 203
Lignite coal, 124
Lime-soda process, 173–174
Line (spray) desuperheater, 85, *85*
Liquid-filled Bourdon tube thermometers, 157
Liquid-in-glass thermometer, 157, *157*
Live plant start-up, 186–187
Live steam, 92
Log, *182, 183, 184*
Low pressure gas burners, 98–100
Low pressure gas system, 53, *53*
Low pressure steam boilers, 2
Low water fuel cutoff controls, testing, 80, *180*, 182–183

M

Main feedwater line, 77–78, *77*
Main stop valve, 36
Maintenance, routine, 191–192
Manometer draft gauge, 110–111, *110*, 155, *155*
Manual shutoff cock, *98*
MATT, 127–128

U

Ultimate analysis, 124
Underfeed stoker, 57, *57*, 101
U-tube manometer, 156, *156*
U-tube type draft gauge, 110, *110*

V

Vacuum (suction) gauge, 155–156
Valve flow meter, 160–161, *161*
Vapor-pressure Bourdon tube thermometer,
    157, *158*
Vaporstat, *97*, 99
Variable-area flow meters, 160–161
Variable orifice steam trap, 83–84
Vent condenser, 69
Venturi tube, 160
Vertical fire tube boilers, 7, *7*
Viscosity, 124

W

Water alarm whistles, 25
Water column, 25–29, *25, 26*, 81, 182
Water hammer, 81, 171
Water level in boiler, 190, *190*
Water softening, 173–175
Water treatment, *See* Boiler water treatmer
Water tube boiler, 2
    fittings on, *20*
    and soot blowers, 35
Water tube steam boilers, 8–10, *8*
Waterwalls, 8–10
Weight-type alarm whistles, 27, *28*
Wet method, boiler lay-up, 189
Windbox (plenum chamber), 110, 116, *116*

Z

Zeolite, 174–174
Zones, of regenerative air heater, 114